Allan,

Many thanks for your help.

Best wishes,

Niall;

Brooklands, September 2015

UPON A TRAILING EDGE

UPON A TRAILING EDGE

RISK, THE HEART AND THE AIR PILOT

MICHAEL JOY
OBE, MD, FRCP, FACC, FESC, FRAeS

Matador
9 Priory Business Park,
Wistow Road, Kibworth Beauchamp,
Leicestershire. LE8 0RX
Tel: 0116 279 2299
Email: books@troubador.co.uk
Web: www.troubador.co.uk/matador
Twitter: @matadorbooks

ISBN 978 1784624 729

British Library Cataloguing in Publication Data.
A catalogue record for this book is available from the British Library.

Printed and bound by CPI Group (UK) Ltd, Croydon, CR0 4YY
Typeset in 11pt Aldine by Troubador Publishing Ltd, Leicester, UK

Matador is an imprint of Troubador Publishing Ltd

This book is dedicated to Brooklands, and to the people who worked there between 1907 and 1989, when British Aerospace closed the site. It is also in memory of nearly ninety aircraft workers who died, and over 419 who were injured, when it was bombed by the Luftwaffe on 4th September 1940.

It is the birthplace of British aviation and of motor sport. Some 18,600 aircraft were designed, built and flown from there. Now it is in nemesis as a retail and business park. Brooklands Museum occupies part of the old site. It is a charitable trust which is dedicated to the inspiration of a new generation to help restore our engineering excellence to some of its former glory.

Recently the Heritage Lottery Fund made a substantial grant to develop the listed Belman aircraft hangar as a wartime aircraft factory. Any royalties from this book will be donated to the trust.

CONTENTS

ILLUSTRATIONS

TEXT

1. A Red Kite
2. A Common Tern
3. *Wellington*
4. *GO 99* at Brooklands
5. The Napier Railton
6. A Young Barn Owl
7. *Outhwaite*
8. North American Harvard T1
9. Fairoaks Airport, 1958
10. Boeing Chinooks at RAF, Odiham
11. Kitfox Showing off its Flaperons
12. Group Captain Sir Douglas Bader
13. Warbirds at Goodwood
14. Leeds Castle
15. Flight Deck of Piper Navajo G-BJLO
16. Kim's Gun
17. Guard on the Khyber Pass
18. Cricket up the Khyber
19. DC10-30 AP-AXE, Karachi, February 1981

PLATES

1. Great-uncle Jack
2. Dr David Joy
3. Sir Hiram Stevens Maxim
4. Samuel Franklin Cody
5. Claude Grahame-White

PROLOGUE

An aerofoil is a wing, or the blade of a propeller. As it moves through the air it generates lift, or thrust. At the wing tips, the higher pressure below the wing contaminates the lower pressure above with vortex formation. Vortices contain energy and vortex drag reduces the efficiency of the wing. There are parallels with management. At the trailing edge of an aircraft wing there are smaller aerofoils. These influence events. This is a story about flying told from a personal perspective somewhere behind the aeroplane.

1. *A Red Kite (Milvus milvus), a cousin of the Shitehawk (Milvus migrans), keeping an eye on our picnic near Didcot. The high aspect ratio wings with slotted tips are superbly adaptable for slow speed flight. Here they show a Hoerner configuration to gain the best lift from wing-tip vortex energy. At other times they are contoured upward like a classical winglet. This helps conserve the lower pressure over the upper surface from dissipation.*

2. *More trailing edge devices, this time on a Common Tern (Sterna hirundo) enjoying the Henley Royal Regatta with us. It maintains a high aspect ratio to its wings (the square of the wingspan divided by the wing area) whilst loitering but reduces the span and increases the loading to enable a high speed plunge to catch a fish.*

ACKNOWLEDGEMENTS

Some authors are diarists, or keep an archive. Others rely on recollection and fragments of memory. The flying logbook was helpful. And there were photographs. Certain records, such as the minutes of the First Cardiovascular Study Group meeting at the International Civil Aviation Organisation (ICAO), Montreal in 1980, survived. Much material had been shredded for reasons of confidentiality or space.

Submission of a paper to a scientific journal is easy in comparison with penetrating the maquis that is publishing. But as Oscar Wilde said: *Never speak impolitely of society, only those who cannot get in do that.* Indeed not. Then Jeremy Thompson, from Matador, flew in with his Rockwell 112A, and saved the day. For that I am very grateful.

As this is a story about aviation, written by a doctor, it needed guidance. Encouragement did come, from some for personal reasons, from others out of professional curiosity. Texts on personnel regulation within the aviation industry are a niche within a niche. The following helped in diverse ways with criticism, some reading and editing the whole or part of the manuscript.

In alphabetical order, Dr Claus Curdt-Christiansen, former Chief of Medicine at ICAO; Dr Ken Edgington, formerly Chief Medical Officer (CMO) of the UK Civil Aviation Authority (CAA) and Dr Michael O'Brien, emeritus consultant neurologist to Guy's Hospital and neurologist to the CAA, copy-edited the complete manuscript. Captain John Turner, Director of Aviation Affairs, the Honourable Company of Air Pilots; David Learmount, Operations and Safety Editor, Flightglobal; Dr Robert Hunter, Head of Safety and Security, BALPA; Allan Winn, Director of Brooklands Museum; Philip Clifford, Brooklands Museum Library; Brian Riddle, Chief Librarian, National Aerospace Library, Farnborough; James Maconochie-Joy, artist and author; my sons – David and Toby Joy – both pilots, and others contributed – some anonymously. To all of them I am most grateful. Captain Mike Bannister, the last Concorde Chief Pilot, commented on Chapter 27 and Captain Ian Fogarty, Chief Training Captain, Airbus, Cathay Pacific, did the same for Chapter 16 in discussing the strange mores of the Airbus.

The following gave kind permission for the use of photographic and other material: Meriel Bennett, John M Dibbs, Brooklands Museum, Sophia Coningsby, Claus Curdt-Christiansen, Guillaume Nededec, Sylvio Finkelstein, Sarah Forman, Getty Images, Valda Keyte, James Millar, Michael O'Brien, Graham Pitchfork, Julian Temple, Jonathan Turnbull, Peter and Polly Vacher.

Lastly I would like to thank all those flyers I met professionally over a period of nearly forty years for their unfailing courtesy and forbearance. My thoughts are with them, sharing as I do their love of the air and its ways. I am especially grateful to those who kept watch with me on the airways of Europe, thereby helping to ensure that this story could eventually be told.

Front cover
Photograph of the port wing of a Boeing 777 demonstrating the in-board (high speed) aileron which droops with the flaps (between certain limits) to become a flaperon, responsible for both roll and lift/drag in the landing configuration. The outboard ailerons also act as flaperons when the landing flaps are selected. These are locked in high-speed flight to avoid torsion of the wing. The spoilers are stowed in the picture but may become active in roll or gust alleviation. The electrocardiogram records a cardiac arrest complicating a heart attack – the premature complex is rapidly followed by a fall in the blood pressure to zero (lowest trace).

PREFACE

I suppose we shall soon travel by air vessels; make air instead of sea voyages;
and at length find our way to the moon, in spite of the want of atmosphere.
Lord Byron (1822)

This is a story about aviation, its risk and the heart of the pilot. It is both a personal and a professional one. It is an eclectic and affectionate glance from the perspective of a journeyman cardiologist who was at once a teacher, pilot and adviser to regulators, rather than an aeronautical boffin. It explains risk and failure, not heroism or triumph of the human spirit at the frontiers of speed, or of altitude. It touches upon the pioneers in design and construction, and looks at history. It tells of some remarkable people and places. Sometimes it is technical in the medical, aeronautical or regulatory sense; sometimes discursive in order to develop and explain. Occasionally it is polemical. It is not a scientific text, although it employs scientific terms; it is for the curious, not the spoon-fed. The reference material, quoted at the back, is unannotated.

Aviation, its regulatory environment, and indeed medicine, continuously evolve: the concerns of one day are history the next. Judgement moves more slowly. Sometimes it is helpful to reflect on what has gone before and this is an attempt to do so in an area which has received relatively little attention. Every effort has been made to achieve accuracy and give credit, but hopefully the author will be forgiven for venturing into areas which are better known to others. Views expressed may divaricate from those with a more intimate knowledge of aeronautics, or of aerial history. On regulation, many have a mind-set. One or two names have been changed to preserve privacy; others have either given permission, or the details are already in the public arena.

In postscript, it is a lament for the passing of an age, an industry, and a time in which the United Kingdom once held the high ground.

The Athenaeum, London, SW1: June 2015

INTRODUCTION

The United Kingdom Civil Aviation Authority (UK CAA) was set up in 1972 following an act of Parliament. It has a number of regulatory functions, including personnel licensing of aircrew; this involves not only assessment of flying competence but also of medical fitness. By a set of curious chances, I was appointed as cardiologist to the newly formed CAA in 1974 as a result of the Hawker Siddeley Trident 1 disaster. This had occurred at Staines two years earlier. A contributory factor to that accident was concluded to have been the cardiovascular incapacitation of the Captain. Some of the foregoing relates to the steps that were taken in the hope of minimising the risk of recurrence of such an event.

★ ★ ★

One morning at the Civil Aviation Authority building in Gatwick South Area, a pilot presented himself in my consulting room for cardiological examination. He had been referred by Dr Michael O'Brien, a neurologist at Guy's Hospital, London (see photo plate 28); both he and I were advisors to the CAA Medical Department. The story was an unusual one and involved an executive jet flight between Milan Malpensa and Biggin Hill; the pilot I saw that day had been in command. The trip was uneventful, until the landing, when he had turned to the co-pilot and asked,

"Where are we?"

"Biggin Hill – where did you expect us to be?" his astonished colleague responded.

"How did we get here?"

He had completed the trip, apparently behaving appropriately, and yet had no recall of having made it. He had suffered an episode of TGA (total global amnesia), a recognised benign neurological condition which usually disappears in a matter of hours, and which has a low risk of recurrence over the next year or two. Its pathogenesis is not understood but an organic brain syndrome (OBS) had to be excluded and Michael sought my advice as to whether there was any cardiological abnormality. This would have included a search for a source, perhaps, of cerebral embolism. (An embolism may be a clot of blood, free in the circulation, which can trigger a stroke.) Following clinical examination, echocardiography (ultrasound) and electrocardiographic (ECG) rhythm monitoring, none was found. The decision on fitness to fly, following further investigation including magnetic resonance imaging (MRI) and electro-encephalography (EEG), rested with the regulator, this time with input from Michael as the neurological advisor.

The restoration of flying privileges would have been determined by the completeness of recovery, which should have been absolute in the case of TGA. Also for consideration would have been the likelihood of recurrence, time interval at which the chance of recurrence would have been considered remote, and the likely impact on flight safety if there was a further episode. Risk to flight safety could be mitigated by restricting the pilot to flying on multi-crew operations only. The starting point for the fitness decision would have included examination of the available data on the natural history, the probability of a relapse and a definition of 'remote' in terms of regulatory tolerability. Had the blood pressure been elevated – a common observation in middle years and beyond – a brief salvo of atrial ectopic beats observed on the ambulatory ECG recording, and/or a small area of increased density in the brain identified on MRI, what then? Would, or should, these additional findings have modified the fitness recommendation and what additional consideration should have been applied?

This Bowdlerised story serves to illustrate the breadth of the medical issues and their potential consequences which sometimes confront the regulator. They cannot be resolved in an office with a handbook and require a clinician accredited in the relevant speciality, ideally with knowledge of the conditions under which the pilot undertakes his duties. This, after all, is the requirement of the International Civil Aviation Organisation (Annex 1 – 1.2.4.5.2.), to which the UK is a signatory. The resolution of such questions in an expeditious and professional manner is in the interest of public safety, the pilot, and the operational capability of the organisation which employs him. In the UK this is the mandated responsibility of the CAA. It is culpable if there is adverse performance in terms of delayed or faulty decision making. The latter has the potential to cost the pilot his or her livelihood.

Fifty years ago civil aviation was a different world. The first generation of jet aircraft were becoming established, the training of co-pilots on certain aircraft was not mandatory, CRM (crew resource management) did not exist, medical cause accidents were not uncommon and the retirement age for the pilots of the British Overseas Airways Corporation (BOAC) was fifty years of age. There were also Flight Engineers (FE) and even Flight Navigators (FN). Flight time limitation standards were not to become law in the UK until the Bader committee report of 1975. Being a long-haul airline pilot at that time was regarded as stressful, although most would only admit that hours of boredom, interspersed with moments of terror, was a closer approximation to reality. For a long time there was a paucity of data on the lifetime survival of aircrew. This changed in 1996 with the publication of a review of retired American Airlines pilots. Their life expectation was compared with a matched group of sixty-year-old white American males over a period of twenty-five years. The results showed that a pilot aged sixty years had a better than five-year additional survival advantage, when compared with his non-flying contemporaries.

More recently it has been reported that the standardised mortality ratio (SMR) of airline pilots is slightly over half that of their peer group. In other words their death rate is half that which would be expected at any given age. But in spite of this, pilots still suffer from the medical problems of the general population and this may impinge on their ongoing fitness to fly. The risk (likelihood) and consequences of a disabling event need clarification. Such mishaps may be Hollywood-style and dramatic, or subtle and missed by the pilot or his/her colleague. The cursor of the fitness decision has to be derived from the continuum of increasing (cardiovascular) risk, and presented as a binary statement – fit/unfit. This has parallels in other aspects of aviation – if the MEL (minimum equipment list) of an aircraft is deficient, it is a no-go situation.

As the story unfolds it will become clearer how we addressed the problems of cardiovascular medicine in the context of fitness to fly in a safe, fair and proportionate way. In some of the commoner conditions it was achieved by mathematical modelling. Elsewhere there had to be reliance on what might be called the gestalt of licensing. This reflects an overall philosophy evolved through knowledge of the environment, and experience with similar, related conditions. No-one has a monopoly of wisdom on these issues. The opinions expressed are those of the author and are in good faith. They do not necessarily reflect the mainstream – this is the challenge of academic argument.

But now, back to the beginning…

MEMORY

Men do not learn much from the lessons of history and that is the most important of all the lessons of history.

Aldous Huxley,
Collected Essays, 1959

History seems most poignant when it is just out of reach. For my generation, born at the outbreak of the Second World War, the 20th century is forever cleaved by the events of that time. Everything that had happened seemed to have done so before the war, during the war, or, increasingly, after the war. Following conception at about the time of the Molotov-Ribbentrop pact (23rd August 1939), my arrival coincided with the Battle of France. Trouble lay ahead. Childhood was full of wartime artefacts. Army coats, great, winter warm, hung in the hall hitched over Barr and Stroud binoculars marked with an arrow and the initials WD (War Department). The Prismatic Compass Mk III we take on walks had been with my father in the Western Desert, at Tobruk and El Alamein, then Sicily and finally on to Gold Beach for Operation Overlord on the 6th June 1944. Now it helps us find our way around the Somerset levels. The vast army blanket upon which my sister, Elizabeth, was ill on a picnic near Stourton Tower in Somerset sixty-five years ago is still in the oak chest but thinner and corrupted by moth.

Great-uncle Jack, clean-shaven and in his Sam Browne, watches from the sideboard in aquatint, recalling Laurence Binyon's poem published in the *Times* in 1914: *They shall grow not old as we that are left grow old…* (see photo plate 1). He had been a married solicitor, aged thirty-seven years and was a major in the Hertfordshire Regiment. He died in a preliminary skirmish three days before Ludendorff's last great offensive on the Somme on 21st March 1918. It was also two weeks after the treaty of Brest-Litovsk, which had been dictated to the nascent Bolshevik government of the Russian Soviet Federated Socialist Republic. This ended Russian participation in the war. Things looked bad for the allies at the time with the German armies focused on the west. The treaty had been brokered in part by Leon Trotsky, who fell out with Stalin and was later murdered on his orders in 1940. He was in exile in New Mexico. Trotsky had not supported the Molotov-Ribbentrop pact. We should be mindful that extrajudicial execution remains an instrument of Russian domestic and foreign policy. There are worrying historical parallels.

The consequences of the Brest-Litovsk treaty echoed through the treaty of Versailles in 1919, the Second World War and the Yalta conference, the breakup of the Soviet Union and most recently, Vladimir Putin's efforts in the Ukraine. We should learn from history and not dramatise it. Jack Gough lies in the war cemetery of Ste Emilie Valley outside Villers-Faucon, near Peronne, as peacefully as is possible between a sugar beet factory and a field of broad beans. We visited in August 2014 in *Wellington*, our 1926 Barker Cabriolet de Ville 'Prince of Wales' Rolls-Royce New Phantom, which waited stiffly as we walked about in the rain. Many of the graves are of soldiers of the 16th (Irish) Division who died in March 1918 and are buried with ten German combatants. They might have marched to the front line past the pits being dug by the Labour Corps in wait for their corpses. Perhaps they would have been singing Ivor Novello's anthem of the Great War:

> *Keep the home fires burning,*
> *While your hearts are yearning.*
> *Though your lads are far away*
> *They dream of home.*
> *There's a silver lining*
> *Through the dark clouds shining,*
> *Turn the dark cloud inside out*
> *'Til the boys come home.*

Great-uncle Jack had served in the war to end all wars, but did not live to see the German offensive ultimately fail eight months later. The allies were victorious under the supreme command of General Foch.

My maternal grandfather had also served, as an engineer, but survived against the odds. Life expectation was about three weeks for a junior infantry officer at the front. He repatriated a 78 rpm gramophone record, *When Paderewski Played the Baby Grand*, which had a deep notch in it. This was caused when a German shell burst overhead whilst it was being played on a wind-up gramophone. Ignaz Paderewski was a concert pianist and the Prime Minister of Poland; he travelled with a concert grand piano in his luggage. In August 1914 we had gone to war in defence of Belgium, following the German violation of its neutrality, established by the Treaty of London in 1839. There were three other treaties of London; in 1518, 1913 and 1915. There had been no legal obligation to join combat but there had been no conspiracy either, unlike the more recent invasion of Iraq. The architect of the plan of attack, Count Graf von Schlieffen, had retired in 1906, dying the year before the war and leaving his ideas to be modified and implemented by Helmuth von Moltke the Younger.

"Mobilisation means war," von Schlieffen had correctly predicted, but did not live to see his point proven. Twenty-five years later we went to

3. *WELLINGTON, our 1926 Rolls-Royce Barker bodied 'Prince of Wales' Cabriolet de Ville outside the cemetery near Ste Emilie Valley, Villers-Faucon, near Peronne. Great Uncle Jack Gough lies buried there. He died in March, 1918, at the age of thirty-seven years.*

war again to honour our treaty obligations to Poland. Had we not done so the world would have been a different place, and I would not have been initiated into the mysteries of the earth gyroscope at Oxford by a Polish pilot who had fought on the allied side.

★★★

A month after I was born the British Expeditionary Force was evacuated from Dunkirk in Operation Dynamo. Nearly one third of a million allied troops were taken off the beaches of northern France. Years later, in 2011, as High Sheriff of Surrey I was to take part in a celebration of this event with surviving 'small ships' still lying on the River Thames. My father (see photo plate 2) a General Medical Practitioner in Frome, Somerset, was of an age at which he would have expected to have been called up. He volunteered instead, to gain some latitude as to where he was likely to be based. He guessed, correctly, that if he joined a northern regiment he would be stationed in the south. This came about when his unit, the 6th Battalion of the Durham Light Infantry, was camped under canvas near Bridport, Dorset. There were two available motor vehicles of which he, as the medical officer, had one. It was a baker's van. He had been commissioned in the Royal Army Medical Corps (RAMC) in the Tees and Tyne Regiment, which recruited in the area bounded by the two rivers. His experience gave him a lifelong affection for the men with whom he served – some of them were Durham miners. He continued to visit his old batman, and his driver, each year until very old age.

He had raced a Roesch Talbot 90 at Brooklands before the Second World War, which he had acquired from a Harley Street radiologist, Dr Roth. Those were the days when an X-ray dispensed as much radiation as a tactical nuclear weapon. Its registration was *GO 99*. "Say ninety-nine" was a trick at that time, used by doctors to assess the auditory and tactile vocal fremitus in the diagnosis of inflammation of the lung. This technique relies on modification of low tone (spoken) or high tone (whispered) speech through inflamed lung, as heard through the stethoscope or felt with the side of the hand. Other diphthong phrases – "Boy oh boy" and "Toy boat" – were sometimes used as an alternative. Now Computerised Tomography (CT) scanning is employed which surely is an improvement as it is so much more expensive.

4.   *My father in action in his Talbot 90, practicing for the BARC Mountain Handicap at the Brooklands Whitsun meeting - 1ˢᵗ June, 1936. He was the 'limit' car and came second to CH Masters in a Balilla F.I.A.T. He averaged 60.52 mph over the five laps. During the race he was number 15. The registration plate - GO 99 - and head- lamps were removed to enhance speed. The fastest lap that day, on the full circuit, was 140.29 mph by Oliver Bertram in the Barnato-Hassan special.*

At five minutes to midnight on March 17th 1935, in white tie and tails, my father claimed, improbably, to have been the last man to have driven legally down Piccadilly at 100 mph. The only interesting thing that happened to me in Piccadilly, in September 2002, was on the Countryside March when someone mooned out of an upstairs window of the Ritz. He won an onyx ashtray from the British Amateur Racing Club (BARC) at the Whitsun meeting, 1ˢᵗ June 1936, at Brooklands at a time when it was fashionable to smoke. The car was written off on the Barnet bypass the following year, but not by him. Medicine and impending marriage had put a stop to all that.

He had a morbid fear of flying, never having done so during the war, and never having needed to do so after it. When he went with the 8th Army to Alexandria, they travelled by sea via the Cape of Good Hope and Port Elizabeth. Years later he and my mother visited Michelle, a former au

5. *A real muscle car, seen here at the 'Wings and Wheels' meeting at Dunsfold in 2014. The 1933 Napier Railton holds the ultimate speed record at Brooklands of 143.44 mph when it was driven by John Cobb. The 23.944 litre Napier Lion aero-engine produces 580 brake horse power from twelve cylinders in three banks of four. It is owned by Brooklands Museum Trust, Weybridge. Only a favoured few are allowed to drive it.*

pair, in the Lebanon and remarkably, travelling by car from the UK. By the time I ventured to lecture in Beirut with Dr Ken Edgington, Chief Medical Officer (CMO) of the UK Civil Aviation Authority (CAA), at the invitation of Dr Claus Curdt-Christiansen, Chief of Medicine at the International Civil Aviation Organisation (ICAO) in October 1997, the place had been flattened by war. My mother disliked flying too – she said it gave her the Wilis. It is unlikely she came across one since a Wili is the spirit of a dead maiden deceived by her lover; they are best spotted late at night in Rhineland glades: confer *Giselle*. There should be no confusion with the Rhinemaidens (Woglinde, Wellgunde and Flosshilde), who were water-nymphs featuring in *Der Ring des Nibelungen*.

The winter of 1940–1941 was particularly severe, especially under canvas where they were bivouacked at Litton Cheney, near Bridport in Dorset. He and some of the troops stationed there developed frostbite during training in a blizzard on Exmoor. His unit laid a minefield in the hope of defending the coast against the anticipated German invasion, should it come up the Bristol Channel. There was also the possibility of a landing by enemy parachutists dressed as nuns and carrying bicycles. Presumably they would have concealed their *pickelhaube* helmets under their wimples. According to A. J. P. Taylor, the story about German insurgents disguised as nuns originated in the Great War when the prevailing advice was to look at their legs – if they were hairy, they were German infantry. There seems to have been no experimental study which confirmed the diagnostic accuracy of this test.

"Halt! Who goes there – report friend or foe? Good evening, Sister, please raise your habit that I might examine your legs?"

Food was not plentiful but its supply was enhanced when a bull in a field near their encampment escaped and trundled around before treading on a newly laid mine. The other mines blew up in sympathy, taking with them the unfortunate creature to a happier pasture in the sky. His commanding officer had told him to stitch it up, but some things are beyond the surgeon. The steak was good, he said. The 6th Battalion travelled from Cullompton to Gourock, embarking upon the *Duchess of Windsor* for Alexandria via the Cape of Good Hope.

He was away for much of the next five years, turning up now and then in uniform; but memory is fickle, especially early memory. Most of us have recollections we assume reflect earliest consciousness but these are sparse, fallible and not easy to prove. On New Year's Eve 1943, my parents stayed at the Savoy Hotel in the Strand to celebrate the return of my father from Sicily to commence preparation for Operation Overlord (D-Day), 6th June 1944. Restaurant food prices were controlled during the war by the Meals in Establishments Order (1942) at 5/– (25p) for dinner, but the luxury hotels could charge more – 7/6d (38p) for three courses. That evening oysters were available at an extra 3/6d (18p).

These occasional trips to London were a feature of their early life together. Sometimes I was left with Mrs Pitman, who used to 'help'. She and her husband, Fred, lived in a gaslit terraced cottage at the end of Plumbers Barton, off Christchurch Street West, Frome. With the increased girth of old age the tiny cobbled lane seems impossibly narrow today. I was given the bedroom of their son, Kenny, complete with a nimbus cloud of goose down cover which would now be called a duvet. It was unmanageable. I was cuffed for calling Mr Pitman "Fred" – his first name.

The highlight of the stay was a flying display by Kenny in his Spitfire. Nearly seventy years later, at my garden party as High Sheriff of Surrey, I was fortunate to have another Spitfire flyby. This time it was accompanied by a Hurricane. At the appointed time we all assembled in the lane and waited. Eventually a rather noisy aeroplane appeared, turning and looping above us. It seemed too small to be the legendary aeroplane which every boy wanted to fly in combat. I had expected a ride, but an attempted landing in Portway might have demolished the Express Dairy chimney.

The earliest event I can recall, but I have no idea where it occurred, was seeing an enemy aircraft caught in the crossed beams of searchlights. During the summer holiday of 1944 we stayed in a seaside hotel in Bude, Cornwall. The Americans were there too and I was almost squashed by a half-track armoured personnel carrier, probably a White Motor Company M3, of which, more later. It came lurching and grunting over the cliffs where we used to collect window – the silvered black paper strips dropped by aircraft to confuse enemy radar. It is now called chaff and is still used as an electronic counter-measure. The monster belched blue smoke and flumped into a dirty brown puddle covering my mother, brother and myself with foul-smelling mud. There was a lot of shouting about a limey kid (small goat?) and I was hit in the face by a package. *Spearmint*, it said, before it was taken away on the grounds that chewing gum was a dirty American habit. Like the Dutch, the Americans shout a lot.

Later on an American supply ship was said to have hit a mine in the Bristol Channel and flotsam was washed up along the beach. We collected cartons of brackish chocolate mint creams, an unheard-of luxury in those days of rationing. Typewriters were collected further up the coast. The flat sea was covered in an iridescent film of bunker oil which merged with the horizon. Paddling was forbidden to me. Belinda Wells, a confident eight-year-old role model with blond pigtails, suffered no such inhibition and emerged with her cylindrical legs embellished by tidemark rings of oil. Looking back it's surprising that such an unremarkable event could be indelibly recalled, but recognition of the morphology of a girl's legs must be part of our programming.

We share our makeup with much of nature – even *drosophila*, the fruit fly with pink eyes, has 50% of our genes. And the hatchling swallows in our barn are pre-programmed to fly around, catch insects on the wing, discuss their flight plans on the television aerial, depart for France, the Pyrenees, Morocco, the Sahara desert and South Africa, and return the following year if they not shot by Spanish or Maltese 'sportsmen'. If you want to see beauty, aerobatics, navigation of the highest order and wonder at the universe, forget about quarks, naked singularities and string theory, and praise the glory of these wonderful creatures. If morphological biodiversity is what you seek, try the Underground.

There was a non-aviation related incident that holiday which had implications for the future. My brother Richard devised an onomatopoeic game which involved spinning a chamber pot like a trencher – a trencher is a medieval wooden plate used by scholars at Winchester College. It was eaten in hunger by the Trojans, as prophesied by Calaeno in the *Aeneid*. Richard would sing, *"Pim-wim-wim goes the potty…"* repeated ad nauseam. The winner was the one who caused the potty to spin for the most turns before settling down. On this occasion there was a calamity. Richard spun it with such vigour that the unfortunate receptacle smashed against the wardrobe. Its frowning pediment and Edvard Munch-like oval mirror scowled fiercely down on the little boy with a tear in his eye, whose faded blue rompers had one linen-covered button held on by a single thread. The incident was an early exercise in accident causation on the Swiss cheese (actually French – see below) model of James Reason. This will be examined later, but for now, if there had been attention to any one of the three points below, the accident might have been averted:

*   The potty was being operating outside its design envelope for a purpose for which it was not originally intended.
*   It was frangible, enamelled steel potties having been pressed into war service.
*   Insufficient training had been given to ensure its safe usage.

Richard had a penchant for wardrobes. On the day we went off to our prep school for the first time, in his excitement he climbed into the wardrobe in our bedroom. That seemed very silly, so I pulled him out – sillier still when he hung on. The contraption fell over with an almighty crash, trapping him, and bringing the ceiling down in the dining room below, where our parents were having their tea.

There were two legs sticking out and a small voice cried, "Lemme out!" I met them on the stairs. "Something dreadful has happened," I said redundantly, as the ceiling was on the dining room table. Fortunately he was unhurt apart from a cut on his face.

The final event of that holiday had more far-reaching consequences. One day a communications aircraft made a precautionary landing near our hotel. We went to take a look, but it was guarded by a Corporal Jones-like figure in battle dress standing at ease with a Mk III SMLE (Short Magazine Lee-Enfield) service rifle. Or maybe it was a Great War P17 American Enfield, which were used in large numbers by the Home Guard in the Second World War. The difference was important enough for the American version to have a red band painted upon it; the former has a calibre of 0.303" whilst the latter is 0.30.06". He eyed us suspiciously. Looking inside was against orders in case I was a dangerous enemy alien, but he made an exception. I was fascinated by the levers, instruments and that mysterious aroma of rubber, adhesive and anticipation which is an enduring feature of service aeroplanes across the generations.

The moment was Delphic – from then on I was determined to fly.

REQUIEM

Under the wide and starry sky, Dig the grave and let me lie…

Robert Louis Stevenson
(1858–1894), *Requiem*

Before my father died we went together to Arromanches-les-Bains in Normandy and looked upon what is left of the caissons which made up one of the two Mulberry harbours. The second was on Omaha Beach further up the coast to the west. It was a time for reflection. It was here that he had come ashore at Gold Beach on 6th June 1944 – D-day, at H hour + 6. He was with the 6th Battalion of the Durham Light Infantry. It was part of the 151st Infantry Brigade of the 50th (Northumbrian) Infantry Division of the British Second Army, and was commanded by General Sir Miles Dempsey. The initial assault began at 07.25. By midnight the 151st had reached Bayeux, having landed 25,000 men for some four hundred casualties. He never spoke of it beyond the fact of D-Day – the anticipation during embarkation leave, the seasickness which vanished on landing, the death and injury on the beachhead. He felt that there was not much he could do as a medical officer who had trained as a general practitioner, but the troops valued the presence of a doctor and its effect on morale was significant.

He was more forthcoming about his time in the desert. He gave the impression he would have preferred to have stayed there, rather than be involved with general medical practice in Frome. It had been difficult to survive on the water ration of one gallon per man per day, some of which was removed by the cookhouse. The remainder had to cover personal consumption including washing and shaving. Kidney stones were common. It was very cold in the starlight, even in midsummer, when the pre-dawn night was illuminated by showers of Perseids. Sometimes the strains of *Lilli Marlene*, sung by the German troops, could be heard in the distance.

> *Vor der Kaserne*
> *Vor dem grossen Tor*
> *Stand eine Laterne*
> *Und steht sie noch davor*
> *So woll'n wir uns da wieder seh'n*
> *Bei der Laterne wollen wir steh'n*
> *Wie einst Lili Marleen.*

The song was adopted by the allies, too – Lilli Marlene, the girl who waited for her man at the barrack gate; the dream of soldiers everywhere.

He spent the days watching such wildlife as there was, his father being the naturalist Norman H. Joy. He was involved in the whole of the desert campaign with the Eighth Army. There were some memorable events including a road traffic accident, which damaged his cervical spine and reduced his ability to turn his head. And an incident during the retreat through Mersa Matruh, in which his driver ran over an Italian machine gun nest with his Red Cross Bedford flat-nosed truck. This was before the first battle of El Alamein in July 1942. In spite of the doubts of the presiding vicar he asked for the scene to be recalled in his eulogy. This single act of daring fulfilled his need to do his bit as a non-combatant. There were redacted trips to Cairo for R&R (rest and recuperation). Back in Normandy we visited the cemeteries, British and German. After losing two world wars it is an irony that Germany today, justly dominates Europe politically, financially and industrially, with a manufacturing gross domestic product twice that of the UK.

★★★

The Royal Navy had blockaded Germany in the Great War following the inconclusive Battle of Jutland (May/June 1916) led by the cautious

Admiral Sir John Jellicoe against the German High Seas Fleet under the nimble-minded Vice-Admiral Reinhard Scheer. British losses in men and tonnage of shipping were twice that of Germany, but the German fleet did not venture forth again. This was to be the task of the U-Boats which indirectly brought the USA into the War, and assured eventual success to the allies. The Royal Navy also contributed to the protection of our island from Unternehmen Seelöwe (Operation Sealion) in the second conflict. The planned invasion of Britain in the summer of 1940, over which the Battle of Britain was fought, failed, in part on account of our naval strength.

The Royal Air Force in 1939 had 135 squadrons, the majority of which were bombers, with a total strength of 2,600 aircraft, many of which were obsolescent. The total manpower was 173,985 of all ranks. Now repeated defence cuts inspired by a politicised civil service and a limpid, self-serving political class, ignorant of defence issues, have reduced the fully trained strength of the Royal Air Force to 33,000. This is a Spartan denouement reflecting the values of a nation inured to *panem et circenses* – Juvenal (AD 60–140), Satire X – in decline. There are now (2015) seven front line RAF squadrons remaining; there had been 37.5 in 1991.

With the retirement of the Tornado in 2019 and of the tranche 1 Typhoons at the end of the decade, there may be but five front-line squadrons left. Out of this will have to come four for homeland defence – the QRA (Quick Reaction Alert) response to the Russian threat, with one to cover Baltic (and Falkland Islands) defence and expeditions in Iraq and Syria. We are debating whether to send a few elderly Tornados to Syria as this is written. The Royal Navy has done badly, too, inspite of the awaited (aircraft-free) carriers. Currently (summer 2015) it has 23,260 men and women on its "trained strength" - a shortfall of 7,000 on that needed to man fully what is left of the fleet. The army at the end of 2014 had a strength of 94,000 - on target for 80,000; in theory this will be shored up by un-recruitable reservists.

We live in increasingly dangerous times and yet money, borrowed on behalf of the taxpayer, is thrown at corrupt regimes to sanitise the Tory brand in preference to re-enforcing our homeland defence. The peril we face today may be as great as that in 1938, when the Anschluss in Austria, and the occupation of the Sudetenland in Czechoslovakia, echoed to the march of fascism. And yet there is only a reluctant commitment of 2% of our annual GDP to defence, and this may have been achieved by creative accountancy. When the history of this time is written, the depth of the failure of these latter-day Muppets of Munich will be laid bare as the Germans and the French take the lead in Europe, and provide for its defence.

★★★

In 1919 the boundaries of Europe were redrawn, unsuccessfully as it turned out, and following victory in 1945 the country was exhausted. Statecraft, leadership and common sense withered, together with the sense of duty and sacrifice which until lately had shone for common purpose. The electorate became apathetic and political life a fusion of expediency, deception and spin beneath an increasingly stifling penumbra of corrupt and unaccountable European bureaucracy. The electorate in the Western world lost confidence in its politicians; short-termism at home laid waste to our manufacturing sector and there was greed and corruption in our financial services.

In 1945 we were effectively bankrupt and were bailed out with other European nations by United States Marshall Aid. This ended in 1952. Our war effort had been prodigious. Not only had we increased our manufacturing output six-fold, but we had built and manned the factories to produce more than 100,000 aircraft of all types, including more than 10,000 heavy bombers and 38,000 fighters. Some 722 heavy ships were launched and over five million tonnes of merchant shipping constructed. One hundred thousand tanks and armoured cars and nearly a million other vehicles were produced. There were telecommunications, ordnance and all the paraphernalia of the battlefield. The Royal Air Force over the six years to 1945 had grown to over 9,200 aircraft, with more than one million allied and Dominion men and women serving.

It is difficult to understand how seventy years later we are almost bankrupt again, mainly due to weapons-grade self-serving political ineptitude. The budget deficit in 2013 was the highest it had been since the Second World War and the national debt higher than it had been for fifty years. There are now no significant British-owned car manufacturers and the aviation industry has disposed of its interest in Airbus to concentrate on United States defence contracts and foreign weapons sales, some of which have been investigated for evidence of bribery. Rolls-Royce Holdings, one of the few jewels in our manufacturing crown, sold its 32.5% interest in the International Aero Engines consortium (IAE) V2500 intermediate size turbojet engine to United Technologies, the parent company of Pratt and Witney, in 2012. It has no replacement. Furthermore, Rolls-Royce Motors, founded over lunch at the Midland Hotel, Manchester in 1904, is owned by BMW (Germany), with Bentley Motors being owned by Volkswagen (Germany). Both are successful companies manufacturing in the UK, but are German-owned.

At the stroke of a pen the Secretary of State for Transport, the Right Honourable Philip Hammond, PC, MP, rejected Bombardier, the remaining (albeit Canadian-owned) Crewe-based railway manufacturer in favour of Siemens (Germany) for the production of 1,140 railway carriages, worth £1.6 billion, for the Thameslink project. This threatened the closure of one of the two remaining Bombardier production lines. The senior civil servant responsible, and the Secretary of State himself, spoke as one when they told me that the contract turned on the better credit rating of the German firm. No other European nation would be as deranged as this. At one time over 20,000 people were employed at Crewe, by no means the only centre of railway production, and over seven thousand steam locomotives were constructed there; now only one thousand employees remain. Britain built the first railways and at one time exported them to the world. Patriotism before power and party has gone.

There is a glimmer of hope for the future in that Hitachi is to base its European railway manufacturing business in Newton Aycliffe, County Durham. This is to fulfil a £1.2 billion deal to make the next generation of inter-city trains for the Great Western and East Coast main line services. It was the same pen that ordered our aircraft carriers to be scrapped, and our Hawker Harrier squadrons. We invented the only operational vertical take-off combat aircraft in the world at the time; the Americans bought in to it and we were equipped with them. The Secretary of State for Defence got rid of them in what Joseph Kennedy, US Ambassador to the Court of St James in 1939, would have called a fire sale settlement.

"Dieu protége l'Angleterre," to paraphrase Sir Winston Churchill in his London broadcast of 21st October 1940 to the people of France.

Just as we led in railway and aircraft design and construction, telecommunications and ship building, we have won more Nobel Prizes than any other country apart from the USA. We were first in nuclear power generation; now the French and Chinese may build our power stations. It is astonishing that we give predatory nations access to strategic assets such as power generation and transport. The majority of our utilities are now foreign-owned and exploited. Our Chairmen and CEOs often have little in-depth knowledge or understanding of the industries for which they are responsible. What dawned as the Age of Aquarius has evolved into the age of entitlement exemplified by kleptocratic bankers, over-rewarded QUANGOcrats and increasing distance between the haves and the have-nots. Engineers and manufacturers are out of fashion. So is social justice.

★★★

Much of European airspace was closed for five days in April 2010 following the eruption of the Eyjafjallajökull volcano in Iceland. Dame Deirdre Hutton, DBE, formerly of the Consumer Council and the Food Standards Agency, had been appointed Chairman of the CAA six months beforehand; at the same time Andrew Haines had been appointed CEO, following a career in the railways. The British mistrust of experts is in our DNA, but it might have been helpful to have had someone with a career in aviation in at least one of these two posts. A test pilot or senior engineer, maybe? The civil service elite is mainly composed of generalists with arts degrees, unrelated to the offices they will fill and ignorant of or unsympathetic towards technology. It has also become increasingly politicised.

Career politicians, generally without gainful employment experience and otherwise unemployable, are appointed briefly to ministries for which they have no qualification and to which they lay waste. They construct policies with short-term objectives for short-term political ends. There is a national shortage of teachers, engineers and doctors – half of the doctors working in our hospitals qualified abroad as we are too incompetent to train/retain our own.. Even London Heathrow Airport, our largest national hub, has had its development stunted by political indecision over runway capacity, out of consideration for votes in constituencies to the west of London. The third runway should have been built thirty years ago. Heathrow operates at 99% of capacity much of the time and a couple of snowflakes regularly close it in the winter. It is owned by a Spanish consortium (Ferrovial).

Finally, to our grammar schools, which were once amongst the best in Europe, and the best of social levellers. Now our state secondary education, judged on international performance in terms of opportunity for pupils from a poor background to advance, is one of the worst in Europe. The poor white working class are at the bottom of the heap, in every way, in terms of achievement. Part of this downward trend relates to the adoption of trendy teaching methods, indolence and a tolerance of failure, but above all, there is political interference. Commitment to excellence, discipline and achievement has been lost. Baroness Shirley Williams (St Paul's Girls' School and Somerville College, Oxford) and Anthony Crosland (Highgate School and Trinity College Oxford) were responsible, with others, for the destruction of selective entry. Their policy is now supported by all the main political parties, including those whose leadership is thickly Etonian.

"If it is the last thing I do I will destroy every f★★★ing grammar school in England, and Wales, and Scotland," said Crosland, whilst Williams (testament of pathos) said recently that their closure was her finest hour.

Crosland had shared a tutor at Oxford with Sir Tommy Macpherson, one of the most decorated soldiers in the history of the British Army. He was later tutor to HRH the Duke of Kent. Macpherson later recalled that he (Crosland) was a notable *bon vivant*. Whether socialist programming changes the brain permanently remains to be shown, but it is strangely unresponsive to rational argument and common sense. There is emerging, possibly relevant, pharmacological evidence that neuro-transmitter blockade can be associated with neuro-anatomical change: perhaps socialism does the same. Hugh (later Lord) Scanlon did recant in later life, acknowledging the damage that the unions had inflicted upon the country. Similar to the closure of the grammar schools, perhaps; but by then he had become an establishment figure. There is no bigotry more cosy and secure than the certainties of left-wing dogma. Oscar Wilde visited the problem in *The Soul of Man Under Socialism* but, true to form, saw it as enlightened individualism – social anarchy in the pursuit of art. *The new individualism is the new Hellenism*, he declared. Try selling that in Islington. How fortunate that the boys of the old brigade are not here to see how we have managed their legacy and their sacrifice.

Where are the boys of the old brigade?
Who fought with us side by side?
Shoulder to shoulder, and blade by blade,
Fought till they fell and died!
Who so ready and undismayed?
Who so merry and true?
Where are the boys of the old Brigade?
Where are the lads we knew?

Edward Slater; words by Frederic
Weatherly, 1881

ORIGINS OF
FLIGHT

*The whole problem is confined within these limits, viz. to make a surface
support a given weight by the application of power to the resistance of air.*

Sir George Cayley, 1809

When I was seven years old my parents purchased an old rectory from
Queen Anne's Bounty. This now defunct body merged with the
Ecclesiastical Commissioners in 1947 to form the Church Commissioners.
The house stands at the top of Locks Hill, Frome, almost opposite the
Beehive Inn. There had been more than half a dozen breweries in Frome
when the Lamb brewery, which had stood at the top of Bath Street, and
Frome United Breweries in Vallis Way, amalgamated in 1955; only to go
into liquidation in 1960. Locks Hill was so quiet in those days that Bruce,
my father's black Labrador, used to lie in the road and had to make way for
the fishmonger and the rag and bone man, with their horses and carts. The
house was cold and damp. It was also the home to armies of woodlice.

The woodlice wandered about the house and lived in large numbers in the
Parish Room, a dark, damp brick-built affair beneath a large horse chestnut
tree. When we first moved in, shrouded figures would gather for evenings
of droning incantation by gaslight. It contained a cache of incense which
had been left behind by the departed Rector. This, Richard and I used to
burn when we were short of the ingredients for making gunpowder. Such
activities were not part of any religious or political ceremonial. To one side

of the Parish Room was a shed where my brother's barn owl lived. He slept most of the day but used to join us for supper in the kitchen; after a fly-by he would watch proceedings from the dresser.

Owls have such good wing boundary layer and tip vortex management that they fly silently whilst listening and looking for their prey. This contrasts with the peregrine falcon, which is one of the fastest and most widespread raptors on earth. They do not worry about tip vortices and if they choose to beat you up, as once happened to us in France, they do so at speeds sometimes exceeding 200 mph. And they whistle as they swoop by.

After he had eaten his supper, usually dog meat wrapped in feathers, Wol would depart behind the massive Electrolux fridge, stamp his feet, evacuate his bowels and noisily bring up pellets. They smelt of melaena (partly digested blood), but Brandy, our yellow Labrador, would eat them if he could. Eventually Wol departed whilst we were away on holiday, although he would sometimes return at sunset in reply to calls. Once he turned up to show off his girl (or boy) friend to his old folks. He was followed by a coven of three stroppy little owls with permanent scowls and street manners. They compared unfavourably with the baroque Wol with his quizzical look, when he was not dozing or asleep.

The back of the Parish Room overlooked an electrical substation, the Co-op and Miss Cayley's house. Miss Cayley was very old and always muffled in shawls of one sort or another. My mother used to visit her occasionally. One day I was taken along too. Her drawing room was gloomy and its walls covered in Anaglypta. Moustachioed grandees, male and female, looked sternly down from their dark gilt frames, hung on wire by hooks from the picture rail. The Victorian paintings were covered in a bitumen wash, muting the colours and giving a sepia tone to the whole scenario. The chairs had antimacassars. There was a faint sepulchral odour about the place. On her desk was an ink stand with a neglected fountain pen which I coveted for its gold nib. She told the story of her great-grandfather, Sir George Cayley. Unknown to me at the time, I was in the presence of a descendent of the man who is considered by some to have been the world's first aeronautical scientist, not overlooking a personal hero, Leonardo da Vinci (1452–1519).

6. A teenage barn owl (Tyto alba) from a water colour by Sophia Coningsby. Wol used to join us in the kitchen for supper and bring up his pellets behind the fridge. He flew silently with the help of superb boundary layer and wing-tip vortex management.

Leonardo invented the ornithopter, a flapping wing aeroplane, the helicopter (lifting screw), and the parachute five hundred years ago. His best-known work hangs in the Louvre in Paris. He also studied the contribution of vortex generation in the root of the great vessel of the heart (the aorta) to the closure of its valve, more than a hundred years before William Harvey published *de Motu Cordis* in Frankfurt in 1628. He built a glass model, having seen and wondered at an ox heart at his local butcher. Using hayseed suspended in water he studied the turbulent (vortex) flow in the sinuses of Valsalva. Unsurprisingly, not many cardiologists know that.

Sir George Cayley, 6th Baronet Brompton (1773–1857), was briefly the Whig Member of Parliament for Scarborough, but that should not detract from his other accomplishments. He founded the first Polytechnic Institute – now the University of Westminster – and defined the four aerodynamic forces of flight – lift, drag, mass and thrust. He carried out some of his experiments in rotary lift in the stairwell of Brompton Hall. He conceived the cambered aerofoil (wing) and demonstrated the importance of dihedral (upward) angulation of the wings for stability. After experimentation at the dawn of the 19th century he built his first model glider, which had all the features of the modern aeroplane. Writing in 1923, Charles Dollfus, creator of the Musée de l'Air in Paris, declared: *The aeroplane is a British invention... Sir George Cayley is the veritable inventor of the aeroplane.* Sacré bleu!

It is probable that the first flight in a heavier-than-air machine (i.e. not a balloon), and which carried a passenger, was in one of Sir George's box gliders in the 1840s. This involved an unidentified ten-year-old boy. If that is the case, he anticipated Samuel Franklin Cody by sixty years. Cody did the same with his stepson, Vivian. The flight recounted by Miss Cayley is well known. With the help of her grandfather, George John, and their live-in engineer, Thomas Vick, Sir George constructed a glider in 1853 which flew across Brompton Vale, piloted by a hapless footman. There is dispute as to whether the intrepid pilot was a footman, coachman or butler. He seems to have been a footman, as I recall Miss Cayley imagining his powdered wig, stockings and coat tails flying in the breeze. What is not in dispute is that on landing the poor man resigned on the spot, exclaiming that he had been appointed as a footman and had no intention of re-mustering as a pilot.

It was on the afternoon of 17th December 1903 from Kittyhawk, four miles from the Kill Devil hills in North Carolina, that Orville Wright sent a telegram to his father, the Very Reverend Milton Wright, stating: *Success four flights Thursday morning all against twenty one mile wind started from level with engine power alone average speed through air thirty one miles longest fifty seven seconds inform Press home Christmas.* It was the first time in the history of the world that a machine carrying a man had lifted itself under its own power. The flight had lasted twelve seconds and the craft had covered 120 feet. On the fourth and final flight of the day Wilbur flew for fifty-seven seconds at about thirty miles per hour, covering 852 feet. Forty-four years later Chuck Yeager broke the sound barrier over the Mojave desert and thirty-two years after that, in 1976, the Anglo-French Concorde was flying scheduled passenger services across the North Atlantic Ocean at the twice the speed of sound (Mach 2) – faster than a rifle bullet. This outstanding Anglo-French achievement and its subsequent service lasted for twenty-seven years.

The success of the Wright brothers fired enthusiasm for aviation in Europe. Sir Hiram Maxim (1840–1916) was an American by birth, later becoming a naturalised British subject (see photo plate 3). He was knighted by King Edward VII for services to machine gunnery. He had been a prolific inventor, apprenticed in Maine, before coming to England. It can probably be claimed that he was the first man in Europe to have made a powered ascent. His many inventions included a tricycle, a mousetrap, a blackboard and an automatic sprinkler. He got into dispute with Thomas Edison over the ownership of the patent for the incandescent light bulb and lost. He is best known as the inventor of the Maxim gun, which was later developed as the Vickers machine gun. He also invented a flying machine. In 1893 there was a brief flight in his captive craft, which had a wingspan of 110 feet and weight of 3.5 tons. It was driven by two steam engines, fired by naphtha and ran on rails. It seems to have lifted off but the 'flight' was abandoned to the relief of the good people of Bexley, Kent.

There was much interest in aviation at the turn of that century in France. There are many names. These include Ernest Archdeacon and Henri Deutsch de la Meurthe, who founded the Aero-Club de France and awarded a prize for the first flight longer than twenty-five metres. Henri Farman, the Voisin brothers (Charles and Gabriel), Léon Delagrange, Louis Bleriot and others all contributed. The Voisin brothers formed the first commercial aircraft factory in Europe: Appareils d'Aviation – Les Frères Voisin, having bought out Louis Blériot in 1906. Charles first flew at Bagatelle near Paris on 28th February 1907 in a biplane pusher. It had a fifty horsepower Antoinette

7.   *Outhwaite, our 1929 4 ½ litre le Mans 'WO' Bentley, late for lunch in Honfleur: Spring 2015. On a different occasion he went to dinner with Diana Barnato-Walker.* ©Guillaume Nedelec

engine and the flight covered thirty-three feet. Years later we visited the site in *Outhwaite*, our 4.5 litre WO Bentley, at the invitation of Louis Vuitton. *Outhwaite* had risen to the occasion when *Black Prince*, our 1937 two litre Aston Martin, had expired at the top of Reigate Hill. We drove through northern France late at night in a rainstorm, with primitive weather gear, to be told "typical English" when we arrived, just in time, at Bagatelle. An excitable (and exciting) lady from Italian television could not be dissuaded that the Bentley was not an Aston Martin; after all, the placard was clear.

The prize rewarding the first person to fly in Europe went to a wealthy young Brazilian, Alberto Santos-Dumont, the son of a coffee planter. He started by developing an airship, but in his cellular biplane – *the 14-bis* – on 23rd October 1906, he flew 180 feet at a height of fifteen feet, also at Bagatelle. He had asked his friend Louis Cartier to produce a watch which would allow him to keep both hands on the controls. This was the birth of the wristwatch. He committed suicide in São Paulo in 1932.

Aviation in the United Kingdom lagged behind the French and the Americans. There are many household names. Horatio Phillips, the son of a gunsmith, built the first wind tunnel to study the lift generated by double curved aerofoils (wings), which he patented in 1891. He demonstrated that airflow over the upper surface of such a structure increases in speed with consequent reduction in pressure (lift), the reverse occurring on the lower surface. This was a practical demonstration of the theorem published in 1738 by a Swiss mathematician, Daniel Bernoulli (1700–1782), who had studied fluid mechanics and the properties of Newtonian fluids. Phillips made a short hop of forty-five feet in his Multiplane in 1904. It was little more than a Venetian blind on a tricycle and was longitudinally unstable. Three years on, a later version with two hundred aerofoils covered 450 feet. It was not controllable and cannot be considered to have been an aeroplane. He quit after that.

Other pioneers in England include Claude Grahame-White (1879–1959), who was an engineer and aviation pioneer (see photo plate 5). He was the first to make a night flight during the *Daily Mail* London to Manchester air race in 1910. Harry Hawker (1889–1921) was an Australian who was so impressed by the first demonstration of flight he saw at Diggers Rest in 1910 that he journeyed to England and joined Tommy Sopwith, soon to be his test pilot. He died as the result of an aviation accident, possibly from a contributing medical cause, at Hendon aerodrome in 1921. He had suffered an in-flight haemorrhage, maybe related to co-existing spinal tuberculosis.

Sopwith was born in Kensington in 1888 and died aged 101 years in Hampshire in 1989. In 1912 he set up the Sopwith School of Flying at Brooklands with the prize money he earned for the longest flight in a British-built craft from England to the Continent. He had covered 169 miles in three hours forty minutes. With Fred Sigrist (whose company Reid and Sigrist made gyroscopes for the turn-and-slip blind flying indicator) Sopwith set up his eponymous aviation company. It built over 18,000 aircraft in the Great War, of which 5,747 were Camels. Sopwith Aviation closed down after the war with charges of profiteering, to be restarted with chief test pilot Harry Hawker as H. G. Hawker Engineering Co. Ltd. Later it became Hawker Siddeley Aviation. Sopwith competed in the Americas Cup in 1934 and 1937 in *Endeavour* and *Endeavour II*. He crossed the Channel to Dunkirk in 1940, taking part in Operation Dynamo in *Endeavour II*, to rescue the British Expeditionary Force (BEF) and other allied troops.

John F. C. Moore-Brabazon, 1st Viscount Tara (1884–1964), was the first Englishman to fly, in a French Voisin, on the Isle of Sheppey. The date was 2nd May 1909. Alliot Verdon Roe (1877–1958) was the first Englishman to fly in a machine of his own design, built under a railway arch on Walthamstow marshes. The date was July 1909, and the venue adopted following a disagreement with management at Brooklands. There is always disagreement with management. The aircraft was a Roe Triplane. The company he formed with his brother Humphrey was called A. V. Roe Aircraft and some 8,300 of his Avro 504 fighter aircraft were built during and after the Great War. He later left the company to found Saunders Roe, which built flying boats. The Avro Company built the Lancaster during the Second World War, and the Vulcan bomber after it.

Geoffrey de Havilland (1882–1965) joined the Balloon Factory at Farnborough in 1910, bringing with him an aircraft he had designed, and which he sold to the establishment for £400. It subsequently became the Royal Aircraft Factory. De Havilland quickly moved on to Airco and later founded his own company – the de Havilland Aircraft Company – first at Stag Lane aerodrome and later at Hatfield. In 1960 it became part of the Hawker-Siddeley Company. He was his own test pilot. Of his three sons, two were to die in aircraft accidents – Geoffrey in an in-flight beak-up in the DH108 tailless experimental aircraft. In this disaster, whilst in a Mach 0.9 dive, a high-speed shock stall caused failure of the main spar – critical Mach numbers were not well understood at the time. John was killed in a mid-air collision involving two de Havilland Mosquitos – one of the most versatile aircraft ever built (of wood). Over 7,400 were constructed and it was operated by twenty-one nations. The later de Havilland Vampire was operated by thirty-one nations and 3,268 were built.

Henry Folland (1889–1954) worked at Farnborough from 1912 and designed the SE 5a (Scout Experimental) fighter. This aircraft went into production in six different factories and 5,265 were built during the Great War. The propeller from the Viper engine of one hangs in my garage, slightly afflicted by woodworm. It was purchased in an East End street market for £4 when I was a senior registrar at the (Royal) London Hospital. Later Folland joined the Gloster Aircraft Company which was taken over by Hawker, whereupon he moved to found the Folland Aircraft Company. The Folland Gnat became a successful small jet trainer and was used by the Red Arrows for their aerobatic displays. It was sold to several countries. Finally, Frederick Handley Page founded Handley Page Ltd in 1912 at Cricklewood, which was the first publicly traded aircraft company in the UK. The firm specialised in large aircraft – bombers and transport aircraft. For many years a large aircraft might be called a Handley Page in the same manner that a vacuum cleaner tends to be called a Hoover, or increasingly a Dyson.

The plaudits for being the first man to fly in England went to another hero, an American born in Iowa – Samuel Franklin Cody (1867–1913). He had started life as a cowboy and was expert with the horse, the lasso and the rifle (see photo plate 4). He settled permanently in England in 1889 and sometimes is confused with Buffalo Bill Cody. He developed a stage show with his wife Maud (Lillian), and later his assistant Mrs Elizabeth King, who subsequently adopted the name Lela Cody after Maud had returned to the United States. One of his tricks, years before the Health and Safety Executive took the fun out of the simple pleasures of life such as playing conkers, was to shoot cigarettes or glass balls out of Lela's mouth. He could also split a playing card, sideways on with a rifle bullet, taking aim between his legs. One of Lela's great-grandsons is John Simpson, the BBC Foreign Affairs editor.

Cody's early success in aviation was in the development of his patented man-lifting kites. This excited the interest of both the Army, for artillery spotting, and the Royal Navy, for use as observation posts. In 1904, Lieutenant Colonel John (later Major-General Sir John) Capper was appointed to the Army Balloon School at Aldershot. Capper was responsible for the Service development of balloons, and extended his interest to kites. He negotiated a contract for Cody as an army kiting instructor with the Royal Engineers in 1906. Number 1 Company of the Balloon School subsequently became No. 1 Squadron, Royal Flying Corps in 1912 and later No. 1 Squadron, the Royal Air Force in 1918. Later Cody was to experience difficulty in the recovery of the £5,000 promised by the War Office for the use of his patent. With the encouragement of Capper, Cody drew on his experience with kites to build a glider in which his stepson, Vivian, was to be seriously injured.

In 1906 Capper obtained a two-year contract for Cody with the War Office and although the Army Council maintained its indifference to heavier-than-air machines, the course had been set. Capper and Cody collaborated on the building of the British Army Dirigible (balloon) No. 1, also known as *Nulli Secundus* (Second to None). It was constructed in 1907 in the balloon shed on Laffan's Plain, now Farnborough Airport following the privatisation of the Royal Aircraft Establishment (RAE) in 2001 by the Ministry of Defence (MOD). On September 10th 1907, the plum-coloured balloon was heaved out of its shed, inflated and floated away to huge acclaim; Capper was the pilot and Cody the engineer. On October 5th 1906 they took off again. This time they flew over Farnborough common, waving at Napoleon III's widow (Empress Eugenie – she was an aficionado) and shouting to Lela at his home in Frimley that he would be back for dinner. Then they headed for St Paul's Cathedral, via Whitehall, where the Army Council stood waiting on the roof of the War Office. They saluted one another.

When their engines overheated, partly due to a persisting headwind, like Lady Agatha d'Ascoyne in *Kind Hearts and Coronets* he came to earth not in Berkeley

Square, but at the velodrome in Crystal Palace. Cody had a competitor, Lieutenant J. W. Dunne, whose secret aircraft project was removed thereafter to Blair Atholl. The Army Council of the country with the biggest navy and empire the world had ever seen responded with a flourish and awarded him £50 towards the cost of building British Army Aeroplane No. 1.

Cody experimented with the airframe of his aeroplane whilst he waited for an engine. He studied the effect of the controls, when there was sufficient wind, by tying his craft to a tree and recording the effect of airflow over the wing surfaces. When the engine arrived, he measured its power output by tying the aircraft to the tree with a Hooke's gauge. Cody's tree, now a replica made in aluminium alloy by Farnborough apprentices, stands outside the QinetiQ Headquarters in the Cody Technology Park in Farnborough. Formerly it stood outside the RAF mess near the threshold of Runway 24. After much trial and error he is credited with the first flight of an aircraft in England, on 16th October 1908, when he covered 1,390 feet but damaged the aircraft on landing. As a reward for his success he was visited shortly afterwards by R. B. Haldane, the Secretary of State for War, who explained that the military could see no use for aircraft in war and that his contract with the army was cancelled. He was, however, allowed to keep the aircraft and to work at Laffan's plain. Dunne's aircraft was scrapped. This heralded the start of a century of procurement blunders and extravagance which still plagues the MOD to this day. The elephant is alive and well in SW1.

Cody continued with his experiments, funded by prizes and appearances at air shows. Lela became the first woman to fly in the British Empire and North America on the 15th August 1909; his first passenger had been his friend and supporter John Capper. The next aircraft he developed – the *Flying Cathedral* – was the largest in the world. He was made an English citizen at a ceremony he set up at the St Léger meeting at Doncaster racecourse the same year. He died as a result of an inflight breakup of his float plane variant in 1913. About 100,000 people attended his funeral. He was outlived by his only son by four years – Samuel Franklin Leslie Cody fell in combat with the RFC, *fighting four enemy machines*, in 1917. Heroes were heroes in those days, not posturing narcissistic celebs. His was not the first fatal accident in aviation in the UK – that attribute belongs to the Hon. Charles Rolls in 1910, also as a result of an in-flight breakup. With

Cody's death, the plans for an aviation company bearing his name died with him.

There were two failed attempts by a Frenchman, Hubert Latham (1883–1912), to cross the channel in 1909, during which he executed the first ever ditching. He does get the credit, however, for being the first person to shoot a duck from an aircraft. It was stuffed and is to be seen at Château de Maillebois, the family seat. He died in the Congo, either being gored by a buffalo, or having been murdered by one of his bearers. On 25th July 1909, Blériot, in a monoplane, crossed the English Channel, known as *la Manche* by the French and *der Ärmelkanal* by the Germans. It took him just over thirty-six minutes to fly from Les Baraques, between Sangatte and Calais, to his crash landing point near Dover Castle.

But as aviation made its shaky and dangerous start, the Triple Alliance of Germany, Austro-Hungary and Italy (the central powers) were squaring up with the Triple Entente of Britain, France and Russia. Italy was to later change sides under the terms of the secret Treaty of London (1915) to get into practice for October 13th 1943 in the second world conflict. The Royal Flying Corps had been commissioned two years before the Bosnian Serb student, Gavrilo Princip, murdered Archduke Franz Ferdinand, heir to Emperor Franz Joseph of Austria, and his morganatic wife, Countess Sophie Chotek, in Sarajevo on the 28th June 1914. "Please don't die, Sophie," were the last words of this unpopular man. Princip survived the gallows on account of his age – nineteen years – but not the firestorm, the excuse for which he provided. He died in jail of disseminated tuberculosis in 1918.

Four weeks later, on July 30th, Winston Churchill, then First Lord of the Admiralty, moved the First and Second Fleets from Spithead, where they had been reviewed by HM King George V, in secrecy and under cover of darkness to their war stations at Scarpa Flow. "The lamps are going out all over Europe," said Sir Edward Grey, Foreign Secretary, in August 1914. The conflicts ahead would change the world forever, and aviation, in spite of Mr Haldane's doubts, would play a central part.

On the idle hill of summer,
Sleepy with the flow of streams
Far I hear the steady drummer
Drumming like a noise in dreams.

Far and near and low and louder
On the roads of earth go by,
Dear to friends and food for powder,
Soldiers marching, all to die.

East and west on fields forgotten
Bleach the bones of comrades slain,
Lovely lads and dead and rotten;
None that go return again.

A Shropshire Lad: XXXV, A. E. Houseman (1859–1936)

EARLY YEARS

With the end of the Second World War my father returned to the general practice he had purchased before it had started. It had cost him £3,000, a fortune in those times. Following the birth of the National Health Service in 1948, under Aneurin Bevan, the whole sum was sequestered and paid back much later as part of his pension. During the war he also had to pay a locum, one Dr Ogilvy, out of his own resources. She was, by reputation, a rather indecisive lady whom he called Oggie. She soon faded away.

Petrol was first rationed in 1939 and this was not lifted until 1950; likewise food, clothing, soap and paper. Rationing was finally abolished in 1954. There was a brief return to petrol rationing during the Suez crisis in 1956. It made life difficult and Ivor Novello (*Keep the home fires burning…*) was jailed for a month for the misuse of petrol coupons. He was the hero of my first patient when I was a medical student, who, as a blind street musician, used to sing Novello's songs to me in one of the long Nightingale wards at St Thomas's Hospital. This went down badly with the ward sister as it spoilt the preferred ambience of the mortuary during the consultant ward round. Here the dropping of a pin sounded like a demented bedpan being restrained by a straightjacket.

My father conducted vast un-booked surgeries, and hand-wrote referral letters with a new invention – the Biro; free refills were guaranteed if the ink ran out before a given date. He repeatedly beat the clock and the warranty was discontinued. The scarcity of petrol did not deter him from what he called visits and the Americans call house calls. This involved driving in his pre-war Ford 8 around the countryside of East Somerset. It was not much of a performer and its main vice was the abrupt failure of the suction driven windscreen wiper upon acceleration. As it frequently rains in Somerset this was hazardous.

Sometimes Richard and I would accompany him to a local farm where we would be given an egg. During the darkest part of the war the adult ration was one egg per week, though pregnant mothers and children did better. A national minimum diet was extensively researched and tested by academic investigators in Cambridge. They lived on it for a time to study its long-term tolerability, but it was never needed. The health of the nation improved during the war with more balanced food, but reportedly flatulence increased due to the higher carbohydrate content. Now one quarter of the population is obese; two thirds of males and three fifths of females are overweight. The dietary benefits of wartime have gone into reverse.

The Nichols Farm at Whitham Friary was particularly favoured as Mrs Nichols used to bake a sponge cake for us. The farm was lit by a single-cylinder Lister diesel generator which charged a large array of lead acid accumulators. It puffed away in an outhouse quite happily, needing little attention until it was stopped – when it snorted black smoke in indignation. Later on when my family went away I used to stay with them, catching the stopping train from Frome hauled by a Swindon built Great Western Railway 0-6-0 pannier tank engine. Later I attended a course to learn to drive one. It was there that I saw my first calf born – appalling, "was larnt" to drive a tractor, and shot rabbits with a poacher's 0.410 shotgun with a hollowed-out stock. This could be concealed down the trouser leg along, with luck, the rabbit.

One day we met two German prisoners of war, working on the farm, who had remained in spite of the cessation of hostilities. They were rather jolly and not the grizzled fellows of the wartime cartoons. There were many millions of souls who had been uprooted by the war. By the end of 1945 some two million remained in camps for DPs – Displaced Persons – all over Europe.

Many were still in camps up to five and ten years later. The camps contained representatives of diverse nations, survivors of the Holocaust, Poles, Czechs and Hungarians not wishing to return to their Russian occupied homelands. In Britain there had been axis prisoner of war camps, too, although many were sent to Canada and elsewhere. These must have contained half the male population of Florence at one time or another, judging from the number of purportedly ex-prisoners of war I met there when I was a student in the 1960s. It is with a sense of déjà vu that the early part of the 21st century has opened with genocide and millions of DPs, this time in the Middle East, the Ukraine and Africa.

Under the Geneva Convention officers were not allowed to work, but that did not apply to the other ranks who were sometimes seconded to farms, where they lived with the families. Thus it was that we met these two. We wondered why they did not escape but there was nowhere for them to go. Their names are lost to memory but they offered to make Richard and myself a model plane each in exchange for packets of Craven A cigarettes – *Does not affect your throat* (but gives you cancer later). He chose a Spitfire and I chose a Mosquito. Bearing in mind the simple tools available they carved and painted two handsome models which went on sorties round the lawn. Sadly, during a move, they were thrown out by my father. One of them married an English girl and they had three children. He became a panel beater in Brighton.

There was also a displaced persons camp at our preparatory school, Port Regis, in Dorset. We were sent there together in 1950, Richard being just eight years old and I was nine and a half. As we waited for the departure of our parents, I thought how small and lonely he looked. In the days of the Empire parents might not see their children for several years if they were serving in India. But the Empire was in retreat and we lived only twenty miles away – my mother suffered from what we call 'acopia' in medicine. At one edge of the site there was some land upon which a camp had been constructed. It was a collection of Nissen huts and was out of bounds on pain of a beating, this being the normal regulator in schools at that time. As a result we never met the incumbents who lived a troglodytic existence there. They were said to be Italian but nobody seemed sure and we were not allowed to speak to them. One day they disappeared.

There were no local airfields and there was not much aerial activity, although an aircraft did crash three miles or so away from the school one afternoon; why, we never found out. Scavenging, as we did in those days, I found some wire on a dump. Using a cornflakes packet, a brass-bound glass crystal and cat's whisker combination, found in a junk shop, and a pair of high-impedance headphones bought at the church fête for 3d (1.3p), I constructed a crystal receiving set. Thus began an interest in radio communication which plugged the gap until aircraft were again accessible.

At my next school I passed the Radio Amateur's Exam on the way to obtaining a call sign as a 'ham' (radio amateur). There is not much to show for it now, apart from an ex-Royal Air Force Marconi R1155A Bomber Command receiver and a Y Service R206 radio interception receiver (Y being geek shorthand for wireless). There is also a post-war Eddystone 840C communications receiver. It has to be said that the National Radio Company of Massachusetts HRO (Helluva Rush Order) receiver was preferred for the long night watches, when five letter Enigma encrypted Morse code transmissions had to be transcribed with great precision.

The Y service was the listening service which provided the radio intercepts for the more glamorous and interesting code-breaking activities at Bletchley Park and elsewhere. A diverse group of young people – debutantes and amateur radio enthusiasts, both within the military and outside it, served at listening stations in the UK as well as in Europe, and further afield. Enemy radio traffic was both monitored and recorded. It was as vital to the war effort as the much-applauded activities of the code breakers for whom the intercepts were destined.

The R1155 was designed for the heavy bombers; there was also a naval version. It had low, medium and high frequency waveband coverage, together with direction finding (DF) circuitry. It was used with a loop aerial which could be rotated from within the aircraft, and a trailing wire which tended to get forgotten and left on the perimeter hedge. Its Automatic Direction Finder (ADF) operated in the medium wavebands, and is only now being phased out as part of the mandatory equipment for flying in controlled airspace; this in spite of coastal and atmospheric degradation. More than 80,000 sets had been constructed before the war ended. Its other half was the butch T1154 transmitter, which needed respect as it had 1,200 volts on the anodes of its PT 15 power beam tetrodes, generated by a hefty rotary converter. It only radiated some twenty watts in telephony mode and the whole installation weighed more than one hundred pounds. Its warmth must have been welcome to the operator in the dark nights over enemy territory.

Guglielmo Marconi was a remarkable man. On December 12th 1901 he made the first radio contact between Newfoundland and Cornwall. He used a primitive spark transmitter and coherer receiver. He is said to have invented radio transmission and won the Nobel Prize for science in 1909. In 1912 there was a scandal which involved insider trading in Marconi shares by members of the Asquith government. *Plus ça change.* He was made a Marchese in 1924; the downside was that Benito Mussolini served as best man at his (second) wedding. Between 1968–1999 the UK-based company underwent a massive programme of acquisition and expansion. Marconi Electronic Systems merged with British Aerospace to form BAE Systems. In the dot-com boom the remainder got into financial difficulties; in 2006 the wreckage was bought up by the Swedish firm Ericcson. "Typical English," as Thierry was to say at the Bagatelle.

In September 1953 I went to Bradfield College, one of the minor public schools. The choice was made because my grandfather, Norman, had been the Medical Officer and lived in the village before the Great War. Tuberculosis and typhoid fever were common at that time. He was also a naturalist and wrote what is still the standard textbook of British beetles. My father, David, was born there in a large brick house known as Nutter's Furlong. A tame badger and a magpie lived with them. His elder sister ran away with a sailor to New Zealand, which was considered rather non-standard at the time. His other sister, Mary, became a schoolmistress in Chichester. At the time I was at the school, the house was the home of George E. Aisbett, one of the physics masters. Now it is one of the school residential houses.

It is set in some beautiful country, less so following the building of the M4 motorway to the north through the Great House woods. It was cold as there was no heating in the dormitories upstairs. Downstairs there were heated four-inch iron pipes and a fire in the 'houseroom' where the younger boys had their toyses (cupboards) and did their prep (preparation). There was chapel in the morning and house prayers in the evening. The housemaster, Philip Stibbe, was a gallant man. He had fought with the Chindits in the 16th Infantry Brigade under Bernard Fergusson (later Brigadier Sir Bernard) behind the enemy lines in Burma. They were supplied by parachute drops using the Douglas DC3 Dakota. More than 16,000 of these aircraft were built and many are still flying. The jungle is good insurgency territory and the land fertile.

Eventually Stibbe was caught by the Japanese and tortured. Following his release from jail in Rangoon (now Yangon) he wrote a book, *Return via Rangoon*, first published in 1947, which recounted his experiences. We recently visited the large War Graves Commission cemetery outside Rangoon, serene in the Burmese sunshine. Opposite we witnessed the blessing of a new motor car by a Buddhist priest. It was unclear whether this had a favourable effect on the insurance premium.

Discipline at Bradfield was enforced by graded punishment. This included log-cutting for the houseroom fire, runs such as Buscot–Privers (muddy), Privers–Rivers (very muddy), sometimes taken twice, and flogging (beating with a cane). Flogging was an art form with several different levels depending on the infraction involved. It could be boy on boy – by the head of house in the house library, and following house prayers to ensure everyone was in a state of grace. It could be by the head of school and school prefects, in the junior common room (JCR). Nasty. It was alleged that a running 'spiker' over a cricket bat was used by the head of one house on a near-contemporary of mine. The victim was in the sanatorium for two days and the housemaster visited him to ask him not to tell his parents. Remarkably an apology was made, but fifty years too late – the perpetrator should have been expelled, and put on trial, along with those responsible for allowing such criminal activity.

The administration of flogging could also be by the housemaster, or for real prestige, the headmaster. After a couple of years of my time there the former headmaster, John D. Hills, was replaced by Anthony Chenevix-Trench (1919–1979), who greatly raised the game. He could translate Virgil into Greek as he went along, so we were led to believe, was wont to quote Kant's *Critique of Pure Reason*, and lived in a world inhabited by gerundives, fickle subjunctives and an occasional winsome participle. He beat those who regarded Latin grammar as a wasteland, as well as for a large array of other trivial misdemeanours or opinions.

Trench used to flog boys in class for mal-declension of nouns, or non-conjugation of verbs, and in his study for crimes such as smoking. He was also into spanking and the use of the strap. David (Lord) Owen, who was ahead of me in the same house, wrote little about his time at Bradfield in his monumental autobiography, written at half-time, calling him *that strange little man*. Later Trench went on to Eton College as headmaster where, in spite of some changes for the better, he was not a success. He refused to stop his beating activities and developed a liking for alcohol. He died, reputedly of alcoholism, aged sixty years, having been asked to leave Fettes School where he had held his last post as headmaster.

Chenevix-Trench had been a prisoner of the Japanese on the Siam (Thailand)–Burma (Myanmar) railway, where tens of thousands of British, Dutch and Commonwealth soldiers died. The Khwae Noi (river Kwai) and Khwae Yai rivers converge into the Mae Klong river at Kanchanaburi. The bridge(s) – one wooden and temporary and one of concrete and steel (which remains) – spanned the Mae Klong, not the river Kwai as in David Lean's immortal film. The latter had been removed from the Dutch East Indies by the Japanese. It was not until we travelled on the railway to Kanchanaburi, and beyond, years later, that it was clear how dreadfully the local population had suffered; about 200,000 had died on the project. They were human beings too, and are truly the forgotten ones, alongside the 'collateral' in Vietnam, which the Americans called 'Gooks', and non-combatants in Iraq, Syria and Gaza whose lives, mutilation and death at times seem to be little more than a footnote on the ten o'clock news.

There were other inconveniences (sic). The three 'in-College' houses shared a joint lavatory facility. It was known as 'Begans yard'. The lavatories were in cubicles without doors. There must have been thirty of them. The cubicles were covered but the yard was open. It was uncomfortable when it snowed or rained. There were also cold showers in the morning, watched by the beaks (house prefects) from the comfort of their hot baths. Everyone played sport, did PE (physical exercise or 'jerks'), circuit training or ran; I shot and built radio transceivers. On Wednesday afternoons we had 'Corps'.

CORPS

...fear God and honour the King...

Major-General the Viscount Bridgeman,
DSO, MC. *The Cadet's Pocket Book.*

The Combined Cadet Force (CCF) has its origin in 1859 as the Volunteer Corps. By 1860 Rossall, Felsted, Eton, Harrow, Hurstpierpoint, Tonbridge and Rugby had joined. In 1908 the title was changed to the Officer Training Corps (OTC). If a cadet successfully passed both certificates of basic army training (Part 1 and Part 2) he was entitled to attend the War Office Selection Board, known as WOSB (pronounced "wasby") for officer selection. Although the force was initially affiliated to the army, there are now in addition Royal Naval, Royal Air Force and Royal Marine contingents.

Sadly the Cadet Force is still dominated by the public schools, and, as of 2014, involves a total of 259 establishments. There is an ongoing expansion scheme. Over 40,000 cadets are currently involved in: '*Providing a disciplined organisation in a school so that pupils may develop powers of leadership by means of training to promote the qualities of responsibility, self-reliance, resourcefulness, endurance and perseverance.*'

What else? I attended a celebration of its centenary in 2010, in Godalming, as High Sheriff-in-Nomination. In my day everyone joined at the age of fourteen years and spent the first two years in the Army section, unless they had flat feet. No-one was a conchie (conscientious objector). It involved a lot of stamping and shouting but we learnt field craft and how to read a map if you did not already know. The worst insult was to be told at a hundred decibels by Junior Under Officer P. A. Gray ma(jor) that you were "inefficient". Worse than a Buscot-Hogger in the rain. His battle dress creases were so sharp they were almost dangerous.

We wore blouses (battle, men's khaki, etc.) and trousers of some felted material which had the doubtful advantage that when it was wet, it stood up by itself. This was before the more comfortable and practical jersey (men's, heavy, olive, round neck), though they tended to snag on bushes (round, thorn, sharp) and other items when out on 'operations'. Quite why Quartermasters construct their sentences backwards remained a mystery. We also learnt to recognise the three types of tree known to the army at that time – bushy top, poplar and conifer.

My cadet pocket book, price 1/– (5p), exhorted us to *fear God and honour the King*, although by then Her Majesty the Queen was on the throne. There was also a booklet published by the Guardian Press, no less, of London, E17, on map reading, scouting, observation and camouflage. Most relevant of all was Caractacus' last battle at Caer Caradoc in Wales, in the 1st century AD. Caractacus was taken from Cardiff, or some such place, to Rome. As easyJet were not flying to Fiumicino at that time, presumably he went by sea. On arrival he was condemned to death, but was spared by Emperor Claudius on account of his oratory. An early Lloyd George.

Corps was full of puzzling acronyms, such as SMEAC and EGOLAPSWP, to help with sentry duty and patrol and flanking movements in the unlikely event that anyone could remember for what they stood. Researching the problem for this book, in spite of extensive enquiries and some rude retorts on PPRuNe – the Professional Pilots Rumour Network – it seems no-one else can remember either. This was before the era when TLAs (three-letter acronyms) were elevated to the commanding status they now have achieved. Night operations were spent in the local area avoiding capture, or patrolling. We used to black up our faces with burnt cork, and looked like extras from *The Jolson Story*. We yomped about trying to skirt land mines in the form of cowpats, maybe singing George Gershwin's…

Swanee how I love ya, how I love ya
My dear old Swanee
I'd give the world to be
Among the folks in D-I-X-I even know my
Mammy's waitin' for me, prayin' for me
Down by the Swanee
The folks up north will see me no more
When I go to the Swanee shore.

It was all rather inconclusive but we did once rescue a rather sad Perkins minor who was lost, or had been abandoned by his platoon. At the end of hostilities we were rewarded with a mug of cocoa and rock cakes, which were mined locally. For field day we were all bussed off to Aldershot and wriggled around on the heathland on our elbows in the sandy soil whilst concealed by smoke. We were issued with blank (ammunition). My friend Armitage (Martin), with whom I shot in the cadet pair at the Public Schools Ashburton meeting at Bisley, was an accomplished poacher and used to place a pencil down the barrel before the blank round, and shoot rabbits. He sold them to a butcher in Theale, presumably having retrieved his pencil. Sadly, much later on, he was murdered in South Africa.

After Cert A Part 2 one could either stay in the Army section, or join one of the other sections. I joined the signals company. We learnt Morse code and the basis of radio wave propagation. We had plenty of equipment including a base station, not much used, with an R107 receiver and a T12 transmitter. It had an extensive aerial system but when fired up it tended to disrupt local television pictures (there were not many TVs and only one channel in those days), and interfere with the housekeeper's enjoyment of the Home Service. She was called Mrs Roden, nicknamed the Rodent, with the characteristic verbal felicity of the public (i.e. private) schoolboy.

We also had backpack WS 18 transceivers which needed two to operate them. The range was five to ten miles depending on the aerial. The WS 38 sets were worn on the chest and had a range of a mile or two. We used to walk around the countryside calling, "Able Baker one to Easy Fox two, do you read? Over." If we did read we would answer, "Roger" and give our position if we knew it. They cannot be claimed to have been of much tactical value in our hands. Often we did not 'read' on account of terrain or distortion. We also put out netting calls. One day we were told that the phonetic alphabet had been changed to Alpha, Bravo, Charlie, Delta and so on, which has remained to this day. The reason given was that the Russians had got hold of the old alphabet. This seemed a bit implausible by way of an explanation, but it was good to learn that someone was keeping an eye on these things; especially as they had recently exploded the hydrogen (H) bomb.

Field day in the Signals section was different. Three nine-ton half-track signals vehicles turned up at the college fitted out with WS19 wireless transceivers which had been designed in 1940 for use in tanks. The vehicles were probably lease-lend White Motor Company M3s or M5s, over five thousand of which were provided during the war by the USA; they were also manufactured under licence by International Harvester. They were driven by cheerful National Service squaddies, made a lot of noise and took up a lot of room. At five miles to the gallon and with a top speed of 28 mph they had limitations but looked pretty scary with conventional wheels in the front, and a tank track made of rubber at the back. We charged about the leafy lanes of Berkshire like motorised bison. On one corner an unfortunate woman in a Standard Eight met one of us, followed by two more, but by then she has closed her eyes and was in the ditch. We fished her out. We twiddled the aerial variometer and put out netting calls. The only useful thing we learned for all this effort was that the car park at The Bull in Stanford Dingley was not large enough to take half-track vehicles.

Most years there was a ceremonial general inspection in which the whole of the college cadet force turned out. Brasses were polished and a great deal of time spent learning to march in straight lines. Parade grounds for real are made of tar macadam, or grit, and we had to march on grass, not easy if it is soft, with the squelch of four hundred or so pairs of boots coming down out of time. Nor is it easy to keep the Lee Enfield rifle straight when arms are sloped under such circumstances. There was such a difference in height, neck and collar disparity, beret shape and uniform fit (this was before jerseys, men's, heavy, olive, round neck) that some of the younger platoons resembled a march of the mushrooms which lent a Chaplinesque ambience to the day. At least there were no girls…

The parade was called to order and each platoon asked if it was ready. The naval section, as the Senior Service, went first. Lieutenant E. B. Anderton, my physics master, used to reply, "Aye aye, Sir", which raised a cheer to the irritation of the commanding officer. His crisp naval salute with the palm facing the ground was marred by a trigger finger, but he had naval-issue overhanging bushy eyebrows which must have made it difficult to measure the co-efficient of expansion.

The Air Officer taking the salute in my first year in the Corps, in 1954, was Air Chief Marshal Sir Guy Garrod, GBE, KCB, MC, DFC, who had come out of retirement to visit his old school. He had survived the Royal Flying Corps in the Great War, which he had entered in 1915. In 1944, he was temporarily Allied Air Commander-in-Chief when Air Chief Marshal Sir Trafford Leigh-Mallory of Battle of Britain fame (he had been Douglas Bader's commanding officer in 12 Group), was killed in an air crash on his way to take up the appointment. After the war, Garrod was Permanent RAF Representative on the Military Staff Committee of the United Nations and Head of the RAF delegation to Washington DC. He retired in 1948. Maybe as we marched past with sloped arms, roughly in time with the band, we sang to the march by Leslie Stuart (1863–1928):

> It's the soldiers of the Queen, my lads
> Who've been, my lads, who've seen, my lads
> In the fight for England's glory lads
> Of its world-wide glory let us sing
> And when we say we've always won
> And then they ask us how it's done
> We'll proudly point to every one
> Of England's soldiers of the Queen.

Immortalised by Edward Woodward in the Australian film *Breaker Morant*.

My next move proved to be problematic. Major 'Egglips' Coulson had taken over as Commanding Officer (CO) from Colonel O. R. 'Orje' Jones – the CO with BO (BO or body odour was the promotional acronym of Lifebuoy toilet soap in those pre-TLA days) who asked me if I would take over the leadership of the signals section. I would be made a sergeant. Wow.

But my friend Fay (Robert) had spotted somewhere that one could apply for a flying scholarship, funded by the Royal Air Force, if one belonged to their section. I approached Flight Lieutenant, later Squadron Leader, Barry Norwood, and signed on. Then, as they say, it hit the fan. I had written telling my parents of this change in plan and my mother went ballistic. Failure of duty and leadership, acting on a whim and inefficient (oh no), my housemaster told me in faux rage before beating me at the demand of my mother and sending me to the headmaster.

"You are a very naughty boy, tuppence [creep]," he said, showing all the signs of being as baffled as I was about the row, but nothing another beating would not fix. "Perhaps I should beat you again – If I did, what would you say?"

"That I still want to be in the Royal Air Force section, Sir, and I intend to win a flying scholarship."

"You are a very obstinate young man".

So I went into the Royal Air Force section and won a flying scholarship.

RAF SECTION

Per Ardua ad Astra.

Major F. H. Sykes
Proposal for the motto of the Royal Flying Corps on its establishment on 13th April 1912 at Farnborough, Hampshire. Later, in 1918, it became the motto of the Royal Air Force.

The Royal Air Force section was a breath of fresh air. Flight Lieutenant Norwood had a languages master as a fellow officer, called Flight Lieutenant 'Ollers' Oliver, DFC. "It was not an immediate" was all that he would say. Nobody worried if one could not shave (if one had to) in the gleam of one's boot-caps, nor did we wear gaiters. The army section polished its brasses with Duraglit and covered its webbing with Blanco, so called because it was coloured khaki. We did not march, we walked, although we still wore battle dress (blouses, men's, etc.). We learnt about the Dalton navigational computer, meteorology and the theory of flight. But best of all we flew on field days. In my two years in the section, I flew in twelve different types/marks of RAF aeroplanes, excluding the Chipmunk and Tiger Moth in which I also flew on structured courses. The first event was the annual camp at RAF Cranwell.

Royal Air Force Cranwell was founded as Royal Naval Air Service Central Training Establishment on 1st April 1916. Legend has it that a young naval pilot was told to take look around and find somewhere in the neighbourhood for the Naval balloons, kites and airships. Cranwell village seemed to fit the bill and 2,500 acres of farmland was wrested from the Earl of Bristol. When the Chief of the Air Staff, Sir Hugh Trenchard, chose the location he was quoted as saying, "Marooned in the wilderness, cut off from pastimes they could organise for themselves, the cadets would find life cheaper, healthier and more wholesome."

Quite; no women. The Royal Air Force College was the first Military Air Academy in the world. The college was opened in huts on 5th February 1920, gaining its present building, loosely based on the Royal Hospital, Chelsea, in 1933. When we arrived at the beginning of August 1956 we were billeted in barrack blocks which were preferable to the tents, war surplus from the battle of Agincourt, which our contemporaries in the army section had to endure.

We journeyed in uniform on Service warrants by steam train to Paddington on the old Great Western Railway (GWR). After crossing London to Kings Cross we continued to Grantham on the old London North Eastern Railway (LNER). Cranwell used to have its own line from Sleaford, but it was closed that year so we were met by a bus. As we stood in the corridor wondering what lay ahead we were happened upon by some Girl Guides. This was outside the envelope for most of us and looking back, our respective endocrine orchestras were probably a few bars behind their own. Being at an all-boys school few of us knew much about the anatomical, physiological, or, heaven forfend, emotional differences that subtend the female of the species.

We thought little of the encounter, but in his valete speech the Commandant recounted that he – or more likely the duty officer – had been telephoned by the young ladies, who asked for us by name. They told him they were planning a reunion but received the retort that facilities were not available for such encounters on the station, and that if they did appear, thereby reducing the efficiency (oh dear) of HM's Royal Air Force, they could expect to end up in the Guard Room. The following year, he promised, a co-located Guide camp would be considered for the benefit of Bradfield College.

It turned out that we had arrived the day after the graduation ball. I had never seen such a shambles. After a welcome from the Commandant, Air Commodore T. A. B. Parselle, we were shown round the camp. If it moves, salute it; if it does not, paint it, we were told, which explained why every stone larger than a pebble was brilliant white. The first event was a viewing of *The Dam Busters* film which had been released the year before. This told the famous tale of the raid on the Möhne, Edersee and Sorpe dams in the Ruhr valley on 16–17th May 1943. Most of us had already seen it. Some clever dicks even claimed to have spotted the electronic counter-measures Canberras of No. 109 and No. 139 Squadrons, which were stationed at RAF Hemswell, where the film had largely been made. The part of Wing Commander Guy Gibson VC, DSO and Bar, DFC and Bar was played by the late Richard Todd. The march by Eric Coates (1886–1957) was rousing, and is evergreen.

Gibson (1918–1944) was later killed on operations, crashing at Steenbergen in the Netherlands in circumstances which have remained obscure. I looked after his father years later when I was a house physician at St Thomas's Hospital. At about the same time the poet Robert Graves was also in the ward for a fortnight or so. He was permanently surrounded by a coterie of nubile young women, which was odd, as he looked so old and was all of seventy-one years at the time. Poetry, which I could neither fathom nor remember at school, clearly had more pulling power than being a lowly house physician. He drew me into his gilded circle, though there was little time to talk and I had not read *Goodbye To All That*. He gave me a gift of books paid for on his account at Hatchards in Piccadilly, where he knew a namesake of mine.

The week was well organised. We learnt about the Royal Air Force, its organisation and equipment. We learnt to radio navigate with Gee – a system using time measurement between two ground-based hyperbolic radio signals. It had been invented in Swanage during the Second World War and persisted in the V bomber fleet until 1970. We covered theory of flight and had a demonstration of supersonic shockwaves in a tiny wind tunnel. We swam and played soccer. Barry and Ollers stayed in the Officers' Mess where they were encouraged to play the mess trick. For sensible (Health and Safety) reasons this has largely been abandoned. The victim hyperventilates for ten seconds or so following which his chest is suddenly compressed from behind. Involuntarily the glottis is closed and the abdominal muscles contracted (the Valsalva manoeuvre). Consciousness is lost due a fall in blood pressure and thereby in brain perfusion. If the unfortunate subject is not fielded in the subsequent fall, a nasty knock on the head may be sustained.

The mess trick was written up in the *British Medical Journal* in 1951 (August 18th, pp 384–5). The first author was Peter, later Air Vice-Marshal, Howard, who supported me for the fellowship of the Royal Aeronautical Society. He was the last commandant of the RAF Institute of Aviation Medicine, Farnborough, before it closed in 1994. The two other authors, A. C. Dornhorst and E. P. Sharpey-Schafer, were professors of medicine and of St Thomas' Hospital. Sharpey-Schafer, as a medical registrar, had taught my father, as a student at University College Hospital, before the war. Sometimes, late at night, they would pick up their golf clubs, tee off down Gower Street, chip across Bayley Street and return up the Tottenham Court Road. A bit trickier now, for many reasons.

Whilst Barry and Ollers were swooning around in the Officers' Mess, we were up to no good. Nobody liked Harrovians very much so we decided to turn the fire hoses on them and blow them out of their billet. It made an awful mess and we were given a dressing-down by the duty officer about respect for the Queen's property. Harrow was made to clear up, much to our amusement. During the proceedings one of their number attempted to take charge and stood in the midst of it all telling us to behave ourselves. "Come on, chaps…" But he got no further. Whilst he was in transmit someone on the floor above emptied a fire bucket over the poor fellow. He did not flinch. As a reminder of Kipling's:

If you can keep you head when all about
Are losing theirs and blaming it on you…

It had few equals. The expected retribution the following night never materialised.

But it was for the flying that we were there. On 4th August 1956 we mustered on the apron and were each detailed a trip. A long line of Hunting Percival Provost P56 T1s with the Alvis Leonides Mk 25 radial engine and three-bladed propellers were at the ready. We were told how to evacuate the aircraft if necessary:

"Jump for the roundel on the wing, chaps – you won't get there – DON'T pull the D ring until you are clear of the aircraft."

"What on earth is the roundel?" asked someone.

When our turn came we walked out as coolly as we were able whilst being constrained to waddle in our parachute harnesses. We were strapped into our parachutes by the ground crew. My instructor was Squadron Leader Hastie. He had a bad back and got in with difficulty.

"What is your name, laddie?"

"Cadet Joy, Sir."

"Eh? Jolllllly gooooood. Can you take-off an aeroplane?

"Not sure, Sir. You ease the tail up and then pull back gradually?" I said, tentatively echoing my friend Fay (Robert).

"You have control."

"I have control, Sir."

With that he made me advance the throttle. Having seen that I was applying no rudder to counteract the gyroscopic effect of the engine, he did so. At that point, having raised the tail, I pulled back on the stick with exuberance. The tail wheel hit the ground again; *kerbiff.* The feisty Provost seemed to look round in surprise, in the way horses do when you do something unexpected.

"I have control," said the gallant Squadron Leader, wincing – these were the days before Voltarol.

"You have control, Sir."

All at once we were in the air. A Wordsworth moment:

> *Open unto the fields, and fields, and to the sky;*
> *All bright and glittering in the smokeless air.*
> *Never did the sun more beautifully steep…*

"Eh, what, laddie?"

That camp I had three trips in the Provost and one in a Valetta. The Vickers Valetta was developed from the Viking civil airliner, more powerful and stronger, with the aim of being soldier (and idiot) proof. It was neither. In addition to its role in entertaining cadets it was a navigational trainer and had astrodomes, like Pyrex dishes, in its roof for taking navigational fixes. It was a handful on one engine and we were later to fly to Germany in one. The Jet Provost came into service at about that time as a derivative of the Piston Provost, but was not yet available, at least not at Cranwell. Over seven hundred were built and some exported. It was under-powered, being driven by a single Rolls-Royce Viper engine – *constant thrust, variable noise* was the soubriquet applied to it.

The only time I flew in front of such an engine (two of them) was in a Hawker Siddeley 125 to Marrakesh to see a patient who had suffered a heart attack whilst trekking in the Atlas Mountains. As is the form, my lovely registrar at the time, Diana Tait, came too – she is now clinical oncologist at the Royal Marsden Hospital and Dean for the Faculty of Clinical Oncology at Royal College of Radiologists. We watched as the co-pilot glued himself to his fuel burn chart – we were on the extreme edge of the range of the aircraft. In turbulence there was a repetitive banging noise under my seat which seemed to concern no-one. I later discovered that it was due to loosening of the large bolts which anchor the main spar.

But before I could take up the flying scholarship, other opportunities arose. The University Air Squadrons had been mustered before the Second World War and provided a source of aircrew early in the conflict. They encouraged recruitment to the Royal Air Force and gave opportunities for young people to join expeditions as a pathway to character development, introduction to service life, and participation in sporting activities such as shooting.

In 1956 the Oxford University Air Squadron was based at Oxford, Kidlington and the instructors, who were serving officers, were messed at Royal Air Force, Bicester. They passed the time, *faute de mieux*, with gliding and golf. During the long summer vacation they were also encumbered with giving air experience to cadets. Thus it was that we found ourselves billeted in the Officers' Mess at Bicester and travelling to Kidlington each day to fly. The squadron was equipped with de Havilland DHC1 Chipmunks, a primary trainer which had replaced the venerable DH82a Tiger Moth on which I was yet to learn to fly. They were equipped with Gipsy Major III four cylinder inverted air-cooled engines with Coffman cartridge starters. These made a loud bang and emitted a cloud of acrid cordite smoke on the cry of "Contact!" They are not permitted on the civilian version as the carriage of explosives by civilian aircraft is forbidden (See photo plate 6). There were also two excessively noisy North American Harvards, a butch trainer indeed, powered by a Pratt & Whitney Wasp six hundred horsepower radial engine. Part of the noise was said to be due to the propeller tips becoming supersonic at high speed.

Kidlington was established as Oxford Municipal Airport with land bought from the Blenheim estate in 1935 for £19,671.0.0. It became RAF Kidlington during the war and the Elementary Flying Training School (EFTS) was established in 1938. Two years later No. 2 Group Training Pool, later 13 Operational Training Unit (OTU), was established up the road at RAF Bicester, where we were later to stay. By 1940 over one hundred Harvards were based at Kidlington with several Ansons and Oxfords, serving with No. 15 Service Flying Training School (SFTS). Amy Johnson disappeared in a flight from Blackpool to the field in 1941. She had been flying for the Air Transport Auxiliary (ATA).

Our detail was to be trained up to 'solo' standard – the point at which the instructor gets out and you are on your own. It was enjoyable in the peace

8. *North American T-6 Harvard at Kidlington with the Oxford University Air Squadron at the time I was there - September 1956. For a time an advanced trainer with the RAF. A bit like a rhinocerus, or an orthopaedic surgeon; thick-skinned, horny and charges a lot.*

of the late summer although there was less flying than had been planned. Mushrooms abounded on the grass field – there is a tarmac runway now, and an ILS (instrument landing system). We used to beat up (from the air) those who wandered onto the field to harvest them. I completed rather less than eight hours on account of serviceability issues, but was told I was ready to fly solo by the time we finished. There was also a trip in a glider. It was so peaceful – a silence broken only by the whistle of the wind and the creaking of the airframe; but there was no power to get out of difficulty.

As Mrs Patrick Campbell had said, "It was like the deep, deep peace of the double bed after the hurly-burly of the chaise longue", but she had been talking about marriage…

TAF 2 – BAOR

The only way to be sure of winning a third world war is to prevent it.

General George C. Marshall (1880–1959)
Architect of post-war reconstruction in Europe
(the Marshall Plan) and recipient of the Nobel Peace Prize

In the Lent holiday of 1957 there was another trip, this time abroad and to our recent enemy, now our friend. We were to spend a week with the Second Tactical Air Force; British Army of the Rhine – in the argot of the time, TAF 2 BAOR; later 2nd Allied Tactical Air Force, 2A TAF. We assembled at RAF Transport Command, Lyneham, for the trip to RAF Ahlhorn in Germany. RAF Lyneham was opened as No. 33 Maintenance Unit in May 1940. In October 1942, No. 511 Squadron was raised to fly regular services, the first in a Consolidated Liberator to Gibraltar. It also operated the Avro York, a transport variant of the Lancaster bomber, later as No. 36 Squadron and later still as No. 511 Squadron again. At the time we passed through, Nos. 99 (now operating the Lockheed Galaxy C17) and 511 Squadrons were operating the Handley Page Hastings a four-engine transport aircraft. The Liberator flight was later re-formed into 246 Squadron. It became the main base of RAF Transport Command when it was founded in 1943. It was closed in 2011 by Philip Hammond, Secretary of State for Defence, as part of our withdrawal from a strategic role in the world.

There were numerous Vickers Valettas, one of which was placed at our disposal, as they say in the services. The first problem was that we were overloaded and volunteers were called for to stay behind. There was not much enthusiasm for that proposal as we stood with our kitbags trying to avoid catching anyone's eye. The sums were done again (or the weight problem ignored) and off we all went. The Valetta had something of a bad reputation on one engine, but fortunately both Bristol Hercules 14 cylinder radial engines were in a good mood that day.

The Valetta was not pressurised so we bumped along in a seemingly endless layer of fluff at about 10,000 feet. Occasionally we caught sight of the ground that had been secured for freedom by the heroism of the allied forces a decade beforehand. After three hours we landed at RAF Ahlhorn in Lower Saxony. It had been a Zeppelin base during the Great War and was a forward air base for the allies late in the Second World War. Having been rebuilt in the early 1950s it was luxurious by the standards to which we had been accustomed in the post-war period. It was home to No. 96 and No. 256 Squadrons (Gloster Meteor NF11) and No. 213 Squadron (English Electric Canberra B2), and Headquarters of 125 Wing. The Commanding Officer at the time was Group Captain A. G. Dudgeon. It was handed back to the Luftwaffe in 1958.

Once again we were billeted in the Officers' Mess complete with our own rooms, en suite, and a well-endowed bat-*fraülein*. There was unlimited hot water for a change. This was style. We were pretty much given the run of the station and spent a fair amount of time being entertained in the bar by the squadron pilots with tales of derring-do (Chaucer, 14th century: *Troilus and Criseyde*). We did a lot of saluting but this tended to be ignored. Cigarettes were –/11d (4½ p) for twenty Benson & Hedges in tins, and 1/– (5p) for Balkan Sobranies which we smoked in a black holder. We must have looked too silly for words but everyone was too polite to say so. Gin was –/3d (1½ p) a tot. Beer was more expensive. For currency we used 'BAFs' (British Armed Forces) paper money, the lowest denomination of which was 3d. We went on trips into the locality in uniform. Quite what the local population thought of its recent conquerors is difficult to imagine as we all looked so young.

The main purpose, so far as we were concerned, was to fly, which we did. The Gloster Meteor F1 and F3 variants were introduced and saw limited service with No. 616 Squadron, late in the Second World War. A total of sixty-four RAF squadrons were ultimately equipped with various marks of the aircraft, at one time or another. In addition, twelve Royal Naval Air

Service (RNAS) squadrons deployed them. It was originally fitted with the Rolls-Royce Welland engine to be replaced by the Derwent, which was more powerful. It was exported to more than a dozen countries. Construction totalled 3,886 overall, not all in the UK, whilst total operational losses were 890, including four on one day on one occasion. Such attrition would be intolerable today as a month or two would rub out the Royal Air Force. One day when we were at dispersal, the AOC of TAF2 – Air Chief Marshal Percy Bernard, 5th Earl of Bandon, GBE, CB, CVO, DSO, blew in, in his personal Meteor. He wore a dazzling white flying suit. We all saluted.

The Meteor briefly held the world speed record for a jet aircraft in 1945 when it achieved 606 mph. The NF11 variant was made by the Armstrong-Whitworth Company and differed from its forebears in that it had a long nose with a Westinghouse radar within, and two seats, the rear being for a navigator. It had drop tanks – both ventral, and under-wing. As a first generation jet aircraft it had a short duration of flight – just over an hour. The NF14, of which there were a few around when we were at Ahlhorn, was a further development which must have been good at telling fibs as it was characterised by an even longer radome.

I flew on two sorties in the NF11 and one on the Meteor 7 – forty minutes' dual training, I recorded in my logbook. In the NF11 I sat in the back and tried to work the Gee navigation system, which was an upgrade of that met at RAF Cranwell the year before. I concluded that we were over Hunstanton, Norfolk, rather than Lower Saxony. Our first outing was an air-to-ground firing detail. Wing over, dive, fire at an invisible (to me) target and get a bollocking for going too low was the SOP (standard operating procedure).

On the first occasion I was unprepared for the g (gravitational force) induced by the recovery and 'greyed out' due to reduction of blood supply to the brain. In this state one remains conscious but is unable to see. It is related to the high oxygen demand of the retina in the presence of reduced blood perfusion. One can still hear and otherwise function. We made several runs and regularly pulled four g, which was combatted by clenching what are now known in women's magazines, and elsewhere, as the abs. We were told that one more height incursion and we would be sent home in disgrace. Combat pilots now wear 'faggots' (FCAGTS – full coverage anti-g trousers) and CCPG (chest counter-pressure garments). Less fun, but safer.

On another occasion I was given a trip in the Canberra B2 Night Interdicter, also nominally on air-to-ground firing. The aircraft carried no external weapons stores and on this occasion it had a cannon pack in the bomb bay. The Canberra was a remarkable aircraft which first entered RAF service in 1951, retiring from service fifty-six years later in 2007. It was originally intended to serve as successor to the DH Mosquito. It set a world altitude record in 1957 of 70,310 feet and served as a tactical stand-off nuclear strike aircraft as well as excelling in electronic and photographic reconnaissance. It was equipped with two Rolls-Royce Avon 101/RA3 engines, over nine hundred being built in the UK, and more than four hundred under licence in the USA.

I was invited to sit on the collapsible 'rumble' seat next to the single-pilot. The navigator and observer/bomb-aimer sat behind without any forward vision (unless in the nose position to aim the bombs). They seemed to be playing cards. They had upward ejection seats, a benefit not enjoyed by their similarly placed colleagues in the Vulcan bomber. Six months previously that fine aircraft (XA 897) had carried out a record-breaking flight to Australia. It had been planned to return to London, Heathrow airport. On arrival there has been a recent claim that the co-pilot, Air Marshal Sir Harry Broadhurst, GCB, KBE, DSO and Bar, DFC and Bar, AFC, RAF, elected to proceed in spite of being advised of bad weather on three occasions. The aircraft landed some one thousand metres short of the runway and lost its main landing gear, becoming airborne again at which point the pilot and co-pilot ejected. The remaining members of the crew died as their escape would have been through the floor. The pilot put the Canberra through its paces for my benefit. He shut down an engine and we crabbed about for a bit. Then at what seemed to me to be a remarkably low level he performed a barrel roll over a reservoir, I imagine having first relit the idle engine. It was discomforting to see so much water above one's head.

Towards the end of our stay there was night flying. We were not invited but it was impressive, notably for the noise during the 'circuits and bumps' which are part of training. We were in the bar when an emergency was declared. This emptied it at once. One of the Canberras could not get its undercarriage gear to extend. Those who have had to put out a PAN (urgency) or a Mayday call at an aerodrome will know that the immediate response is the emptying of all personnel from hangars and related facilities, in all weathers, to watch. In the

Services, I am told, if you are witness, this exempts you from the subsequent Board of Enquiry. As this stops you flying, naturally you go and watch. This was the case that night when a wheels-up landing was inevitable. To our morbid disappointment we were not allowed to go and join everyone else for the show.

The legend was that the pilot instructed his two crew to blow the explosive bolts of their hatch and bang out (eject). They apparently refused – "We are staying with you, skip" – which sounded like the right stuff, but also a bit like mutiny. Years later I would meet him. Reportedly a good landing was made on the parallel grass runway apart from the severing of some electrical cables with an associated pyrotechnic display. There was no fire but the stricken craft skidded along and with a final flourish like Odile, the dying swan in Tchaikovsky's ballet, slewed across the main runway before coming to a halt. Following this everyone rejoined us in the bar.

"Cat 4" (almost a write-off), we were told when we drove out to inspect the wreckage the next morning. Back in our trusty Valetta on the way home I said to Squadron Leader Norwood that I was planning to join the Royal Air Force as a pilot. But hard on our heels was the 1957 Defence White Paper, which was to do lasting damage to our armed forces and the aircraft industry.

★ ★ ★

Duncan Sandys was still the son-in-law of Winston Churchill at the time, divorcing his wife Diana in 1960. He was wounded in the Second World War and held posts in Whitehall including the chairmanship of a cabinet committee responsible for defence against flying bombs. It was from this that his interest in missiles arose. In one of the endless defence reviews which have plagued our armed services and defence-related industries over the decades, the White Paper, which became known as the Sandys Report, was published. "The era of the manned fighter is over," he intoned. "The future lies with missiles." And this was at a time when missiles were little more than fireworks with a couple of EF50 thermionic valves stuck on. He showed prescience, but maybe he had other things on his mind.

Margaret, Duchess of Argyll, was the third wife of Ian Douglas Campbell, 11th Duke of Argyll. She had a reputation for being a *grande horizontale*, *magna cum laude* – there is no direct English translation. She was involved in a scandal in which she was the subject of a photograph in a certain position performing a certain task on an uncertain headless man. The picture was taken on a Polaroid camera allegedly borrowed from the Ministry of Defence. It has been claimed that it was the only one in England at the time. Rubbish: someone at school had one. The identity of the gentleman in question was the subject of great debate and the Right Honourable Duncan Sandys ended in pole position, although Douglas Fairbanks Junior was in the final furlong; and more recently a married lover, Bill Lyons, sales director of Pan American Airlines.

The long list of co-respondents at her divorce trial in 1963 was recorded as eighty-eight, a record which probably still stands, but the shortlist contained only four, who were named. The horrified judge gave a 40,000 word judgement and His Grace was blackballed by his club, Whites. Notwithstanding these adventures it was reported in her obituary in the *Independent* newspaper that she fell out with her daughter, the Duchess of Rutland, objecting to her grandchildren being raised as Anglicans. Sandys was ennobled, as would be expected, for services, inter alia, to the wrecking of our aviation manufacturing base. His vision of the future, rather than his escapades, ended my brief aspiration to be a fighter pilot.

FLYING SCHOLAR

He rises and begins to round,
He drops the silver chain of sound,
Of many links without a break,
In chirrup, whistle, slur and shake...

George Meredith (1828–1909)
The Lark Ascending, 1881;
set to music by Vaughn Williams (1872–1958) in 1914.

Once in the Royal Air Force Section, the business of winning the flying scholarship came next. This involved travelling with three others to RAF Hornchurch where aircrew selection took place. We had to wear uniform as we held service railway warrants. On the way Gowring minor and I were up picked up by some weirdo outside the Railway Lost Property Company in Praed Street, Paddington; probably par for the course in London, W2. He was harmless. Royal Air Force Hornchurch had been a Sector Airfield of RAF Fighter Command, 11 Group, commanded by Air Vice-Marshal Keith Park in the Battle of Britain. It was extensively bombed. In 1952 it became the RAF aircrew selection centre before it was closed in 1962. We were billeted in barracks with some who, to my untutored eye, did not seem to be likely aircrew material. Food was surprisingly plentiful and much better than at school. The process took three days. We had intelligence tests, a prolonged medical examination which involved marching around in the buff and passing our water into small pots, leadership tests and an aptitude test – tracking a moving spot on a cathode ray screen.

Then there was the interview. The Chairman was a Squadron Leader with a bristling orange moustache and such protuberant teeth that it was difficult not to respond directly to them. "So you want to join the RAF as a pilot?" At that point I had not decided and deflected the question by stating that I was planning to see if I won the flying scholarship first. It seemed to do the trick.

The scholarship was good value. The only contribution required was 5/– (25p) towards board and lodging, which was provided otherwise free along with all clothing and accessories. Rail travel warrants were also provided. The RAF paid for training, which had to be in a service-approved aircraft. In practice this usually meant the pre-war de Havilland DH82a Tiger Moth, which we regarded as old-fashioned (lacking cool). How wrong we were – it is a wonderful, though rather cold, aeroplane; if you can fly one you can fly anything.

One or two, such as my later friend and colleague Michael (now Professor Sir Michael) Rawlins, learnt on the new de Havilland Canada DHC1 Chipmunk. He got lost on his final cross-country over a snowscape. Happily he executed a forced landing with such panache that whilst both wings came off the aeroplane, he was unhurt as he bellyflopped into a field of potatoes.

"Is the aeroplane alright?" asked the anxious instructor when Michael telephoned with the news. "Are you alright?" he added as an afterthought. Otherwise we would not have shared a flat, driven round Europe together as students (we bought some fake gold watches together in Rome) and lectured on the Medical Unit at St Thomas's Hospital.

The summer term of 1957 was good. Exams in the form of 'O' Levels were in a rather modest bag, and 'A' Levels seemed a long way off. One spent the time walking in the countryside and shooting either on the full bore range on the other side of 'Hogger' – Hogs Back Hill, Bradfield – or at the National Rifle Association ranges at Bisley Camp, near Brookwood in Surrey. One day Flight Sergeant Sparks turned up in a van laden with flying goodies for the forthcoming scholarship in the long summer holiday. I was kitted out with a sheepskin flying jacket and matching trousers. When wearing these with any usual underclothing one resembled M. Bibendum, the cheerful Michelin man from Clermont-Ferrand. It later proved difficult to get into a Tiger Moth wearing this gear even with gravity on one's side, and almost impossible to get out again. Fortunately the good Flight Sergeant also provided a canvas flying suit which was more manageable until I got hold of a cooler (in use, much cooler) grey poplin jet flying suit. All this was eventually surrendered, apart from the gauntlets which I was allowed to keep, and the leather fleece flying boots which were purloined by a flying instructor.

The required aircraft, the de Havilland Tiger Moth DH 82/82a, is a fabric-covered biplane. With production commencing in 1931, 8,611 units were constructed before it ceased in 1945. Over one thousand are believed to have survived as of 2009, many in Australia and New Zealand. The airframe is made of tubular steel, spruce and plywood, covered with doped fabric. The wing, tail unit and top decking spars are of fabric-covered spruce, with plywood formers and ribs. There is internal bracing of the wings which are separated by braced struts. The engine is an inverted air-cooled Gipsy Major 1 with dual magneto ignition and fuel gravity fed from the single tank between the upper wings. (See photo plate 7.)

There were ailerons on the lower wings only. These are operated differentially via a bellcrank to offset adverse yaw; the rudder and tail plane are relatively small. There were no brakes originally, but there was a steerable tail skid. Communication was by Gosport speaking tubes, as seen in country houses and high-value limousines of the 1920s. There was a mouthpiece in each cockpit and this was connected via flexible tubing to the headset of the other pilot. It was sometimes called 'the blower', which was also service slang for the telephone. It worked so well at Bristol that some silly ass at Fairoaks had felt it necessary to downgrade it to the ex-Bomber Command A1134 intercom set. This sulked in its new role, mainly due to battery problems. Maybe it was missing its Lancaster.

At last the day arrived and I set out with my rail warrant, my student pilot's licence and my *Personal Flying Log Book (Aircraft Operating Crew): CA 24*, published by Her Majesty's Stationary Office (HMSO) for the Ministry of Transport and Civil Aviation. I caught the train to Bristol (via Radstock, Bradshaw's directory said). At that time there was still coal mining in

Radstock. Having arrived at Temple Meads, Brunel's lovely station which had been bombed in the blitz, I asked a railwayman which train went to Whitchurch Airport. I had been instructed to report there. He eyed my slender frame and ill-fitting RAF uniform.

"What do you want with Whitchurch?" he asked.

"I am going to learn to fly," I said, assuming a military posture.

"You'll not there," he said. "It's shut – try Lulsgate."

This was an early initiation into the efficiency of large organisations.

Bristol Whitchurch had been a municipal airport which opened in 1930. In 1938, No. 33 Elementary Reserve Flying Training School (ERFTS) opened, whilst in September 1939, Imperial Airways and British Airways Ltd merged to form the British Overseas Airways Corporation (BOAC). BOAC moved from Croydon and Heston to Whitchurch, which remained one of the few operational civilian airports during the war. There were services to Lisbon, Shannon and the USA. The Bristol and Wessex Aeroplane Club, based there, joined the Civil Air Guard in 1938 to train pilots for the anticipated hostilities. No. 33 ERFTS was to train Royal Air Force Volunteer Reserve pilots. In 1940 the Air Transport Auxiliary (ATA) formed No. 2 Ferry Pilots Pool, which was based here. In 1957 Whitchurch was closed and everything moved to RAF Lulsgate Bottom, so called because it was set on the top of a hill.

Royal Air Force Lulsgate was opened in 1940 in spite of its known poor weather. Low cloud formed during warm frontal conditions, and fog associated with westerly winds blew in from the Bristol Channel. As a training venue for bad-weather flying the Royal Air Force found the weather too bad. Now it would be called 'the wrong sort of bad weather'. On one occasion I had to leave the Christening of my goddaughter, Alice Watkinson, in Bristol early, as the airport was due to be fog-bound later in the afternoon.

The new airfield was opened unexpectedly by the arrival of a German Junkers JU88, successfully confused by electronic countermeasures. No. 286 (ack ack co-operation) Squadron was initially based there before No.

3 Flying Instructor School (FIS) arrived. After the war there was little activity until Whitchurch Airport moved in. At the time I was there, the only scheduled aircraft visiting were the Aer Lingus DC3 Dakota and the Cambrian Airways de Havilland Heron, a small airliner with four Gipsy Queen inverted air-cooled engines. They joined the circuit unannounced to our non-radio aircraft. The airport, in common with much of our infrastructure, is now foreign-owned, by the Ontario Teachers Pension Plan group. Any foreign reader who has got this far in the book will be relieved to learn that there are a few strategic assets still left for stripping.

We were billeted with a landlady about a mile or so from the airfield and walked in each day along the A38. On one occasion we came across a motor caravan lying on its side with all its household appurtenances spread across the road – napkins, books, smalls, pots and pans and Daddies Favourite Sauce. Apparently the driver had become distracted by a wasp which had hitched a lift and caused him to lose control of the vehicle. Of the wasp there was no sign, it wisely having scarpered, not expecting the A38 to be quite so dangerous. It was a good first lesson – under all circumstances, no matter how grave, fly the aeroplane first and foremost, or, in this case, drive the car.

I reported to the Bristol and Wessex Flying Club to find that there were five other cadets as well as myself. But there was worse news to come. There was only one approved aircraft, a Tiger Moth, G-AJHU, and one approved instructor, Harry Armitage, also the Chief Flying Instructor (CFI) because he was the only flying instructor. And if any club member turned up wanting instruction, we took second place. As a result progress was painfully slow. On my first trip, on the basis of my Chipmunk experience, I was invited to fly a circuit, which I did tolerably well until turning onto the final approach (finals). Suddenly, wrench, wrench on the control (joy) stick and a kick on the rudder bar. Over the blower came a fierce voice.

"I have control – leggo of this aeroplane! Airspeed! If you let your airspeed drop on turning finals you will spin in and that would spoil my day."

Mine too.

Due to the prevailing arrangement, or scam as it would now be called, I completed only three hours and forty minutes in the ten days that I was there that summer before the aircraft 'went tech'. It was due its fifty-hour check, so I went home.

During the following Easter holidays, in the run-up to 'A' Levels, I returned with the other hopefuls. This time I completed a further eight hours in nearly three weeks of hanging around playing snooker. I did take to riding a borrowed motorbike to the maintenance hangar to chat to the Scottish engineer. He had the morphology of a prep school geography master in his resemblance to an animated pipe cleaner. I also met Dicky Trounson, the divorced father of my first girlfriend, who had purchased a Piper PA 20 Tripacer at who knows what cost at that time. This seemed to be the last word in luxury when compared with the draughty Tiger Moth. When I enthused about it to my somewhat Aspergic engineer friend his only comment was "Not built for mag(neto) serviceability."

But there is a limit to the time one can spend listening to the music of Lonnie Donegan and Johnnie Duncan, whilst drinking the locally brewed scrumpy (a strong Somerset cider with the appearance of infected urine) at the Waggon and Horses, costing –/11d (4 1/2 p) a pint. Bitter was 1/–d (5p). Flying then did not cost much either – £2/15/–d (£2.75p) per hour on a Tiger Moth and £2/17/6d (£2.87 ½ p) per hour for the grander Auster J1/N. So I went home again. Several cadets must have complained about the unsatisfactory arrangements to the Royal Air Force because approval was withdrawn. But before I left, I did go solo.

The first solo flight is a dogleg moment in one's life (there are others), and it came about after some seven hours on the type. It happened on a windy day, 22nd April 1957. After some circuits and bumps Harry spoke over the blower and said, "Would you like to have a go on your own?"

Heck. "Do you think I am ready, Sir?"

"Of course I do, you idiot, otherwise I would not have asked. Remember, bags of common, bags of common [sense]." He got out and secured the front harness (the Tiger Moth is flown from the rear seat). "I will wait here and you come and pick me up."

"Any last tips, Sir?"

"Never wear brown shoes with a dark suit."

"Righto, Sir."

I taxied over to the runway threshold to do the pre take-off checks, several times:

Trim – *two notches nose-heavy*
Throttle friction nut – *tight (loose in the front)*
Carburettor – *wired hot*
Fuel – *on and sufficient*
Auto-slats – *locked*
Altimeter – *set to QFE (the altimeter pressure setting to register zero feet at ground level)*
Engine temperature and oil pressure – *in the green*
Compass heading – *set*
Harnesses – *very tight indeed*
Hatches – *closed*
Stick – *full and free movement*
No red lights from control

I advanced the throttle and sped off, becoming airborne in a jiffy. The aircraft had never climbed so well and the first task was to get used to a gap where the instructor's head had been. A wide circuit allowed for thinking time. Downwind, and a glance at the signals square by the control tower. This revealed the controller running out to change the landing T – a large T-shaped board to indicate the direction of landing to non-radio aircraft. Was he wearing brown shoes? The runway direction had been changed on account of the wind direction, though what meteorological happenstance could possibly have occurred in five minutes to justify this one was a mystery.

Don't panic. Fly the aeroplane. Reselect the runway. Downwind – do the checks; base leg – do the checks; finals – do the checks. Crikey, the ground speed seems high. The outer perimeter (peri) track flashed by, then the inner one. Lucky the westerly runway is long. On and on we floated, with the aircraft enjoying flying as much as I was hoping it would feel like coming to earth. Eventually we settled, rather well I thought, and taxied back to my instructor. He leapt into the aircraft, opened the throttle without a word, and taxied at the speed of sound back to the apron. He jumped out, also without a word, and drove off. As I entered the crew room my friends burst out laughing. In my anxious state I had landed with the wind instead of into it. This explained the impressive ground speed. Harry, who was rumoured to enjoy an assignation most lunch times somewhere in Bristol, was in a better mood when he returned.

But I had done with the fog of Lulsgate Bottom and it would be some eighteen years before I flew in there again. The Royal Air Force cancelled their arrangement with Bristol and I was reassigned to Fairoaks, near Woking in Surrey.

★ ★ ★

FAIROAKS '58

9.   *An unsigned pen and ink drawing of Fairoaks in the summer of 1958. There were six Tiger Moths based there at the time. The large '7' shows the direction of take-off on the grass field (70° magnetic). Behind the control tower to the left of the hangar is Dolley's farmhouse. I checked out in the Auster, J1/N - G-AJDV (seen on the right) at the end of the flying scholarship. It was written off at Bisley five years later. There were no fatalities.*

The history of Fairoaks as an airfield started with the bankruptcy, in 1930, of the then-owner of the Ottershaw Park Estate, Miss Susan Schintz. The sale included Dolley's Farm and the farmhouse, which is now part of the airfield and its buildings. The farm was purchased by Colonel Louis Strange in 1931. Colonel Strange was involved in flying at Spartan Aircraft Ltd, Cowes, on the Isle of Wight and applied for permission from Bagshot Rural District Council in May 1935 for the construction of a private airfield. The following year the airfield was requisitioned by the Air Ministry for use as a training school under the RAF Volunteer Reserve. It cost £8,750.0.0 for the property, with hangars and other facilities to be constructed.

It was operated by General Aircraft Ltd as No. 18 Elementary and Reserve Flying Training School (E&RFTS) and became No. 18 EFTS (Elementary Flying Training School), having combined with No. 19 E&RFTS which had been based at Gatwick at the outbreak of war. DH Tiger Moths, Hawker Audaxes, and Hinds, were based there together with a Fairey Battle light bomber; it was a hopeless aeroplane. I found one once on a gunnery range which had been used for target practice. A sad ending to a pretty useless machine. One of the tricks played for a bit of sport by the trainee pilots during the war was to bounce their aircraft on the top of locally disposed barrage balloons. As a rule this was harmless but on one occasion one caught fire and the pilot was lucky to get back to the field with much of his fabric burnt away. How he explained the mishap is not on record.

Wing Commander Arthur, AFC, commanded No. 18 E&RFTS before the war and No. 18 EFTS during it. He transferred to No. 18 Reserve Flying Training School (RFTS) in 1947, which had been formed from the EFTS. Universal Flying Services took over the school in 1946. He was still the Chief Flying Instructor when I was there in 1958. He retired in 1967 having flown 10,000 hours on the Tiger Moth alone. In 1958, the airfield was unchanged from its wartime configuration. There was a pronounced hillock towards the north side which could be entertaining. The Tiger Moth has no brakes and turns on the ground with the help of a steerable tail skid; this damages the surface after a while, to the chagrin of the airport manager. As related, it has no ailerons on its upper wing surfaces and not a lot of tail/rudder area. For this reason it should preferably take off into wind and avoid prepared runways. The hump was bulldozed and a hard surface runway finally laid in 1979, although the site works had been carried out, without permission, by Douglas Arnold when he owned the field a few years earlier.

We were billeted in the old wartime ground crew huts, now gone. We ate in what had been Dolley's farmhouse – bacon and eggs for breakfast each day. The summer was glorious and brought to mind the music of Vaughn Williams. Being a grass airfield it was populated by large numbers of skylarks which, during their display-flight, climb through the air almost vertically, singing their hearts out. They nest on the ground and as a result, due to intensive agriculture, are in serious decline. The whole attitude of the flying club could not have been more different. There were half a dozen Tiger Moths and several instructors. We flew all the time and I completed the remainder of the thirty plus two hours (on account of the delayed completion) needed for the Private Pilot's Licence (PPL), in ten days. This was in spite of an air show at the field into which we were press-ganged to help. I finished off converting to the Auster J1/N which seemed more grown-up with its enclosed cockpit. It was also quieter and warmer. Wing Commander Arthur did a crazy flying display at the air show which seemed pretty pointless to me. Later one of the oldest surviving Tiger Moths, G-ACDC, was almost written off during such activity.

During the first trip I was introduced to aerobatics. My instructor, a chap called "Call me Sir!" Thornber, asked if I was strapped in tightly and then abruptly went into a dive, followed equally abruptly by a climb. He misjudged the top of the loop and the aircraft hung upside down. My precious 'half mil' (1:500,000) map and equally precious chinagraph pencil fell out, fluttering down to land somewhere near Dorking. Worse, I was left hanging half out of the cockpit, dangling from my Sutton harness and clinging onto the combing.

"Now you do it," he said when I had got my breath back.

Blow that for a game of darts, I thought, and put the aircraft into a prolonged dive followed by a tight round-out, which I held, pulling positive *g* over the top. I stayed in my seat.

"Fly like that, Joy," he said, "and you will come out of the bottom of the aeroplane."

After a while we were encouraged to 'improve our confidence' by taking an aircraft to perform aerobatics over the Hogs Back to the south. This was carried out with the confidence of the ignorant but in spite of loops, spins, and spins off the top of maximum-rate turns, somehow we got away with it. Rolls never seemed to work out, and anti-spin strakes were not fitted, nor had we heard of them. Once a Gloster Javelin interceptor known as the Flying Flat Iron – a large delta-shaped aeroplane with a T tail, out of Farnborough – came snorting round too close for comfort. He quickly disappeared when I headed for the deck. It had an unloved flat spin characteristic, although 436 were built and went into service. It was retired in 1968. The second prototype was lost in a deep stall, probably the first occasion upon which this new aerodynamic problem was experienced. A prototype BAC 111 and the HS Tridents G-ARPY and G-ARPI were also disastrously lost due to this phenomenon, as will be described later.

In the short time that I was there I completed all the requirements for the PPL, including a Vne (velocity never exceed) dive to restart the deliberately stopped engine; it has to be switched off and the aircraft stalled. The airframe whistled and shuddered alarmingly before the propeller jerked about and eventually decided to get back into action. I also did it on my own, once – not a very good idea; the practice procedure is now banned. I also completed short and long cross-country exercises. These gave an opportunity to come to love the Surrey countryside through which I would travel frequently during my time as High Sheriff, more than half a century later.

The long cross-country exercise involved over two hours' flying and landing away at White Waltham and Oxford, Kidlington. It was not completely without incident – I became uncertain of my position, a euphemism for lost, somewhere near Woodstock. The railway station had been built by the Duke of Marlborough in the 19th century to bring guests, horses and other paraphernalia to Blenheim. To aid map reading I flew low over it in an attempt to read the station name board. It turned out that it had been closed the year before though I did frighten the life out of someone, possibly a train-potter also unaware of the changed circumstances. There was very little theoretical tuition, which was potentially dangerous, and the full measure of which I was unaware until I did the ground studies for my instrument rating at Oxford twenty years later.

I nearly botched the General Flying Test due to an incompetent crosswind landing which had the aeroplane stepping a tango. I had clearly not practised that exercise enough.

"You have been doing too much solo," said Ron Cobbett, the Deputy CFI, Wing Commander Arthur being on leave at the time.

True.

"But you won't kill yourself."

Hope not.

And with that I was given my pass certificate and was subsequently issued with my Class A (landplanes) licence by the Ministry of Aviation, number 50317. Then I left flying for nine years, during which time I learnt to be a doctor.

SIGH FOR A NIGHTINGALE

The very first requirement in a hospital is that it should do the sick no harm.

Florence Nightingale (1820–1910)

There are £24 billion worth of outstanding claims against the NHS at the time of writing (2015), one quarter of its annual budget in England and Wales. Either it, or the legal profession, will have to be wound up eventually.

St Thomas's Hospital was an ancient foundation in Southwark, even in 1215. It was named after St Thomas á Becket. Originally an order of Augustinian monks and nuns, it provided for the welfare of the poor and the sick. The Lord Mayor of London, Richard Whittington (and his cat) founded there in the 15th century what would now be called a mother and baby hostel. The monastery was closed during the reformation under King Henry VIII but reopened four years after his death in 1551 under King Edward VI. It was rededicated to St Thomas the Apostle in view of the earlier problem with St Thomas á Becket. One of the governors, Sir Thomas Guy, founded Guy's Hospital in St Thomas's Street in 1721 to take those who could not be cured by St Thomas's Hospital. These would now be called bed-blockers. The beds are still blocked. Guy's Hospital remained there but St Thomas's left Southwark in 1862 for Lambeth, to make way for the construction of London Bridge station.

In 1871 the hospital opened on its present site on the Thames embankment opposite the Houses of Parliament. It was not a good place to be during the war because many attempts, some successful, were made to bomb the Palace of Westminster. St Thomas's received some forty-six hits and as a result three blocks were destroyed, with the roofs being blown off two others. Dr Aubrey Leatham was a cardiologist with whom I later trained at the National Heart Hospital. He wrote shortly before his death in 2012 that the resident doctors, of which he was one, used to play hockey on the bombed-out top floors using the fireplaces at each end as goal posts. Nursing and medical staff were killed, but no patients were lost. They had been moved to the ground floor and basement. There the beds were so close together that the wards were called 'Scutari', after the tented wards during the Crimean War tended by Florence Nightingale. After the war the psychiatric unit moved there, and to this day even after a further relocation, part of the department is still called Scutari.

Having arrived at the Medical School in 1961 by a circuitous route, it was 1966 before I qualified as a doctor. At that time there was a compulsory 'pre-registration' year which had to be completed before gaining full registration with the General Medical Council. Postgraduate education and training has been considerably expanded, and there has been a concomitant reduction in the number of hours worked under the European Working Time directive. The result is that doctors now have more structured training, but are far less experienced than they used to be in the past when they take up their appointments. If one worked hard and caught someone's eye (not always in that order) one might be appointed to a house job in one's own hospital. This carried some prestige and was usually helpful in career development, which was still not plain sailing. At one Appointments Committee a name was put forward:

"I object to this man," said Sir John, later Lord, Richardson, physician to Harold Macmillan, later the First Earl of Stockton.

"On what grounds, Sir John?" came an enquiry.

"On moral grounds," replied Sir John.

"In that case I will have him as my House Physician," said Professor Sharpey-Schafer, ex-scholar at Winchester and Kings College, Cambridge, erstwhile golfing partner of my father in Gower Street, and at that time the Professor of Medicine.

Rumour control had it that Lady Richardson had caught the man in question with one of their popsical daughters in the pantry at a students' firm party. *Dit ne plus.*

After qualification I was appointed as a house physician to Dr John Bishop Harman (father of the Right Honourable Harriet Harman, MP) and Dr Brian Creamer, later Dean of the Medical School. It was hard work. In those days off-duty was restricted to a notional two weekends a month and maybe an evening during the week if it was not *Major Week*, when we were on call twenty-four hours in the day, for seven days in succession. With forty-two beds, including patients, to look after and any number of other beds spread around the hospital for emergencies, sleep was at a premium. We were paid £770 a year although this was increased to £1,100 per year within a few months following a review. But morale was high and it was a privilege to be at such a place and pursuing such an interesting career. And there was the social life.

The Nightingale training school had been founded in 1860. For years nursing was regarded as a calling and young women from all walks of life trained there. One or two bore the courtesy title of 'lady' due to aristocratic birth. Many nurses had similar academic qualifications in 'A' Level terms to our own. In the school of physiotherapy the standard was even higher. The reason that the young ladies did not become medical students was in part the attitude of the schools – "Our gels do not go into medicine" – and partly lack of parental interest: nice girls got married. At the time you went to Guy's to learn medicine, St Bartholomew's to get married and to St Thomas's to be a gentleman. No wonder the old adage ran that you could always tell a Thomas's man, but you could not tell him anything.

All this was a fertile ground for socialising at the numerous hops where there seemed to be a constant stream of lovely young ladies. And it was the fabled 60s – "If you can remember the 60s, you were not there." Not true in medicine as I saw no drug misuse, although for the purpose of that declaration, alcohol is not a drug. For the hearty there were the various club (cricket, rugby, squash and so on) balls or dinners at which black tie was *de rigeur* and which cost a guinea each (£1/1/– or £1.05p), drinks extra, or £5 on New Year's Eve when there was all the champagne you could drink. The ground turned out to be so fecund that the Dean, Mr Robert Nevin, MS, FRCS, was constrained by Matron, it was said, to read the riot act in his welcoming speech to a new intake of students, explaining that the nurses were primarily there to nurse…

If you were a house physician, as opposed to a house surgeon, your time was spent admitting (clerking) patients, attending ward rounds with your seniors and carrying out procedures of one sort and another. There was a 'charge to housemen', which was put to music and sung as a psalm at one Christmas show. *Thou shalt visit thy patients once by the day and once by the night* was one line.

The night round could not begin before the patients had received their medication, which included night sedation so that the medical staff could get some sleep. At that time alcoholic drinks were available on prescription for the patients and were free for the doctors. Whisky, gin, sherry and brandy in glass-stoppered bottles. During one of the recurring financial crises the only economies which the consultants' committee could suggest were the removal of sealing wax from their dining room and the discontinuation of brandy from the wards as it was imported from France.

If you were on five wards as I was, and bone tired, temptation was at hand. On more than one occasion my friend Jon Pritchard, who became a paediatric oncologist at Great Ormond Street Hospital, and I had soda water fights in which everything would get soaked. "Had a good night last night, din yer, Doc?" some drenched Lambethian stalwart would say to our embarrassment the following morning. It was a climate of mutual respect and affection; nowadays such louche behaviour would get into the red tops in the twinkling of an eye.

There was a song traditionally sung at the end of each Christmas show:

> *Underneath the lamplight, golden curls aglow*
> *Darling I adore you, I will never let you go*
> *Lady, won't you light your lamp for me?*

That was about the ambiance – the long Nightingale ward with thirty beds, politically incorrect now, but the best way to provide care, some still feel. Everyone can see and be seen. The noise of wind displacement, a trumpet voluntary audible in all directions and sometimes resembling Jeremiah Clarke's *March for the Prince of Denmark*; there was the snoring. Ill-lit, but a pool of light radiated from a single bulb under the green glass shade above Sister's desk in the middle of the ward. There sat the night nurses, mostly students – pink stripes for the junior ones and blue stripes for the more experienced. Black stockings, starched aprons and white belts, lace hats, slender arms – they comforted the ill and the dying. They also wrote up the notes, filled in forms, talked and knitted. They were chatted up by the housemen. Sometimes I did a line or two – knit one, purl one – in between writing up the bed tickets (prescription charts).

One also met one's friends and talked sailing, especially with my friend Philip Poole-Wilson, later professor of cardiology at the Royal Brompton Hospital, President of the European Society of Cardiology and much more. Philip prevailed upon me to fix up a date with Mary, later his wife, disregarding the point that I had no idea who she was. He had a pre-war sailing boat called *Melody A*. For the price of scraping its bottom and painting it with copper arsenide, or something equally ghastly as an anti-fouling agent during the winter, one would get invited to sail to Cherbourg in the summer. Wet work, as being an old design it was practically a submarine. I was only allowed the graveyard watch at the helm – midnight to 4am. It is extraordinary how one can fall asleep in a rainstorm, in a big sea, to be woken by the crack of the boom with the boat unintentionally changing tack. At that time Henri Riste would provide duty-free *vin et Gitanes* at the harbour-side out of a battered old grey corrugated iron Citroen H van with a cigarette glued to his lower lip.

I returned, by chance, to Cherbourg much later, this time to the airport on a weather diversion. I was on the way to pick up my daughter, Annabelle, from Sainte Nazaire. The Gulf of Sainte Malo was occupied by wall-to-wall thunderstorms (Cbs), with no clear way through. There was a plaque in the terminal building to commemorate the Silver City Airways operation in the 1950s–1960s in which 250,000 passengers were carried without loss. The aircraft involved was the Bristol 170 Freighter/Super Freighter which also had the capacity to carry three cars. Air Bridge Holdings merged Silver City and Channel Air Bridge to form British United Air Ferries at the beginning of 1963. The operation eventually ceased due to competition from the ferries.

But back to the night round, when one evening one of the Nightingale nurses said she was learning to fly…

WINGS ONCE MORE

Once you have tasted flight, you will forever walk the earth with your eyes turned skyward, for there you have been, and there you will always long to return.

Leonardo da Vinci (1452–1519)

If you were a nurse at that time you could fly for £3 an hour. Norman Jones was a businessman and aviation enthusiast who built the French-designed single-seat Druine Turbulent at his company, Rollason Aircraft, in Croydon. It was powered by a Volkswagen engine. He had a penchant for nurses. He also built a small two-seat aeroplane, the Rollason Condor, based on the Turbulent, which was powered eventually by a one hundred horsepower Continental engine. Only forty-nine were built, of which thirty-six were still flying in 2006. He was a founder member of the Tiger (Moth) Club in 1956, which came about at a dinner at the Royal Aero Club. He gave the club five Tiger Moths, including the much-reproduced G-ACDC, the second oldest DH82a still flying. It was first registered in February 1933 and spent most of its early life at No. 28 EFTS at Wolverhampton.

Jones was keen to get UK aviation products accepted as light aircraft production at that time was dominated by the French and the Americans. This led him to offer aircraft on favourable terms to certain flying clubs, including Fairoaks and Rochester. I have no recall who the Nightingale aviatrix was who turned my thoughts to flying once more, but the days were short, there was no free time, and at that point I was about to leave St Thomas's for my second pre-registration house appointment.

My surgical appointment house was with Mr Tom Fenwick, FRCS, at Queen Alexandra Hospital, Cosham in Hampshire. He was a Lancelot Spratt persona, a good surgeon and remarkably patient teacher. But he could get quite 'upset' in the operating theatre which meant things tended to fly around. After a while I had my own Saturday morning operating list, flattening the bulging inguinal fossae and removing the appendices of the citizens of Portsmouth without supervision. Tom used to carry out the Thursday morning clinic in gumboots with his two black Labradors sitting under his desk. Neither they nor the patients felt it either necessary, or appropriate, to comment on the arrangement. After the clinic he would go back to his farm until Monday.

Portsmouth Municipal airport opened in 1932 when Portsmouth, Southsea and Isle of Wight Aviation moved from the Isle of Wight and the first air ferry in the south of England arrived at its grass airfield. During the war the company concentrated on maintenance and repair. Airspeed had moved there in 1933 and was taken over by de Havilland in 1940. Between 1938 and 1945, four thousand, four hundred and eleven of their Oxford twin-engine training aircraft were constructed at Portsmouth for the Royal Air Force, and others. After the war some were converted to civilian use. At the time I was at Cosham, in 1967, the Hants and Sussex Flying Club were operating light aircraft including a J1/N Auster. Channel Airways operated from Portsmouth a service which included the Channel Islands, Southend and Paris.

Whilst I was working in Cosham on the 15th August 1967, two Hawker Siddeley 748 turbo-prop aircraft crash-landed within two hours of each other. There was no fire and no-one was injured. The cause was poor braking on wet grass with no incremental distance factored in to allow for this. The regulator had made this a requirement when the aircraft were sold to New Zealand, but not in the UK. Shortly after the event this restriction was made mandatory and operations ceased as they were no longer economical. It transpired that the airfield had always been unsafe in wet weather. I was later to have some doubts about the HS 748 operation following an incident of my own.

As the spring of 1967 approached I took some flying lessons with the Hants and Sussex Flying Club in the Auster J1/N. After only seventy-five minutes of familiarisation, following a gap of nine years, I was deemed fit for the solo cross-country. I had covered stalls, spins, practice forced landing and powered approaches, in what I recorded as *lousy weather* during this time. The trip had to be of at least two hours' duration and there had to be two landings away. My flight plan took me to Thruxton, then Shoreham, and back to Portsmouth. Not feeling very confident, the first error was to let the instructor set the magnetic compass, "to be on the safe side," he said. Soon after take-off I realised that flying down the Solent was not the quickest way to Thruxton, which is near Andover. It was a non-radio aircraft and as both RNAS, Lee-on-Solent, and Southampton were active I turned north hoping that nobody was looking. The worthy instructor had set the compass one hundred degrees out. Another lesson: do it yourself, then check and re-check.

Eventually Winchester Cathedral came into sight and I reset my course. But my problems were not yet over. The visibility was not particularly good and Thruxton remained elusive. Eventually I found a grass airfield with a lot of activity, mainly DHC Chipmunks. As I had no radio there seemed little to do but to join the general mêlée and land. As I stopped I looked at the control tower. For the first time there was an intermittent green light, clearly intended for me. Lamp signals to aircraft are uncommon in the era of radio; non-radio aircraft have to advise the control tower by telephone of their intentions. This may be locally, or from a distant field before departure. After rapid consultation with my Air Law booklet the interpretation was 'cleared to taxi' (to the control tower). After shutting down the engine a crisp army captain appeared.

"What are you doing here, dear boy?" he asked.

"Is this not Thruxton?" I replied, somewhat superfluously, as all the aeroplanes had military markings.

"I thought so. This is Middle Wallop [HQ of the Army Air Corps]. Would you like to come into my tower and have a cup of tea?"

It turned out that Thruxton was only about five miles away and I soon was on the ground again. After all this messing about I need to refuel, which was just as well that I supervised. It was rumoured that the airfield had some sort of financial problem and there seemed to be few people about.

The chap who attempted to refuel the aircraft had to be restrained from filling the oil tank with Avgas. He smelt of aldehydes (alcohol degradation products). On another occasion, in the Piper Navajo, the ground crew, against my instructions, refuelled the outboard, instead of the inboard, tanks, thereby upsetting the balance of the aircraft and requiring an external transfer of fuel. In spite of this, the centre of gravity remained too far forward which became evident when loss of aileron authority drew attention to the problem whilst in the air. The aircraft is nose-heavy and needs tail ballast with only two on board and outer tank fuel loaded. The forward centre of gravity required elevator pitch up, resulting in earlier aileron boundary layer separation until sufficient fuel had been burnt off. A further lesson – always supervise the refuelling of your aircraft.

When I got back to Portsmouth there was a certain amount of ill-concealed anxiety. ("We were just beginning to get worried…")

I should have recognised Thruxton as I had been there before – it has two (previously three) hard runways. It was opened in 1942 and was used by both the RAF and the United States Army Air Forces (USAAF): 366th Fighter Group, 9th Air Force. It became civilian once more in 1947. The previous visit had been by road with the Royal Air Force Section from school. We were treated to an aerobatic display by Millard – at public school, at that time, the use of first names caused raised eyebrows, doubtful glances and turned shoulders. He was a boy in the Army house who had won a flying scholarship. We watched his loops and rolls in the Tiger Moth with respect. Remarkably, he took as his passenger his housemaster, the Reverend J. B. Swinbank, who presumably had celestial insurance as well as his safety harness. Whatever his concerns, 'Swinners' used the occasion to preach a later sermon in the chapel on being humble in role reversal: "He was the teacher and I was the pupil…" Yawn.

The other point of interest on that visit was a squadron of de Havilland Mosquitos, en route for disposal somewhere. We were allowed to sit in them and play with the switches and the control yoke. I pressed a button and an engine started to turn, luckily without starting or knocking anyone's head off. It was just as well that they were not armed.

I returned to Middle Wallop, years later, at the invitation of Lt Col (Dr) Ken Edgington (see photo plate 8). He was a helicopter pilot and senior Consultant in Aviation Medicine to the Army whilst with the Army Air Corps. He also served in Cyprus, Norway, Germany, Australia and the Ministry of Defence (MOD). Later he became the Chief Medical Officer (CMO) at the CAA and Head of the Personnel Licensing Division. I was to work with him on cardiological aspects of European harmonisation with the Joint Aviation Authorities (JAA). He invited me for lunch and a spot of flying which involved stalking deer on Salisbury plain for three hours in a helicopter. After a visit to the mess we were kitted out and took off in an Aérospatiale Gazelle. Having got used to the absence of (visible) wings, its controllability was impressive and he gave me a prolonged flying lesson. After a while, to demonstrate his prowess, he dropped the craft into a woodland clearing no larger than a rabbit scrape, blowing leaves, twigs and the local wildlife to kingdom come.

We subsequently went to many meetings together including a memorable one in Beirut. On this occasion, which was during a somewhat fragile ceasefire, an impressive young lady sashayed up as we left the aircraft and invited us to come with her through immigration. Things were looking up. The lady vanished, as they say, to be replaced by a scruffy, rather shifty-looking fellow wearing a sack, who beckoned us to the 'official' car. As he headed off through West Beirut, passage through which had been advised against by the Foreign and Commonwealth Office (FCO), we wondered if we were going to suffer the same fate as Terry Waite. In the event, we had been hijacked by a taxi driver who demanded no worse than $30.

Years later I was treated to another helicopter ride, this time whilst High Sheriff in Nomination. I flew with the Chairman of Surrey County Council, Geoffrey Marlow, who had served in the Royal Air Force. We were to fly in a Boeing Chinook out of RAF Odiham. (See photo plate 9) It was a jolly in the local area as part of the ongoing military effort to gain acceptance for their operations. Almost unbelievably, there are those who complain about such activity. Having researched activity-sensing cardiac pacemakers with Dr Bill Toff in the Chinook previously, it was interesting to interpret why they (the pacemakers) seemed so spooked by the machine. Once the engines had started, they ran to the upper extreme of their pacing range, 120 beats per minute, and remained there until the engines were shut down again. In flight the aircraft has a curious yawing trajectory at low level, rather like riding an elephant; yaw is movement of an aircraft about an axis which changes its orientation but not its direction. It also vibrates, which must have been the cause of the piezo-electric difficulty.

★ ★ ★

Being very short of money, flying time was not easy to come by, but after completing five hours, the privileges of the PPL for Class A landplanes (single-engine piston) were restored. One way to find an excuse to fly was taking one's friends up for a jolly. On one of only three further trips that summer there is a note in my log that John Betts, a colleague at the hospital, came with up me *and was terrified*. I have no memory as to why, but it did not stop him coming up again. On that occasion I took the remaining three on-call doctors at Queen Alexandra's Hospital up too. The wind was variable and there was some activity with the arrival of a Channel Airways flight. I made an approach on the north-easterly runway but the aircraft floated and I decided to go around.

10. *'Three little maids from school are we' (confer W S Gilbert). Boeing Chinook HC2 helicopters during our visit to RAF Odiham in 2010. Three Squadrons, Nos. – 7, 18 and 24, are based there. It is a most versatile battlefield support aircraft.*

On the second approach the same thing happened; the aircraft, whilst stable on the final approach, began to float on with a decaying airspeed but unexpectedly high ground speed. I decide to put it on the ground. As we tore along the runway the boundary fence was looming up fast. It was too late for a go-around so I braked – carefully, an abrupt application might have put the aircraft on its nose. Then harder, next as hard as I could. Fortunately the brakes were not set up evenly and we did a ground loop – a swerve – and stopped just before the fence. No sooner had we landed and I had noted the pea green appearance of my friends than an HS 758 was rushing towards us, stopping a few yards away. When I met John many years later and reminded of this scrape, he remarked "I thought you always landed like that".

We both had experienced wind shear, a phenomenon in which there is a difference of wind speed and direction over a short distance. I had never heard of it at the time. It can occur in relation to thunderstorms, temperature inversions and frontal activity. It is a potent source of accidents in the take-off and landing mode, an example being the loss of the Delta Airlines flight 191 Lockheed 1011 Tri-Star at Dallas, Fort Worth, in August 1985. There was thunderstorm, specifically microburst (a localised severe downdraft), activity in the area local to the airfield. Wide fluctuations in airspeed were experienced by the aircraft during the final stages of its approach. The resulting loss of energy (lift) led to 137 fatalities; there were only twenty-six survivors. On discussion of our own experience, later, it transpired that the Channel Airways aircraft had been following me in and made the assumption that the line I had taken, into wind on the grass field, was appropriate. Then he, too, ran into the wind shear. It did seem at the time that there had been no margin for error on the part of either of us, and that if the runway had been wet as it was two weeks later…

I did not fly for a year after that trip and on the next occasion it was in a Rollason Condor at Fairoaks, where the Nightingales also flew. Then it was off to Rochester where I was living for a few months. The Condor is a wooden aeroplane with good manners but with a maximum load of the order of 550 pounds. Two adults leave little scope for fuel or a map unless one is a slender Nightingale. With the 100 rather than the 130 horsepower Continental engine, performance is limited – hardly enough to pull the skin off a rice pudding, as they say. This was evident on one occasion on take-off when I found it was difficult to get out of ground effect with a heavy passenger whilst heading uphill on Runway 20 at Rochester. Sometimes I took my daughter, Annabelle, up although she was only about three at the time. Years later I used to take up my elder son, David, at much the same age in the Beechcraft Baron 95-B55 G-SUZI. Even though he could not see over the combing, in spite of two booster seats, he was remarkably good at straight and level flight, which he achieved by keeping the wing tip on the horizon. He could also climb and descend. He now has a PPL and until recently owned a Kitfox.

The land for Rochester Airport had been purchased compulsorily in 1933 by the City Council, Short Brothers moving there a year later, together with Pobjoy Airmotors. Short Brothers subsequently took over Pobjoy. The major construction project by Shorts was for the S29, a four-engine bomber known as the Stirling. The Esplanade, Rochester, also saw the construction of the Empire and Sunderland flying boats; in 1946 the company relocated to Belfast. In 1938 No. 23 ERFTS arrived and was equipped with Avro Tutors. After the war RAF No. 24 EFTS replaced it

11. *David's Kitfox showing trailing edge devices, in this case 'flaperons', which act differentially as ailerons (to control bank), and together as flaps to increase lift (and drag) for landing. Note the Hoerner down-turn of the wing tips (confer the Red Kite) which reduces contamination of the upper wing surface by the wing-tip vortex. An early application was on the Messerschmitt Me 162A jet fighter in 1945 - and the Red Kite, before that.*

for a few years. Channel Airways operated Douglas DC3 Dakotas and de Havilland Doves to the continent for the two decades after the Second World War. It co-operated with British European Airways in providing a feeder to the BEA operation at Southend; this was eventually discontinued.

By September 1968 I had completed both my pre-registration year and a further year as a Senior House Officer, at first in Portsmouth then back at St Thomas's Hospital. At this point I was offered a research fellowship on the Professorial Medical Unit under Professor Bill Cranston, working in a laboratory with Dr Robert Lowe, later Dean of St George's Hospital Medical School. I was investigating the neuro-humeral control of the circulation – the interaction of the endocrine (hormonal) system with the nervous system, in the regulation of the circulation. As my net income was only £99 a month, funds for flying were scarce. I continued to hire club aircraft at Rochester, Fairoaks and later Biggin Hill from a small club, the South London Aero Club. It had aircraft including a Cessna 150 and a Piper PA28/160 Cherokee with the advantage that it gave a 10% reduction to members of the University of London. It got into trouble, reportedly, due to the involvement of a club aircraft in the smuggling of illegal immigrants. This was well ahead of the game at the time. After that I transferred to the Surrey and Kent Flying Club, also at Biggin Hill.

Biggin Hill was first used by the Royal Flying Corps in the Great War. No. 141 Squadron was based there with Bristol Fighters as part of the inner patrol zone of the London Area Defence against the Zeppelin raids, and attacks by Gotha bombers. It could claim one kill before the war ended. After the Great War, the Army School of Air Defence and the Experimental Searchlight Establishment were established there. No. 56 Squadron flew the Sopwith Snipe, and later the Armstrong Whitworth Siskin, until these were transferred to North Weald in 1927. Vickers Vimys (of Alcock and Brown transatlantic fame) also flew there with the Night Flying Unit. It was closed between 1929 and 1932 to build new hangars. When it reopened it was joined by Nos. 23 and 32 Squadrons equipped with Hawker Demons and Bristol Bulldogs. Later Nos. 32 and 79 Squadrons were equipped with Gloster Gauntlets and joined by No. 601 (City of London) Squadron flying Bristol Blenheims.

The story of Biggin Hill during the Battle of Britain, and beyond, is legendary and needs no retelling. Many squadrons of Spitfires including Nos. 92, 72, 74 and 610 were based there, as part of 11 Group, and remained active in spite of repeated attacks on the airfield. It saw continuous service during the war; afterwards it was transferred to No. 46 Group in Transport Command flying Royal Canadian Air Force DC3 Dakotas (No. 186 Squadron). The United States Air Force (No. 314 Squadron) was also part of the establishment. The Royal Auxiliary Air Force Nos. 600 and 615 Squadrons were reformed there and later joined by No. 41 Squadron. The first two flew Spitfires, later Meteors, and, in the case of the regular No. 41 Squadron, Hawker Hunters. The Auxiliary units were disbanded in 1957. In 1962 the Aircrew Selection Centre moved to Biggin Hill after the closure of RAF Hornchurch, moving again to RAF Cranwell in 1992. Biggin Hill is now a business and general aviation airfield, and the landlord, remarkably, is the Bromley Borough Council. There are still a few national assets left for sale to foreign sovereign wealth funds.

When I first flew out of the airfield in 1968 there was still a Royal Air Force presence. It operated its own Control Tower on the west side of the field together with the main runway, 03/21. It was denied to other traffic without special permission. I flew without significant incident for rather more than forty hours over the next four years, mainly in the Cessna, Piper Cherokee and the Beagle Pup, an over-engineered and under-powered (in its civilian form) aircraft that regularly carried defects. I did suffer abrupt loss of engine power on take-off on one occasion in a Piper Cherokee (PA 140) whilst behind blind flying screens. It was likely to have been due to carburettor icing, although in a normally aspirated (non-fuel injected) engine this is said not to occur on take-off. That is not true. After an age, following the application of carburettor heat, the engine sprung to life again, by which time the Surrey woods had become invitingly close (if one was picnicking). After discussion we decided to go on to our destination, Southend, to practise the VDF (Very high frequency Direction Finding) approaches. As the conditions of high humidity were ideal for carburettor icing, I made liberal use of the heat control. Eventually the knob came off in my hand, so we went home, hoping the ice fairy was not hovering too closely to our inlet venturi.

The second icing occasion was in a different aeroplane (Grumman Tiger AA4 - G-BDYB, aka '*Yogi Bear*'), which I had collected from Elstree following a service. It followed the same pattern, but this time I had a medical student on board. The application of carburettor heat again degraded the performance sufficiently to prevent the maintenance of height, whilst not clearing the problem. So we coughed and sputtered slowly round the airfield, at the same time putting out a PAN (urgency) call which, as already explained, decants the workforce from the hangars no matter what the weather. All was well until the final approach when the good student, who had not said a word hitherto, became agitated by the deliberately held sideslip employed to lose the excess height. His stiff upper lip soon returned and we landed safely to the disappointment of the gathered crowd and to the relief of one aspiring doctor.

Whilst I was still at St Thomas's Hospital, two events occurred which, though unforeseen at the time, were to impact on the future. The first was the formation of the Civil Aviation Authority (CAA) in April 1972, which was later to employ me for thirty-eight years. But before the new authority had had time to get its feet on the rudder pedals a further event occurred, three months later, which was to have a profound effect on the regulatory environment. This was the loss of the BEA Trident 1 G-ARPI (Papa India) at Staines. It was to be the worst aviation accident in the UK until the Pan Am 103 disaster at Lockerbie in 1988.

11
PAPA INDIA

…it is impossible to make the men perfect… and no legislation will make a man have more presence of mind… Or make him more cautious…

Isambard Kingdom Brunel,
Chief Engineer of the Great Western Railway;
Parliamentary Select Committee on Railways, 1841

On Sunday 18th June 1972 at 16.11 hours the British European Airways Trident 1 G-ARPI (*Papa India*) crashed in a field near Staines, Middlesex. It was the BE 548 flight to Brussels and all 118 people on board died of their injuries. The aircraft brakes had been released 150 seconds earlier on Runway 28R (the right-hand runway, whose direction to the nearest ten degrees was 280 degrees). The aircraft was 24kg above its maximum permitted take-off weight, but this was not important. It had both valid certificates of airworthiness and of maintenance. The handling pilot, who was also the pilot in command (P1), was Captain Stanley Key, aged fifty-one years, with a total of some 19,000 flying hours, four thousand of which were as pilot-in-command on the Trident.

The co-pilot (P2), Second Officer (S/O) J. W. Keighley, was twenty-two years of age and inexperienced. This was of concern to the Accidents Investigation Branch (AIB) and its report (4/73) was discursive on the issue. He had completed his commercial pilot training and gained his CPL, and instrument rating (I/R), at the College of Air Training at Hamble in some 225 hours. On the Trident flight simulator he had completed a total of fifty-one hours as P1/2/3 (pilot in command/second officer/third pilot in flight engineer role) with a further seventeen hours of base training – flying the aircraft under tuition of a base training captain. Finally he had flown twenty-nine hours in the aircraft, on the line, under the supervision of a training captain. His progress had been slow and his training reports had indicated the need for careful watching. He was felt to be one who might not react well under stress. Occasionally he had been prompted *to get ahead of the aircraft*. Being 'behind the aircraft' is the aviation equivalent of not being up to speed.

Second Officer S. Ticehurst was flying as third pilot (P3), behind the central pedestal, monitoring the other two pilots. He was twenty-four years of age and had completed over 1,400 hours in total, 750 of them on the Trident aircraft. He was regarded as competent and conscientious. There was also a fourth pilot on the flight deck, Captain J. Collins, who was riding as a passenger; concern was expressed that he might have distracted S/O Ticehurst from his monitoring duties.

The trajectory of the brief flight from brake release to disaster in a fully serviceable aircraft, in 150 seconds, was to be examined minutely in the accident report. One fact was known immediately – that the aircraft had landed more or less in one place, suggesting a near-vertical descent. More forward speed would have left a trail of wreckage. The following day, during the routine Monday meeting of the Medical Unit at St Thomas's Hospital, Professor Bill Cranston wondered aloud why this was the case. Without thinking, I suggested that it might have entered a deep stall. And this is what was subsequently shown to have occurred (see photo plate 10).

An early experience of the stable, or deep, stall involved the second prototype Gloster Javelin in June 1953. The lift of a wing is a function of the forward airspeed and the 'angle of attack'. Under Bernoulli's principle, the increased speed of the air as it deflected over the upper surface of the wing induces a pressure drop, i.e. lift. Further lift is generated by pressure on the under surface of the wing when there is a positive angle of attack. Lift increases with an increased angle of attack until a critical point when the boundary airflow over the upper surface breaks away and becomes disorganised. Lift is reduced and 'drag' – wind resistance in the vernacular – increases. With reduced lift and increased drag there is a point at which the weight of the aircraft is no longer supported. This is the aerodynamic stall and the aircraft will descend, often abruptly.

In an aircraft with a high tail plane, such as the British Aircraft Corporation (BAC) One-Eleven and the HS Trident, the turbulent flow may envelop the 'T-tail' and its elevators, with consequent loss of pitch authority. In this situation there is an additional hazard with turbulent blanking of the air intakes of rear-mounted engines, which may be associated with a compressor stall. Thus the stall may become 'deep' or 'stable'; a potentially lethal problem accentuated by the tendency to forward movement of the centre of pressure (lift) as a secondary effect of the swept wing configuration of high-speed aircraft at high angles of attack.

The first demonstration of this problem in a conventional civil airliner, rather than the delta winged Gloster Javelin interceptor, was on the BAC One-Eleven – G-ASHG – on 22nd October 1963, near Chicklade in Wiltshire. The aircraft is of swept wing design with engines at the rear and a T-tail. It had a crew of seven; the pilot was Mike 'Lucky' Lithgow. It was being flight-tested to assess stability and handling characteristics near the stall with different locations of the centre of gravity. At 16,000 feet (4,900 m) with 8° of flaps, the plane entered a stable (deep) stall at a high rate of descent, in a horizontal attitude, eventually striking the ground with low forward airspeed. Lithgow was a consummate professional and made several attempts to correct the situation with power and control surface inputs, recording the effect, or lack of it, as he did so. They all died.

The now-forgotten but prescient accident to the Hawker Siddeley Trident 1C G-ARPY occurred when it entered a deep stall from which the crew were unable to recover. The aircraft crashed on 3rd July 1966 at Felthorpe, Norfolk, killing all four crew on board. This was the first loss of a Trident aircraft and was due to the deliberate disablement of the stick shake/push stall protection to identify the margin between the stall warning, and the established stall. This provoked a stable flat spin from which no recovery was possible.

In the *Papa India* disaster a similar sequence of events was demonstrated following interpretation of the output of the two 'black box' (painted red) flight data recorders (FDR). There was no voice recording from *Papa India* as at that time there was no requirement on UK-registered aircraft for a cockpit voice recorder (CVR); it was to be one of the recommendations of the subsequent public enquiry for aircraft heavier than 27,000 kg. The weather was poor, with rain and a cloud base with 8/8 (complete cover) and broken cloud at six hundred feet. There was also considerable turbulence. In an airliner such as the Trident, visual references are lost early and flying the aircraft is by reference to instruments once the nose is raised during take-off. Visual cues may be helpful, if available, in extremis.

Start-up and taxiing was uneventful for a Dover One SID (standard instrument departure). Take-off clearance was finally given at 16.08 on Runway 28 Right. It was a de-rated take-off (maximum power was not used). Twenty degrees of flap were set together with deployment of the leading edge 'droop' (a lift device), both normal. On the take-off roll the nose was raised at V1 after forty-two seconds and the aircraft lifted off at 145 knots. Initial climb speed (V2 – the speed at which commitment to take-off is irrevocable) plus 25 knots, known as the Vna, had been planned for 177 knots; only 170 knots was achieved. Captain Key called "Climbing as cleared" at eighty-three seconds after brake release and was already turning for the Epsom non-directional beacon (NDB). At one hundred seconds he reported "Passing 1,500 [feet]." He was cleared to six thousand feet and told to 'squawk' a code on his transponder – a device which identifies the aircraft to the radar controller. This was briefly acknowledged at 108 seconds and was the last call from the aircraft. At 105 seconds, after flap retraction and reduction in thrust for noise abatement, the airspeed had further decayed to 157 knots, twenty knots below Vna.

At 114 seconds the speed was 162 knots (against 177 knots planned) and the droop lever was pulled at an airspeed that was sixty knots too low. Two seconds later the stick pusher (a device which identifies an incipient stall and applies a physical correction to the attitude of the aircraft on the control yoke) thrust it forward, at the same time as disengaging the autopilot which was now outside its operating limits. There were two more stick pushes before the recovery system was manually inhibited at 128 seconds by one of the crew. The aircraft immediately entered an aerodynamic stall followed by a deep stall from which no recovery was possible at that, or probably any, altitude. Twenty-two seconds later and 150 seconds after brake release, all were dead or dying. The cause of death in many was traumatic abruption of the heart which was torn off its conduit, the aorta. The cause of the crash was identified as failure of air speed monitoring and retraction of the droop at too low an air speed. It was concluded that the droop lever could not have moved by itself and that when it was moved, the mistake had passed unnoticed and uncorrected.

Autopsies of the crew members revealed that Captain Key had narrowing of all three of his coronary arteries – the medium-sized vessels which supply the myocardium (the heart muscle) itself. There had been no heart attack (damage to the muscle) as such, although at one point in the left coronary artery there was significant narrowing. There are actually three 'left' coronary arteries – the left main-stem, the left anterior descending and the circumflex vessels; there is also a right main coronary artery. The cardiologist speaking of 'three-vessel disease' is referring to the two branches of the left main-stem, considered separately, and the right coronary vessel. Proximally in the 'left' vessel there was a tear in the its lining – the intima – with evidence of new bleeding into the obstructing 'plaque' of atheroma – a cheesy degenerative material containing deposited cholesterol in its wall. This was not felt to be traumatic – there were plenty of control subjects. Plaque rupture was first described in 1844 and has been the subject of intense research over the past three decades into its role in myocardial infarction (heart attack). The descriptive terminology in the Accident Report is now out of date, but the thrust is the same. The fresh haemorrhage (bleeding) into the plaque did not appear to have been associated with fresh thrombus (blood clot) in the vessel, but could have provoked obstructing spasm of the artery.

Captain Key had suffered his coronary event almost certainly within the curtilage of the pre-flight briefing, start-up and departure. This could have made itself known in several ways. He might have experienced malaise, more probably chest pain, which could have been overwhelming. An alternative was that he developed a rhythm disturbance (arrhythmia) which was distracting. Or, he could have developed a lethal arrhythmia (ventricular fibrillation) which would have led to loss of consciousness within ten seconds, and brain death within three minutes (see photo plate 11). The Accident Report wondered if anything might have provoked the event. There had been a major row involving Captain Key in the crew room about thirty minutes before his departure, although this was said to have subsided quite quickly. Patrick Forman, with whom I was later to share an aeroplane, was working at the time on the *Sunday Times* as their Air Safety correspondent. He said that a reporter, posing as an airline pilot, had got into the crew room a day or two after accident and overheard a conversation. Apparently Captain Key had stumped off after the altercation, following which a fellow pilot asked him where he was going.

"To Brussels."

"How are you going to get there?"

"I am flying, you ass."

"You are not fit to fly, you are not even fit to ride a bicycle."

True or not, he would not have been in a good condition to fly. It has been reported that there is a four-fold risk of heart attack within two hours of a major emotional upset when compared with the same period the day before. The accident report goes into eight pages of discussion as to the cause and concluded that it was primarily a failure of monitoring of the air speed and premature retraction of the droop. Looking back forty years later, the lack of correction of the airspeed in turbulent conditions on the climb out is surprising. It suggests that the handling pilot, Key, was not fully in the loop and possibly out of it after 108 seconds – his last call. Six seconds later the droop was retracted and disaster was inevitable.

Who pulled the droop lever was never established. It is possible that it was Key, in confusion and in the belief that the flaps had been extended in error, which might have accounted, in his mind, for the low airspeed. The use of the stick push dump lever (appropriately known as the tiger's tail on account of its yellow and black stripes) reflected the possibility that one of the pilots had wrongly identified the manoeuvre as a false warning, and was seeking to neutralise the alarming pitch-down, hazardous at the low altitude. At no point was there an application of thrust, a fundamental component of incipient or established stall recovery. The report drew numerous conclusions, many of which were of a technical nature, stating that the underlying causes included: *The abnormal heart condition of Captain*

Key leading to a lack of concentration and impaired judgement sufficient to account for his toleration of speed errors and to his retraction, or order to retract, the droop in mistake for the flaps.

There were a number of recommendations which flowed from the report including:

- Cockpit voice recorders to be mandatory in all UK-registered aircraft over 27,000 kg MTWA (Maximum Take-off Weight Authorised)
- The need for more flight deck training in the change of configuration stall for novice pilots before the assumption of P2 duties
- Training in the recognition of sudden or subtle incapacitation of a crew member
- The advisability of routine exercise electrocardiography as part of the regular scrutiny of aircrew.

This was not the first time, nor the last, that a multi-crew aircraft was lost due to cardiovascular incapacitation of the pilot, although some persist in denying the latter. There had been five fatal aircraft accidents in large passenger carrying aircraft attributable to coronary event in the decade or so before *Papa India*, and twenty-nine accidents worldwide attributable to medical incapacitation in the four decades up to 1985. Thereafter such events have become a considerable rarity in multi-crew operations. This has been due to improved co-pilot training and cockpit resource management (CRM), and training in the recognition of sudden and subtle medical incapacitation. Incapacitation training was made mandatory by ICAO in 1974 and adopted worldwide thereafter.

Following the publication of the Accident Report, the CAA set up an expert committee to examine some of the issues raised. The committee concluded that interpretation of the routine aircrew resting electrocardiogram (ECG) should be centralised to ensure an even standard of reporting. The Public Enquiry had also recommended that should exercise electrocardiography *in future become significantly more reliable* it should be substituted for the resting ECG. The former is, for the detection of occult coronary artery disease, more sensitive but less specific.

During the Public Enquiry there had been a collision of opinion between cardiological expert witnesses as to what Captain Key's last ECG had shown, and whether the tragedy of the 18ᵗʰ June 1972 could have been prevented. The specialists involved were Dr M. M. Gertler (USA), Dr Walter Somerville (UK) and Dr Wallace Brigden (UK). The principal difference lay with the interpretation of the 'mean frontal QRS axis'. Briefly, the sum of the electrical events in the heart at any one instant have a force and a direction and may thus be expressed as a vector. The different vectors reflect, in sequence, atrial (upper chamber) and ventricular (main chamber) depolarisation – excitation, and ventricular recovery (repolarisation). Rhythm change and conduction velocities are derived from time intervals. Dr Gertler insisted that the axis was abnormal and deflected to the left (-49 degrees) whilst Dr Somerville stated that it was -8 degrees – within the normal range.

When I ran the original recording to earth forty years after it had been made, Dr Somerville had been unequivocally correct. The recording was within normal limits. As it was still in its original heat-labile strip format, I mounted and digitised it. What was evident was that it was a poorly standardised ECG with baseline interference, but this had not interfered with its interpretation. In the interest of standardisation and quality control, the committee suggested that the recordings were scrutinised at the CAA by a designated specialist. In the event, that was to be myself. The issue of exercise electrocardiography, recommended by the public enquiry, was pursued, perhaps predictably, by two self-appointed expert committees of cardiologists who published their own reports.

Cardiologists have always spent a lot of time in aeroplanes for one reason or another and felt they should have a hand in the fitness of the pilots flying them about the planet. The first report came from the Eighth Bethesda Meeting of the American College of Cardiologists, published in 1975 after three days of deliberations. The Royal College of Physicians of London followed suit, publishing three years later, in 1978. I gave evidence twice to the latter committee. In the event, of the regulatory agencies involved, neither the US Federal Aviation Administration (FAA), nor the UK CAA, accepted the recommendation that pilots should undergo routine exercise electrocardiography. This was finally laid to rest in 1980 at the first ICAO cardiovascular study group meeting in Montreal, at which I represented the UK and gave evidence which argued against the proposal.

The 220 passengers and nine crew of the Boeing 757-2T7 G-BYAM, inbound on 28th January 1996 to Malaga, fared better. The aircraft was on the approach and cleared to leave FL 150 – approximately 15,000 feet on the standard altimeter pressure setting of 1013.25 millibars (mb) – for seven thousand feet on the QNH (altimeter pressure setting to give the altitude above sea level). The radar heading was to be 180° to intercept the instrument landing system (ILS) for Runway 14. At that point the first officer noticed that the commander was unwell. He declared a medical emergency involving the pilot in command. He was cleared for a further descent to 5,500 feet and later to turn left onto 165° to intercept the localiser from the left.

As the aircraft levelled at the assigned altitude, the ground proximity warning system (GPWS) sounded. It called *PULL UP, PULL UP*, appearing to have been triggered by the aircraft's flight path over a four thousand foot ridge to the northeast of the field. He disconnected the autopilot, applied power and climbed to six thousand feet, whereupon the aircraft broke cloud and the airfield ahead became visible. He joined the ILS from two thousand feet above at twelve DME (distance measuring equipment) miles from the field, and landed safely. The captain was found to be dead on landing. The GPWS warning may have been caused by failure to reset the captain's altimeter, which is on the left, when he was flying the aircraft from the right-hand seat. The First Officer had been trained for the eventuality of medical incapacitation and had 10,750 hours' flying experience, of which 2,470 hours were on type.

The outcome of these two events could not have been more different. Both pilots-in-command had suffered a disabling cardiovascular event; there was one fatal accident and one safe landing. On the one hand the first officer was young and inexperienced, both overall and on type, with no incapacitation training. On the other he was mature, very experienced and had undergone CRM (crew resource management) and incapacitation training.

A NEW DEPARTURE

The secret of getting ahead is getting started.

Mark Twain (1835–1910)

At the time of the *Papa India* disaster I was finishing my doctoral thesis amongst the dusty shelves of the library of the Royal Society of Medicine (RSM) in Wimpole Street, W1. This was years before the Internet. The RSM should issue salbutamol with its library pass to counteract the inevitable bronchospasm induced by the resident *Dermatophagoides pteronissinus* (house dust mite), and its cousin, *Psocoptera psocomorpha* (the book mite), which is generally less antigenic to human beings. The thesis described the location of a receptor site in the hindbrain whereby a hormone (angiotensin) activated by an enzyme (renin), released by the kidney, is involved in the regulation of the circulation. It influences the blood pressure and heart rate via the autonomic (involuntary) nervous system.

The next move was to the National Heart Hospital and later to the Royal London Hospital, where I was a senior registrar in Medicine. This was at a time when the Department of Health, in response to the clamour for better terms and conditions of service for hospital doctors, decided to pay us for being on call. We were to be given Units of Medical Time (UMTs) for after-hours work; there were a lot. The payments were controversial to the extent that they had to be signed off by one's consultant. As UMT payments brought our income to a point above theirs, it did not go down very well, but the sensible realised that they would catch up, which in the end they did. In my case the unexpected bounty was to be spent on an aeroplane.

Following the opening of the CAA in 1972 there was a call for suitable applicants to apply to become Authorised Medical Examiners (AME) to carry out routine examination of aircrew. Being a penniless lecturer on the Medical Unit at St Thomas's Hospital at the time, I applied with alacrity to join the few, only to be told, as in the Battle of Britain sketch in *Beyond the Fringe*, that there were too many already. I forgot about it until Dr James Alexander, Deputy Chief Medical Officer (CMO), whom I had met, wrote and said he had a proposal. The CAA would like to see a civilian medical unit at Biggin Hill which would act as a reference point in civilian aviation medicine. It would carry with it AME status for both the Commercial Pilot Licence (CPL) and the Private Pilot Licence (PPL). There would be no funding. Without stopping to enquire as to which planet James departed on his train from Waterloo each evening, I said that I would gladly accept the accreditation and see if anything could be done about a medical presence there at the weekends. As it turned out there was already an AME in a lock-up room on the field at Biggin Hill who, unsurprisingly, was not keen on someone else mucking in too. So that part came to nothing.

Then Dr Alexander telephoned again. Would I like to attend the CAA Medical Department at Shell Mex House, as there was a proposal they would like to put to me? Thinking that it might be another kite like the Biggin Hill Medical Centre, I was a bit reluctant, but went along anyway. There I met Dr Geoffrey Bennett, the Chief Medical Officer (CMO), for the first time. There were others, presumably from what would have been called Personnel in those days. It dawned on me that I was being 'boarded' – interviewed. It was explained that the expert committee report, following the Papa India disaster, had recommended that a cardiologist be appointed to scrutinise aircrew resting ECGs. This would be at the Medical Department of the CAA. It could be at my own convenience and would be paid £1 each (about £8.80 today using the Retail Price Index). I apprised them of my qualifications, such as they were, and was to be informed within three weeks if the plan was to go ahead.

Nothing happened, so three months later I rang James Alexander. He was dismissive – unlikely to go ahead. Two weeks later I got a further telephone call – could I start next week? Which I did on the 24th August 1974 on the basis of a two-line letter of appointment, stating that the arrangement was to be on the basis of a three-month trial. This was later renewed *for some time to come.* The CAA Clinical Medical Unit subsequently opened in Holborn Kingsway in 1976, and the two clinical sessions for the review of problems in aircrew I attended each week lasted for the next thirty-five years. I was appointed on the basis that I had some knowledge of aviation, as well as cardiology, and was careful to comply with ICAO Annex 1.2.4.5.2: *Designated medical examiners must be familiar with… and have practical knowledge and experience of… the operating environment of the various licence holders. Such practical knowledge and experience should include, whenever possible, actual flight deck experience in aircraft engaged in commercial operation as well as experience in the operational working conditions of air traffic controllers.*

Dr Geoffrey Bennett, the first CMO of the newly formed CAA, had entered RAF Cranwell in 1945. He learned to fly, like all the best pilots, on the DH82a (Tiger Moth), later moving on to the North American Harvard and the Airspeed Oxford. After he gained his RAF wings, he flew for some seven hundred hours in DH Mosquitos with Nos. 204 and 288, and later with Nos. 1 and 29 Squadrons. From the Royal Air Force he gained the Theodore Williams scholarship to Oxford University to study medicine. This was followed by a residency at the Oxford Hospitals and a period in general practice in Berkshire. In 1958 he was appointed research medical officer to the BOAC which gave him the chance to retrain as a part-time airline pilot. Over his lifetime he flew nearly eight thousand hours. The first airliner he checked out on was the Comet 4, but he also flew the Boeing 707 and finally the McDonnell Douglas DC10-30. This was with, respectively, BOAC/BEA, Dan Air and Laker.(See photo plate 12.)

He was a visiting lecturer at Harvard, Oxford and Cranfield, a consultant to the International Labour Organisation, the Federal Aviation Administration, World Health Organisation and the Army. In 1964 he was appointed CMO to the Ministries of Aviation and Technology, becoming CMO to the newly created CAA in 1972, a post which he held until he retired in 1991. It was during his time as CMO at the CAA that he secured the agreement of senior management to fund his type conversion to the DC10, at a cost of £20,000. This was not a good deal for the authority. He was away much of the time flying as a co-pilot on Freddie Laker's DC10 operation, at that time operating out of London Gatwick to Bangor, Maine, in the USA. This was the subject of comment in *Private Eye* in 1979 by Lord Gnome, who recorded that the CMO was very difficult to find at Space House. When he was there, his leadership and knowledge of the industry was outstanding.

★ ★ ★

At the time of the appointment I was living in a flat in South Kensington and having accumulated a sufficient number of UMTs, began to seek a share in an aeroplane. Such opportunities are advertised in the flying press. Eventually a four-man group came to light based around a newly acquired aircraft at Stapleford Tawney, a grass airfield in Epping Forest, north of London. It was the Piper Arrow PA28R/180 G-AVWU and had a fuel injected Lycoming IO-360-B1E engine, a constant speed propeller and a retractable undercarriage. I was later to own a more powerful PA-28R-200 Cherokee Arrow II with the Lycoming IO-360-C1C engine. This seemed grown-up stuff although the weight penalty for these refinements did not enhance the speed by more than a few knots, when compared with the non-retractable version. *Whisky Uniform* turned out to be under-powered – a climb rate of fifty feet a fortnight, it was said, and several later marks were fitted with turbocharged engines.

The linkman was Patrick Forman and we had a series of telephone calls in which his wry sense of humour was evident. He also sent along a lot of figures, *the reasoning of which may seem opaque but it is what is actually needed…* Anyone who could write such a letter must be worth meeting, so I decided to take a look. Then it transpired that the machine in question had its entrails spread over the floor of a hangar in Southend and as result was not airworthy. The only way to get to Southend was by air, so on the 19th October 1974, with my old friend Edward Lyndon-Stanford and two intrepid ladies, we went to White Waltham aerodrome and rented a Piper Cherokee PA 140 aircraft.

★ ★ ★

White Waltham aerodrome is doubtfully claimed to be the largest grass airfield in civil use in Europe. It has three runways which can be muddy in winter. Lying three miles southwest of Maidenhead, it was purchased in 1928 by the de Havilland family for their flying school. Ten years later it was requisitioned by the Royal Air Force and became the headquarters of the Air Transport Auxiliary (ATA), which functioned there between 1940 and 1945. During this time the ATA had expanded from fourteen to twenty-two Ferry Pools. After the war it was used by Fairey Aviation and Westland Helicopters. It remained under RAF control until 1982, preserving an RAF presence in the control tower. When I was flying there in 1973–1974 we used to be given the weather, runway and clearance, RAF-style. This included the transition altitude – six thousand feet; the point at which the altimeter is reset to the standard pressure setting of 1013.25 mb, used on the airways for flight level (FL) determination. It is now the home of the West London Aero Club and is active in flying training. The Honourable Company of Air Pilots (previously the Guild of Air Pilots and Air Navigators) has its flying club there.

I made my first trip across the English Channel from White Waltham. In those days it was quite complicated as departure for France could only be made from a 'Customs' airfield. In this case we had to land at Lympne (now closed), both outbound and on the way back. I took two friends, one of whom was a colleague, Dr Adrian Davies, now a cardiologist in Middlesborough. Having fought through the paperwork, we left Lympne and headed southeast for the light aircraft corridor. Any pilot who has flown a single-engine aircraft over water will know that the sweetest motor seems to grunt and wobble after leaving land. This problem is not evident in twin-engine aircraft when the coast is only a useful position marker. After a short while the low French coastline was emerging from the haze. *Enemy Coast Ahead*, the book by Wing Commander Guy Gibson, VC, DSO and Bar, DFC and Bar, of *Dam Busters* fame, was commissioned by the RAF, detailing his experiences in combat. It was published posthumously in 1946. He died on operations in a DH Mosquito over the Netherlands on 19th September 1944.

The weather was worse on the return and we were followed by a lady pilot who kept up a continuous chatter on the R/T (radiotelephone). Her abbreviated call sign, usually employed once contact has been established, was G-TT, Golf Tango Tango. As she disembarked the aeroplane she was preceded by a magnificent embonpoint. Thereafter those items previously colloquially known as Pringles after a lovely Staff Nurse at St Thomas's Hospital were renamed Tangos.

The ATA was a civilian organisation based at White Waltham for the duration of the war. Initially it was administered by the British Overseas Airways Corporation (BOAC), later the Air Member for Supply and Organisation (AMSO), and thereafter by RAF Maintenance Command for the Ministry of Production. The ferry pools were scattered around the UK and there were two training units. Although the female pilots (Atagirls) tended to attract the attention (there were 166 of them), they were well outnumbered by the males of whom there were 1,152. Sixteen of the women lost their lives for one reason or another, including Amy Johnson who had flown alone to Australia before the war. The male pilots tended to be too old for combat or had degraded medical status – the ATA was said to be an acronym for Ancient and Tattered Airmen.

The pilots were assigned to RAF Reserve Command. The main purpose was to ferry aircraft from their place of manufacture to the operational squadrons, damaged aircraft to the repair organisations and back, as well as communications, freight and ambulance flights. Over their operational lifetime they moved over 308,000 aircraft of 130 types in 414,000 flying hours. The station medical officer was Dr A. Buchanan Barbour who later became the Medical Director of British European Airways Corporation (BEA). Years later I was to be awarded his eponymous prize by the Royal Aeronautical Society, for services to aviation safety.

I was fortunate enough to meet two of the lady pilots of the ATA – Lettice Curtis and Diana Barnato-Walker. They had style. Lettice Curtis went to Benenden School and then on to St Hilda's College, Oxford where she read mathematics. She was a county standard tennis and squash player (Berkshire). She also played lacrosse for her university. She had learnt to fly in 1937 at Ford aerodrome, West Sussex, joining the ATA in the summer of 1940. She remained on its strength until it was disbanded in 1945. She flew numerous different aircraft, and, being tall as well as skilled, was the first woman pilot checked out to fly the heavy bombers. These pilots flew without radios or navigational equipment other than a compass, often in marginal weather conditions. They were given 'Pilot's Notes' on the aircraft they were to ferry which contained all the essential information about the airframe, engines and systems; also the vital power and flap settings, and airspeeds known as 'the numbers'.

After the war she acted as a flight observer at the Aircraft and Armament Evaluation Establishment (A&AEE), Boscombe Down. In 1948 she flew the Spitfire XI belonging to Livingstone Satterthwaite, the US Civil Air Attacheé in London, at Lympne averaging 313.07 mph over a 62.5 mile closed course – a new women's world record. Later in life she became a Flight Operations Inspector with the CAA, finishing with Sperry Gyroscope in Bracknell. In 1992, at the age of seventy-six years, she gained her helicopter licence on the Robinson R22 helicopter. She wrote *The Forgotten Pilots*, published in 1985, which lamented, rightly, the lack of recognition of the contribution of the ATA during the war. She later published *Lettice Curtis: Her Autobiography* in 2004. She died in the summer of 2014 at the age of ninety-nine years.

Diana Barnato-Walker was the daughter of Woolf ('Babe') Barnato, a financier whose wealth had been inherited at the age of two years when his father, Barney, disappeared at sea, possibly having committed suicide. He had been a co-founder of the De Beers mining group in South Africa. Woolf was educated at Charterhouse and Trinity College, Cambridge. He was one of the 'Bentley Boys' and took control of Bentley Motors in 1926 from Walter Owen (W. O.) Bentley during a time of financial hardship. It had always been a time of financial hardship. He raced successfully at Brooklands and won at Le Mans three times (1928, 1929 and 1930). In 1928 he drove the 4 ½ litre car – *Old Mother Gun* – whilst in 1929 and 1930 he drove the 'Speed Six' *Old Number One*. In 1930 he also won a bet of £100 by driving from Cannes to his club in St James' Street in his 'Speed Six' saloon in less time than it took the 'Blue train' to get from Cannes to Calais. The company went into receivership in 1931 at which point it was bought up by Rolls-Royce. One of the most famous cars in the world, the W. O. Bentley was named *le camion de grande vitesse* by Ettore Bugatti. This loosely translates as 'the fastest lorry in Europe'.

Diana was the daughter by the first of Woolf's three wives. She had been a debutante during the 1936 London season, but failed to be presented to

King Edward VIII (later the Duke of Windsor) in the garden at Buckingham Palace on account of a contemporaneous cloud burst. She learnt to fly the Tiger Moth at Brooklands at the age of twenty years. For her twenty-first birthday she was given a dove grey 4 ¼ litre ('Rolls') Bentley as a present from her father; an earlier model of our 1939 'MX' James Young-bodied Bentley, *Algernon*. She served as a VAD (Voluntary Aid Detachment) nurse in France before the evacuation at Dunkirk and drove an ambulance during the London blitz. She joined the ATA at White Waltham in 1941 as one of the first women pilots. Her first assignation was to ATA No. 15 FP (Ferry Pool) at Hamble, which later housed the College of Air Training for future pilots of BEA and BOAC. She delivered eighty different types of aircraft, 260 of which were Spitfires, before she left the ATA in 1945. (See photo plate 13.)

In her book *Spreading My Wings* (1994), she tells of a meeting with Squadron Leader H. T. Gilbert whom she met when she made a weather diversion to RAF Debden in a Miles Magister. Mysteriously the sparking plugs went missing and it was three nights before they could be found. They were engaged within three weeks but he was killed within the month, in a Spitfire, whilst carrying another pilot – it is a single-seat aircraft. She later married Wing Commander D. R. Walker in 1944, becoming Barnato-Walker. For their honeymoon they took a Spitfire each on an unauthorised trip to Brussels for which he was docked three months' pay. He was killed, too, in a bad weather accident in a North American Mustang in November 1945. She never remarried but had a son, Barney, by Whitney Straight, an Anglo-American, in 1947. He never divorced his wife. This was a bit non-standard, as aviators say, by the mores of the day, but she was content, she said. She took the world women's air speed record when she flew in an English Electric Lightning T4 at Mach 1.6 (more than 1,200 mph) in August 1963. She was the first English woman to break the sound barrier. Many did it later as passengers on the Concorde.

I did not know Diana until late in her life – she died at the age of ninety in 2008. She was very striking. One memorable evening we were invited to dinner at her home – Horne Grange, not far from Gatwick. At her request, we arrived in *Outhwaite*, our 4 ½ litre W. O. Bentley, even though there were unresolved carburetion problems. As we departed, the gathering to see us off was enveloped in a puff of dark smoke such that only a rich mixture in a vintage car can produce. The next time I was there was for the reception after her funeral. The service was held nearby at St Mary the Virgin; the church was full to capacity. On her coffin were her wartime flying helmet and flying gloves. She is buried in Englefield Green, Surrey near Ridgemead – her father's home in the 1930s. It was said to resemble the Savoy Hotel rather than a country home.

★ ★ ★

We lined up on the westerly runway at maximum take-off weight authorised (MTWA). I opened the throttle to full power, but the aircraft did not move. It was stuck in the mud. Gradually, and so slowly, we crept forward taking much of the 3,300 foot runway to gain flying speed. No-one had said that it had had a coarse pitch propeller fitted for greater economy when touring. As we neared the end of the mass of muddy grass, the best plan seemed to be to take off – aeroplanes prefer to be in the air rather than lumbering around on the ground. It is said that the average airliner will travel about 200,000 miles on the ground, taxiing, taking off and landing, during its lifetime. Three quarters of an hour later we were in Southend and a tall, patrician man greeted us as the propeller stopped turning. This was Patrick Forman. (See photo plate 14.)

WHISKY UNIFORM

Patrick was a scion of an old Scottish border family whose seat was Dumcrieff,
Moffat, a Palladian mansion. He was educated at Loretto School before
going up to Pembroke College, Cambridge, and reading law at Edinburgh
University. He was initially commissioned into the field artillery, being
posted to an anti-tank training barracks in Catterick, early in 1943. He had a
stammer which ruled out his ambition to fly Spitfires and also the alternative,
to fire guns with the artillery. To his disappointment he was sent off to the
Officers Training Unit (OTU) of the Pay Corps on the Isle of Man; thereafter
to Manchester. Just before D-Day in June 1944, there was an Army Council
Instruction (ACI) which permitted officer transfer to the Airborne Services
with or without the permission of the Commanding Officer (CO). This
went down badly with Pay Corps' CO but delighted Forman, who was off
to join his brother's regiment (Kings Own Scottish Borderers) which had
mustered in Horsa gliders at Woodhall Spa in Lincolnshire.

His unit subsequently embarked operationally on thirteen occasions, only
for each event to be cancelled at the last moment. He had expected to be
dropped at Arnhem from a glider towed from RAF Keevil in Wiltshire,
but suffered a back injury in training and was admitted to a hospital in
Shaftesbury. On 17th September 1944 he saw the gliders being towed past

for the first drop at Arnhem. He discharged himself through a window and hitched a lift to Gosport where a chum arranged his return to RAF Woodall Spa in an Airspeed Oxford, constructed locally in Portsmouth. At that time the airfield was the home of No. 617 (*Dam Busters* Squadron), and a satellite for RAF Coningsby. Fortunately for Patrick, the news came through of the evolving disaster and the second drop was cancelled.

Shortly after this disappointment, in the presence of persisting back pain, he was diagnosed as suffering from spinal tuberculosis – classical Pott's disease – following the intervention of his medical brother, Sholto. Percival Pott, FRS, FRCS was an 18th century surgeon who was on the staff of St Bartholomew's Hospital for over forty years. That should not be held against him. In addition to Pott's disease of the spine, of the scrotum in chimney sweeps (squamous cell carcinoma, or skin cancer), and Pott's puffy tumour – a subperiostial abscess with associated osteomyelitis of the skull – Pott also had a spiral fracture of the lower limb named after him. The last-named used to be common in skiers, but now the knee is the target joint in the sport, rather than the ankle. This upward progress, anatomically, reflects improvement in boot and binding equipment. Pott's puffy tumour was a favourite lesion of Pasty Barrett, of Barratt's ulcer fame. Pasty taught us surgery and gave wonderful parties at his house on Richmond Green. These were attended by what would now be called 'celebs', such as Field Marshal Sir William Slim and Dickie Attenborough. There were no bright young things, apart from his daughters, one of whom was a Nightingale nurse.

In the operating theatre things tended to fly around the place and assisting him could be a trial of patience for everyone. "Pull back on that bloody Deaver, blast you!" Wrench, wrench, following which the thing would be returned to its original position. A Deaver is a ghastly bit of bent metal probably designed by a manager to cut off the hands of the junior staff. On one occasion, after he had dropped a dozen instruments on the floor in frustration when things were not going well, the theatre sister handed him a pair of rib retractors during a rather bloody thyroidectomy.
"What on earth are these for, Sister, dear?" he asked.

"They will make more noise when you drop them, sir."

★ ★ ★

The tuberculous abscess burst into both of Patrick's pleural cavities and he was not expected to survive. There was no chemotherapy at that time – streptomycin was first identified in 1943 by Albert Schatz. He demonstrated that a *Mycobacterium tuberculosis* growth was inhibited by adjacent growth of the soil bacteria actinobacterium *Streptomyces griseus* – a Gram positive spore-forming rod. The antibiotic was developed by Selman Waksman, for which he was awarded the Nobel Prize in 1952. There was a lawsuit too. Para-aminosalicylic acid (PAS) was developed in 1946 and isonicotinic acid hydrazide (INAH) in 1952. Treatment before chemotherapy relied upon rest and exposure to the elements. Patrick was luckier than John Keats (1795–1821), who, when he was dying of tuberculosis in Rome in 1821, wrote home ruefully saying that he was allowed one rusk and one anchovy a day; and that he was being bled once a week. Keats had qualified in Medicine at Guy's and St Thomas's Hospitals by passing the examination of the Society of Apothecaries, but never practised. He preferred to write poetry. "How long is this posthumous existence of mine to go on?" he was quoted to have said in the last days of his illness.

Forman was admitted to a military hospital, but at the request of his medical uncle, Alfred, was transferred to the Wingfield hospital in Oxford where he came under the care of a Catalan refugee orthopaedic surgeon. This was Josep Trueta, who, in 1949, would be given the Chair in orthopaedic surgery at Oxford University.

After a while, at the insistence of Sholto, Patrick was visited by the legendary Evan Jones from St Thomas's Hospital and admitted there to the City of London Ward, on the ground floor. He was encased in a whole-body plaster. One night after his admission a nurse, Jane Henderson, emptied a tiny tabby kitten from her bosom onto his bed. She was to be called Haggis on account of her colouring and had been born in the Gargoyle Club; what Jane was doing there is not on record. Haggis lived in his bed and wore a webbing harness in which she was allowed out to do her business. (See photo plate 15.)

One day she disappeared, to be returned by the matron, Miss G. V. L. Hillyers, who had served as a member of the Queen Alexandra's Imperial Military

Nursing Service Committee. After a year by the Thames she (Haggis) retired to the Scottish Borders. Years later I was attached to City of London ward, as a student, House Physician and later lecturer. The statuesque Nightingale Nursing Sister had been a model for one of the Royal Doulton porcelain figurines of a Nightingale nurse – there were many. I presented her with some violets one day when asking for some time off for one of her nurses.

Patrick was to spend two separate years in St Thomas's Hospital being treated for tuberculosis. The specialists who had looked after him were still there when I was a medical student. Although Evan Jones was almost a deity he was not a good student teacher, perhaps because his ward rounds resembled a comet with a very large tail. It was impossible to hear or see anything, especially as some of it was in Welsh. One day a wizened patient told him she remembered him as a small sandy-haired boy running down the valley with his satchel on his way to school. 'Gaffer' Mimpris later took out part of one of Patrick's kidneys as the disease had spread there too. Gaffer was a large man who operated seated on a bicycle seat at the top of a contraption similar to a pogo stick on wheels. He swayed around alarmingly. On the ward round, the day after his surgery, he boomed at Patrick, "I've done with you" and turned on his heel without further comment. These incidents have a long life.

He was also seen by John Bishop Harman, to whom I was later house physician. There were to be three hospital sojourns and a prolonged convalescence in Moffat, where he was not allowed in the house by his father, who sought to avoid the risk of possible contagion. He survived in a wooden pavilion in the garden. This was rather similar to the tuberculosis sanatorium on the cliffs at Ventnor, Isle of Wight, where, every day of the year, the patients sat in deck chairs pointing into the prevailing south-westerly wind. The belief was that it would blow away the infection.

By the time Patrick and I met he was with Marmaduke Hussey and Harry (now Sir Harry) Evans at the *Sunday Times*. He had been chief legal advisor to the Consumer Council and helped draft the Sale of Goods Act (1979) which had succeeded its eponymous forbear of 1893. At the *Sunday Times* he was the Air Safety Adviser, and a member of the Insight team. One of the early accidents he covered was the Turkish Airlines flight 981 McDonnell Douglas DC-10, which crashed on 3rd March 1974, killing all 346 people on board, at Ermenonville, near Paris. There had been an explosive decompression of the fuselage due to an improperly locked cargo door, secondary to a design flaw. He first heard of the crash whilst airborne over the south of England but could not get clearance to leave UK airspace. His book *Flying Into Danger* was published in 1990 by Heinemann and tells of his involvement in reporting the accident. What he did not record were his impressions of walking over the wreck with its mangled body parts; nor that he saw a man step out of the crowd and pick up a severed hand which he put in his pocket. There are indeed ghouls all about us.

'Duke Hussey' (Rugby School and Trinity College, Oxford) had served in the Grenadier Guards with distinction in World War II and lost a leg at Anzio. He was later chairman of the BBC. When he joined Times Newspapers in 1971 as Chief Executive and Managing Director a note went round the newsroom with the comment: *In the land of the legless, the one-legged man is king.*

★ ★ ★

We looked at the pile of white-and-blue aluminium on the floor of the maintenance hangar. "It *IS* a good aeroplane; it *IS* a good aeroplane," was the mantra Patrick kept repeating. After some negotiation I bought a fifth share in G-AVWU, or *Whisky Uniform* for short, and flew it for the first time on the 1st December 1974. I stayed with the group of five for nearly four years and completed some 150 hours Pilot-in-Command (P1), in addition to other unlogged hours flown with others in the group. We were initially based at Stapleford Tawney, subsequently moving to Elstree. We spent more time arguing than we did flying, partly because the group members tended to have different aspirations. Patrick had gained his Instrument Rating (I/R) largely flying at night on Eric Thurston's Piper Apache PA 23. It was a detail which involved delivering newspapers around Europe in winter with limited warmth coming from a thermos of coffee and an unreliable petrol-burning heater. Mad. I was hoping to gain my I/R but not in a hair shirt. The youngest member, Colin Matthews, wanted to build hours towards an instructor's rating and was not easily persuaded that the new DME (Distance Measuring Equipment) was worth the candle at £1,700 (now about £10,000).

We used the aircraft when we could and made numerous trips to Le Touquet-Paris-Plage on the French coast a few miles south of Boulogne. The resort had been created in 1876 by Hippolyte de Villemessant (1812–1879), founder/owner of the Paris newspaper *Le Figaro*. In 1909, H. G. Wells and Amber Reeves (Kensington High School and Newnham College, Cambridge – the alternative offered by her father, William Pember Reeves, to being presented at court) eloped there (unsuccessfully). Anna-Jane Blanco White was the result a few months later, who, although she was Wells' daughter, took the name of the lawyer George Rivers Blanco White, whom H. G. had arranged for her mother to marry. Her ancestry was an eighteenth birthday surprise.

During the Great War, Le Touquet housed the Duchess of Westminster's Red Cross Hospital for the wounded; 142 casualties are buried in the British Commonwealth war graves cemetery in the town. Noël Coward was a regular visitor before the Second World War. P. G. Wodehouse lived in Le Touquet from 1934 to 1939, from where he was taken to internment in Belgium, then Upper Silesia. *If this is Upper Silesia, one wonders what Lower Silesia must be like...* he remarked.

Later during the German occupation he stayed first at the Hotel Adlon near the Brandenburg Gate in Berlin, and later still in Paris. Having broadcast from Berlin during the war he was regarded as a traitor, but was cleared of treason and went to live in the US after victory in Europe. In 1975 he was partially rehabilitated with the award of a KBE. Now rebuilt, the Adlon is very smart.

There used to be a restaurant on the airfield at Le Touquet, run for many years by a husband-and-wife team; they did as good a lunch as any although for seafood some of the facilities nearer the seafront were difficult to beat. For Easter 1975 we decided to go to Paris via Le Touquet if the weather permitted. As there was no Internet, we had to travel hopefully with regard to accommodation. Patrick and I shared the flying whilst Mandy (see photo plate 16) and her friend were in the back. The TAF (terminal aerodrome forecast) guesstimate, valid for a few hours ahead, and the Actuals (what was really happening) seemed reasonable; anyway Patrick had an I/R. So having cleared customs in Lydd and landed at Le Touquet, we decided to give Paris a go. Before too long the sky darkened and the horizon vanished. It started to snow. Fortunately the snow was dry and showed no sign of sticking to the non-de-iced airframe. It got darker still. Eventually, not without reluctance, Patrick agreed to turn back. *When in doubt, chicken out* is not a bad guideline if you want to stay alive in general aviation.

Having landed back at Le Touquet with two disappointed girls, we were wondering what to do when the little train on the light railway which used to run from the Gare du Nord to Le Touquet-Paris-Plage rattled into sight. We jumped on board and as we wobbled our way through Picardy it was good to be on the ground, but our problems were not over. At the bed bureau in the Gard du Nord there were only upturned palms and a Gallic shrug – the hand signal for *il n'y a absolument rien* – unless of course we would like the bridal suite at the Georges Cinque for which we would have had to mortgage the aeroplane.

Paris in the snow is a bit of a dump if you have nowhere to drop after your escargots, steak frites and bottle of claret. Then Mandy's friend recalled that she had some friends in the *banlieu*, Roissy, near Charles de Gaulle Airport. We telephoned and yes, we could come round for a drink and yes, we could collect the keys to their *grande maison* in the Bois de Boulogne in the 16 èeme Arrondisment; and yes, we could also stay as long as we liked. Why they lived in Roissy with an airliner descending over their house on the ILS every two minutes, rather than in the Bois de Boulogne, defied explanation. Unsurprisingly though, there was some colourful French invective about Concorde and how it should be banned.

On the way there in a taxi the driver said to me, "*Monsieur, vous parlez français comme un belge*", which Patrick said was a compliment but which, as everyone knows, is a French insult. So we stayed for three days in this magnificent house in the Bois de Boulogne, dining off the silver service whilst listening to Patrick playing the music of the Belle Époque on the boudoir grand. After our unexpectedly comfortable stay we unpicked the route on the little train from the Gard du Nord and returned to Elstree in the rain.

Elstree, where *Whisky Uniform* was based, is a small general aviation field between Boreham Wood and Watford. It has a 2,100 foot asphalt runway which in those days was designated 09/27 – take-off was to the East or the

West. Magnetic north drifts annually to the northwest. There is also diurnal variation which might have confused Christopher Robin when he was seeking the Geographic North Pole. The runway was breaking up but has since been repaired. It has a slope of 1.3 degrees which may not sound much but is impressive enough when the aircraft approaches MTWA. Hilfield Park reservoir is to the south, Watling Street to the east, the M1 to the west with power lines all round. Not a good place for a forced landing, or even a landing if you are unfamiliar with it. On occasion, chaps have landed in the reservoir.

Elstree is still owned by Montclare shipping, the major shareholder at that time being (Professor) John Houlder, CBE. His family company specialised in purpose-built ore carriers, gas carriers and drill ships, and later, in semi-submersibles and diving support vessels. He was a remarkable man who held an instrument rating for fifty-nine years, which must be a record. He used to fly solo in a Rockwell Aero Commander to Saint Moritz most weekends, using a huge Decca navigation system with which he had replaced the right-hand seat. He continued to fly, later with a safety pilot, until he was ninety-three years old. He died in 2012 aged ninety-five years. It must have been nerve-wracking at times – he would fly up the valley to Samedan airport, sometimes in cloud, comparing the radar images with photographs he had taken beforehand. He invited me along too, but I was never able to make it.

One day Mandy decided to take off with some nursing friends from the (Royal) London Hospital to a flat in Monte Carlo. That did not pass as a sensible idea at the time so I volunteered to fly down and meet her. We were weight limited when the three of us took off for Nice – Patrick, another friend, Philip Keyte and myself, together with full fuel. There was a long debate as to whether we could take a large candle in case of need for possible camping, Patrick being concerned about degradation of our take-off performance on the uphill westerly runway. In the event we left it sitting by itself in the car. The plan was to stay in a villa borrowed from a colleague in La Croix-Valmer, at the foot of the Massif des Maures hills in the Bay of Cavalaire-sur-Mer. (See photo plate 17.)

Meteorological history repeated itself. I was the handling pilot. Once more, in spite of a favourable weather forecast, all went well until northern

France, when it started to rain. Then it rained harder and harder with the visibility falling to a kilometre, if that. It seemed a bad idea to press on as the weather was still deteriorating, and the VOR (VHF omnidirectional range) navigational system was giving unreliable indications. We called the Flight Information Service, but it was lunchtime. Eventually, with persistence, Reims radar answered and said sure, they would give radar vectors if that was what we wanted, after mocking our uncertain pronunciation of their city. Eventually the twinkling lights of the flare-path emerged from the gloom at about two hundred feet. It is one of the best things there is in aviation when you would rather be on the ground with a cup of tea than struggling with the elements.

We ended up at the Grand Hotel du Nord in Reims in one of those *fin de siècle* hotels decorated with permanently faded paint, and whose rooms resemble large cupboards with high ceilings. One could imagine M. le Décorateur enquiring, "Would Monsieur prefer the faded eau de Nile or the peeling ochre?" Ours had a balcony from which we could watch the carnival and was divided into three sectors – "*Avec des barriers, Messieurs.*" I was bitten by a bed bug (*Cimex lectularis*) which left a handsome crescentic wheal on my back. A deputy cupboard had been constructed in a corner, which we called the gas chamber in deference to the plumbing. That said, it has to be acknowledged that one of the (only, some might say) benefits of the European Union is the striking improvement in French provincial sanitation over the last two or three decades.

The 'Météo' situation was not good. The cloud base was at three hundred feet, if that, and the visibility poor. The pressure gradient was slack with little prospect of early improvement. The two VOR receivers were still in trouble, so we could not take off to check them until the weather improved. On the third day, there was still no means of getting hold of Mandy. Enquiry about the weather yielded nothing more than a flattened palm facing downwards with a slight rocking motion – the Gallic hand signal for 'dodgy' – from M. le Météo. So, feeling a heel, I caught a train to Paris and an Air Inter Dassault Mercure 100 to Nice. (See photo plate 18.)

The Mercure was not a successful aeroplane. Only eleven were sold, all to Air Inter, and none were purchased elsewhere. The range was too short and the Pratt and Whitney JT8D-15 engines noisier and less powerful than the 117 variant wanted by Air France. The modest fleet however completed more than 440,000 movements, losing no passengers, with a 98% dispatch reliability over a service life of twenty-two years. The French build good aeroplanes, but with their own particular touch. I once went on the maiden passenger voyage of an Airbus A300 and on start-up the unmistakable pong of French toilets came hissing out of the air conditioning. Whether their military aircraft have the same characteristic, or share that of their UK and USA equivalents, is beyond my knowledge.

Once in Nice I rented a car and sped to Monte Carlo, incurring a fine the next day for parking on that corner at the end where the buses turn. Mandy was out at a nightclub so I waited until the return of a friend who had the details, and set off to find her. The next day we left for the Golfe de Saint-Tropez. That was not quite the end of the story from the aviation, or social, point of view. We travelled back as separately as we had come. The Alpes-Maritimes are a notorious nesting place for thunderstorms spawned as towering white teacakes known as cumulo-nimbus clouds – Cbs or Charlie-bangers in the trade. That night was no exception. I was sitting in a Sud-Aviation SE210 Caravelle in a 'club' arrangement opposite a lady resembling the late Carmen Silvera who played René's wife in *Allo Allo!* She smoked Gauloises cigarettes continuously, inhaling deeply, and did not attempt to eat the excellent food. She stubbed out each cigarette in the stuffed tomato with a *zish*ing sound resembling the moth in the candle in Thurber's *Fables for our Time*.

This performance did not appeal to the Algerian sitting next to me. He ate the food but the considerable turbulence upset him and his meal was repeatedly recycled into an increasingly distressed sick bag. Eventually we were on the approach to Orly-Sud. Suddenly there was a roar of engines and the aircraft pitched up abruptly. We were going around. The positive *g* proved to be the nemesis of the paper bag, which dumped its contents into the lap of my neighbour. "*Messieurs; Mesdames, je vous en prie. Malheureusement il y avait une Caravelle sur la piste*," said a rather bored-sounding Capitaine Parlant over the intercom.

Patrick and Philip had waited another day in the stable high-pressure system and took off into all the cotton wool, Philip said later. At the time the military ATCO refused them permission for take-off in the fog, but wilted in the face of Patrick's faux *colère*, having explained that UK landmass was permanently *en brouillard* and anyway, he often flew the back beam on the ILS – not true, back beam procedures are denied in the UK. They broke out on top of the cloud at six thousand feet and were radar vectored safely back into Stansted.

OSCAR X-RAY

When you are flying on instruments, always stay flexible.

Geoffrey Rice
Instrument flying instructor, Oxford Kidlington,
July 1978

Many have a dream, some live one; a golf handicap of four, the summit of Mont Blanc, racing a vintage Talbot at Le Mans or sailing the Atlantic Ocean. My personal Waterloo was to gain the Instrument Rating (I/R), a professional flying qualification, and fly a perfect four-minute hold over the Oxford non-directional beacon at Kidlington Aerodrome; call sign OX or Oscar X-ray. Its frequency, 403 kHz, lies in my heart, like Calais in the heart of Queen Mary I; or it did until it was retuned to 376.5kHz. Nerd.

★ ★ ★

When we learn to walk, drive or fly we use the special senses: vision, balance, hearing and proprioception – the means by which we know the position of our limbs without having to take a look at them. We are also able to perceive vibration, pressure, pain, temperature, touch and smell. Smell may not seem too important in an aircraft but it may warn of smoke, and fire obeys no checklists. In one aeroplane I owned it was the only way of telling if the petrol-burning heater was on. These modalities are integrated by the brain and help us to determine where we are in relation to our environment. Flying involves primarily vision but balance and proprioception are of major importance too. Without instruments, in that strange aviation jargon, we fly by the seat of our pants.

The importance of physical fitness was seen early in aviation. In 1912 the Royal Flying Corps assigned two doctors to assess what the fitness requirements should be. Not to be outdone, in the same year, the US War Department also visited the problem. First and foremost were the visual requirements, with hearing and inner ear function (balance) also being examined. One novel test involved the subject hopping on both feet, then on one, forwards and backwards, then repeating the sequence with the eyes shut; not easy and maybe not relevant. Try it.

The search for the 'the right stuff' amongst aircrew applicants made the physical examination tough to the point where the US Surgeon General had to be told to back off in 1914. The examination was almost impossible to pass. One test of psychomotor stability involved the applicant holding a needle between his finger and thumb. A Wyatt Earp clone would fire a Colt Peacemaker unexpectedly behind his head. If blood was drawn at either end of the needle, indicating surprise, there was a presumption of what would be called 'lack of cool' these days, or LMF (lima mike fox(trot) or lack of moral fibre) earlier on. As gunfire is so common in the USA maybe it was not such a good test after all.

In an early audit at the beginning of the Great War, the Royal Flying Corps established that of every hundred pilots killed, only two were from the result of enemy action. A further eight died on account of mechanical defect of one sort or another. The remaining losses were attributed to recklessness, carelessness and physical defect; the last named accounting for a remarkable 60% of accident casualties. This was reduced to 12% over the next two years by the refinement of medical standards. At the end of the war Dr H. G. Anderson suggested in his book *Medical and Surgical Aspects of Aviation* (Oxford University Press, 1919) that *The special aptitude for flying... is most commonly found in those used to playing games... The yachtsman, the horseman, with their finer sense of judgement and "lighter hands"... Every now and then one meets one with splendid physique and unshakeable courage to find that he learns to fly indifferently... and, one meets the weedy pale type... who turns out to be a first rate pilot.*

This statement belongs to the faculty of the obvious in that some are born with the genes to be good drivers, pilots, horsemen, even managers, and others certainly are not. The best pilots wear their aircraft like a favourite overcoat; know its feel, its systems, sounds, eccentricities and responses at every aspect of its flight envelope to the very edge, and maybe beyond. Once we had an unserviceable public address system on a Boeing 747 out of New Delhi bound for London Heathrow – a possible no-go situation if the seat belt warning system was also down. I was sitting next to a heavy crew pilot I knew, on the flight deck.

"Captain," my friend said, "if someone goes to FS [Fuselage Station] 40 or whatever it was, opens the hatch and resets the circuit breaker, it might do the trick." It did.

"Strobe," I whispered helpfully to my friend, pointing to a white flashing light in what was otherwise the impenetrable smelly black velvet of the Indian night.

"Shut up," hissed the Captain as we taxied about while the problem was being fixed.

In November 1996 there had been a mid-air collision west of New Delhi between a Saudi Arabian Airlines Boeing 747-168B en route to Dhahran and a Kazakhstan Airlines Ilyushin Il-76TD inbound to New Delhi. The crash killed 349 people. The Kazakh aircraft had descended below its assigned altitude. There was a single entry/exit air corridor to/from New Delhi due to military airspace restrictions, no SSR (secondary surveillance radar) and no TCAS (traffic collision avoidance system) fitted to the Kazakh aircraft. No wonder the Captain had not welcomed comments, however *sotto voce*.

One of the earliest exercises whilst learning to fly, after the 'feel' of the controls, is to learn to keep straight and level with reference to the horizon. There is a tendency for novices to look at the dials in front of them instead of out of the aircraft. As a wing dips it is easily seen against the horizon and corrected with aileron input. Likewise the nose rises in the climb and drops in the descent, this being affected both by elevator input and power setting. Wind noise helps judge speed; touch – the pressure on the control yoke – unless you are flying an Airbus. In cloud, visual references are lost although the other senses remain, not always to advantage. The attitude of the aircraft has to be judged by reference to a gyroscopic 'artificial horizon'. This is aided by a further gyroscope, and a pendulum – the 'turn and slip' indicator. Finally there is a pressure instrument indicating climb and descent. Subsidiary input comes from the altimeter which may remain steady, or reflect gain or loss of height which will correlate with the air speed indicator (ASI). Compass direction will correlate with any tendency to turn.

Learning to trust the instruments, and not the special senses, is paramount and may not come easily. The first experience of the pilot in cloud is the presumption that all is well. But the inner ear only detects changes in angular acceleration exceeding two degrees/second/second. So the gradual drop of a wing goes unperceived and the result is a spiral dive, or worse, if uncorrected. And when a wing drop is corrected the inner ear thinks movement has been in the opposite direction, so the pilot leans over to correct the impression – 'the leans'. This, the commonest form of spatial disorientation, may end in disaster in an inexperienced pilot in less than a minute or two. It takes training and practice before a pilot can safely take off in conditions of poor visibility, fly in cloud and navigate safely to the destination whilst maintaining radio communication. Eventually the aircraft assumes the form of a mantle and response to multiple sensory inputs becomes reflex. Later, the issue will be touched upon as to whether flight envelope protection built into modern aircraft is always helpful, in extremis, or whether it is an additional burden, especially if training has been inadequate or the pilot is fatigued or unwell.

There are a number of ratings available as add-ons to the basic private pilot's licence for Class A land planes (single-engine <5,700 kg). These include the night, instrument meteorological condition (IMC), twin engine and instrument (I/R) ratings as well as more rarefied ones for seaplanes and mountain flying. In the UK the basic instrument training qualification for the PPL holder is the IMC (instrument meteorological condition) rating. Whilst potentially helpful in poor weather, one of its limitations is its encouragement for the adventurous to fly in conditions for which they are not fully trained. With the development of European harmonisation under the JAA, later the European Aviation Safety Agency (EASA), the scope of the non-professional licence has broadened with different standards for different levels of operation.

The PPL I/R at the time I qualified was essentially a professional standard rating which could also be applied to a single-engine licence. It entitled the holder to fly in all classes of controlled airspace and potentially in all weather. The requirement was for prior experience with at least 150 hours in command (P1) including a significant component of cross-country flying before training commenced. There was a minimum requirement of twenty hours in the simulator and at least the same number on the aircraft. There was also a month of full-time ground studies. Quite a tall order if you worked full-time. In the event I decided to complete the flying before the ground studies, feeling that that would be in the interest of safety. Anyone who has completed the course will know that the two aspects are equally vital and are complementary.

Things started badly. The first problem was that the aircraft was based at Elstree and the training organisation, chosen on the ground of cost, was six miles away at Leavesden. The agreement was that the flying would be out of Elstree, but this did not come about. Secondly, I only had two weeks to complete the twenty-hour course. That August the weather was inclement with a cloud base frequently below one thousand feet – too low for engine-out recovery in a single-engine aircraft. Thirdly, the aircraft VOR receivers, in spite of almost continuous tweaking, could not get on with the new 'Doppler' VOR beacons, sometimes reading backwards. This gave Patrick some columns on a safety-related article in the *Sunday Times*, and my instructor the excuse to break pencils and shout. Such conduct is a better stress test if you are learning to fly on instruments than a needle and a revolver; believe me.

Having arrived at Leavesden and learnt of the changed plan, I hitched a lift in a Piper PA 34 Seneca to Elstree to collect the Arrow. The distance is short but the weather was not good. By the time we got airborne and turned for Elstree, we seemed to be at the base of the cloud at four hundred to five hundred feet or so. A warm front was coming through. In the thirty minutes or so that it took to fettle the aircraft and complete the pre-start, taxi and take-off checks, the visibility had deteriorated further. It was now difficult to determine the cloud base. I took off to the west and almost at once was in and out of cloud at two hundred feet. I set course for Leavesden, but was unable to maintain VMC (visual meteorological conditions) without flying amongst the television aerials. There was nothing for it but to climb into the cloud, un-rated and with little procedural training. Only instrument interpretation was going to save the aeroplane that day.

I called Elstree on the R/T (radiotelephone) and said I was changing frequency to Leavesden. An attempt to return was likely to be as full of hazard as going on. Leavesden did not reply. I was alone, just outside the London Control Zone, under the London terminal manoeuvring area (TMA) and heading towards Bedford Thurleigh Aerodrome. Ominously it was marked on the topographical map by a circle of red dots with the advice *Continuous High Speed Flying*.

Thurleigh saw use by both the RAF and the USAF during the war and subsequently became the Royal Aeronautical Establishment (RAE) Bedford in 1946. It had advanced wind tunnels, and flight simulation research was based there. It was closed in 1997 after becoming the Defence Evaluation and Research Agency (DERA). Subsequent rationalisation led to a presence at Boscombe Down with closure of the remaining assets in 2007. At the time I was in the vicinity it was very busy. All gone now.

In desperation I called London Director, the low-level radar controller covering the London Zone on 119.9 mHz.

"London Director, this is Golf Alpha Victor Whisky Uniform – I have a problem," I said, unintentionally echoing Jim Lovell on *Apollo 13*.

"Whisky Uniform, this is London Director, go ahead."

"I am north of the London Zone, in IMC [flying under instrument meteorological conditions], unrated, and unable to raise Leavesden." All this whilst desperately trying to avoid disorientation.

"Stand by one, I will telephone them… Whisky Uniform call Leavesden Tower on [they gave an alternative frequency]; they are waiting for you."

To my relief there was a response and I was requested to make a procedural turn for identification. My position was two or three nautical miles northwest of Bedford (continuous high-speed flying), and they offered a radar vectoring service to Runway 06. Slowly I was guided onto the downwind leg, minor heading corrections being suggested or reassurance given that the heading was good. I was reminded to factor in a height safety margin and warned that the radar service would terminate at two miles distant on the final approach.

After an age I was on finals. "Golf Whisky Uniform: radar service terminated, your heading is good; call for the go-around." Not likely if I could avoid it, but I could see nothing but soup. Then deliverance – a hole in the cloud base, and there was the ground on late finals. Throttle back, dump gear and flaps, descend as in an Otis high-speed lift and get my heart rate back out of the red. I thanked the ATCO (air traffic control officer), saying that it had been my first attempt. I doubt if he was impressed.

I learnt about flying from that… is a feature article in several aviation journals. Aviate; navigate; communicate. We learn all the time one way and another in a professional environment. In this case the first and foremost task, always: to fly the aeroplane, was shakily fulfilled. Navigation was left to the help on the ground which would not have been there without communication. I should not have attempted even such a short trip in the face of deteriorating weather.

On another occasion no amount of flying skill could have avoided disaster and luck alone would save the day. We were on a free call radar handover from Stansted to Leavesden at two thousand feet below 8/8 (full) cloud cover at about 2,200 feet. Without any warning, and taking up most of the area of the windshield, was the ventral aspect of an aircraft in a vertical descent. It had carried out a loop, entered the cloud layer and was on its way down. He never saw us and if we had been a second or two earlier he would not have known what had killed us all. All we had to confirm that we had not seen a mirage was the bump as we hit his slipstream a second afterwards, and his fast-disappearing airframe, gone from view on the port side of the aircraft. He had done a silly thing but maybe we should have been further away from the cloud layer.

The two weeks were a disappointment. The weather was against us with an instructor unable to cope with the unreliability of the VORs, so the course could not be completed. And all my precious chinagraph pencils had been destroyed. "Book some more leave and we will finish it off," he said brightly as I departed in better weather than on arrival. No fear.

A year later I went back to Oxford where twenty-two years earlier I had flown the DH Chipmunk with the cadets. CSE Ltd, Oxford was the operator of Kidlington Airport at that time. It had training contracts with a number of (mainly foreign) airlines to teach airline pilots as well as looking after some self-funding, 'self-improving' hopefuls, who were often flying instructors. There were also Private Pilot Licence (PPL) holders such as myself seeking the I/R. Two of them had sold their scaffolding business to fund their passion for flying but found the theory tricky. Another, who owned a business in the north, used to arrive on the Monday in a Piper Aztec PA 23, a hefty six-seat twin-engine aircraft with good lifting capability. He was not instrument rated. They said he had a penchant for carrying minimal fuel to add to the general excitement of his flying. He and what was left of his aircraft were found one day on the top of a hill in Yorkshire…

I was assigned an ex-RAF instructor who was as professional as they come. Geoffrey Rice was always way ahead of the aeroplane. He was patient, practical and safe. When the Daventry VOR beacon went down, why not head for Honiley – is it not in the same direction? And why not cut the corner on the airways intersection instead of laboriously crossing the beacon and returning to track? We used a strange aeroplane, a Piper Cherokee PA 28/235. Essentially it was a Cherokee 140 airframe, but with a thirsty 235 horsepower engine and a constant speed propeller (CSU). It was a bit of a dog as it had extra fuel tanks at its wing tips which needed watching – fuel usage upset the trim quite quickly.

Instrument training involves a 'blind' departure, with reference to instruments only, and a procedural join to an airway. Visual references are blocked out by white plastic screens. When everything is relaxed and tidy the airway is left to join the holding pattern of the destination airfield. Commonly this was over a non-directional beacon such as Oscar X-ray at Oxford. At that time Oxford had no ILS. Now it has 4,300 feet of tarmac and an ILS as well. So different from nearly sixty years ago when I was an RAF cadet collecting mushrooms on the taxiway. Instruction from ATC gives a radar or procedural clearance to intercept the ILS localiser – a radio beam which is on the centre line of the runway. Once this is accomplished, usually at two thousand feet, the glideslope (another beam which takes you down to the runway) is intercepted too, followed by the descent as cleared. This requires the interpretation of two needles on the indicator – fly right/ left and up/down. More difficult than it sounds when a half scale deflection leads to an expensive fail and a re-test. I used to see ££ signs if the glide slope deflection began to explore the halfway point.

At the decision height, two hundred feet plus a spare fifty feet to be on the safe side, an automatic go-around (overshoot) is initiated. At that point, after retraction of the undercarriage, the examiner fails an engine which the examinee has to identify, and indicate appropriate action. Zero thrust is then set in preference to feathering the propeller. It is said that more people were killed in training for engine failure in earlier days than were ever killed by such an occurrence for real. The subsequent climb out, return to the hold, and the hold, are flown with asymmetric power. This requires a good deal of welly on the rudder bar to keep the aircraft straight (dead leg – dead engine, so push the opposite side).

Once the hold has settled there is a non-precision approach (using forward and reciprocal bearings off the non-directional beacon on the ADF indicator) and one was allowed to land for the purpose of paying the landing fee. Sometimes I was tutored for the annual renewal examination in the Boeing 737 simulator belonging to British Airways at Cranebank, London Heathrow Airport. David Rostron would patiently watch as I flew the procedures. On one occasion he must have felt that I was getting a bit cocky and switched on a thunderstorm to keep my knuckles white. *If* (confer Rudyard Kipling, 1865–1936) you can cope with all that within the tolerances required (fifty feet altitude and two degrees of heading), you are indeed fit to fly on instruments, and probably a man/woman, too.

After a further sixteen hours or so I took the test with one of the resident CAFU (Civil Aviation Flying Unit) examiners – a pukka Sahib called Captain Edwards, in a blue serge suit with a superior air and several rings on his arm. We used to watch them drinking coffee and wonder if they were in a good mood, in much the same way that patients, I am told, try to read their doctors if they are expecting bad news. I had the misfortune to have the Cranfield route, which had a short airways sector and involved a lot of frequency changing in a short space of time. No autopilot either, unlike the guys in the big jets – that's easy. The one-armed paper hanger route, it was called.

On one approach, I was cleared from six thousand feet in the hold at Cranfield to intercept the localiser on the ILS at two thousand feet. I did not request an extension of the outbound leg due to inexperience and descended rapidly to intercept the localiser smack on the glideslope. Fortunately the examiner laughed at my mortification at this non-standard flying. I passed with Captain Edwards, apart from the holding pattern, even though the second hand had not fallen off the stopwatch as it did on one occasion. There had been a forty-knot crosswind and even with a crafty peep (from behind the blind flying screens) when I could see the non-directional beacon (NDB) aerial taunting me on the ground, I could not make the automatic direction finder (ADF) needle drop. I went up again in the afternoon and passed.

The following spring I attended again for the four-week obligatory, full-time ground studies course. I had to lecture in Iceland part of the way through and got dispensation from the CAA to do so. It was regarded by the regulator as a venial if not a mortal sin. If it is bad weather you are seeking, Iceland is the place to go, with geysers squirting dolefully at the overcast and gales induced by the vast Icelandic low-pressure systems. Back at Oxford we were initiated into the mysteries of the various gyroscopes by a Pole who had flown during the war. The Polish language is a bit like a gyroscope, short on vowels and consisting mostly of Cs, Zs and Ks to the uninitiated. Polish English can be tricky too and was not as fashionable then as it is now. Fortunately there were cutaway instruments which saved the day.

Navigation was painstaking and meteorology is an art dressed as a science; none of the algorithms for explaining thunderstorms on a cold front in winter seemed to work. They had a dispensation, too. Nor was there an explanation as to why they brood, worldwide, over outer marker (OM) beacons. We re-learnt the Morse code which is used in beacon identification. Eventually toil prevailed and I was permitted to exercise the privileges of the I/R. I returned six years later to convert the single-engine I/R to a twin I/R following the purchase of a twin-engine aircraft.

There are advantages to a twin-engine aircraft when flown regularly by a properly trained pilot. These include – usually – greater load-carrying ability and better stability associated with the additional mass; this makes for a better instrument platform. Little experience and/or lack of recency with an engine failure is likely to take you to the scene of the accident. A Beechcraft Baron 95-B55 (two 285 HP Continental IO520 engines) was sourced and re-registered G-SUZI. The initial training for the twin rating had been carried out with Ken Henfrey at Fairoaks. Ken was one of the most meticulously calm and best pilots with whom I have flown. We explored the flight envelope together. He led me through the VMCa (the minimum control speed in the air with one engine inoperative) during which control is gradually lost as the forward airspeed decays in single-engine climb.

And there was the stall. Maybe this was a 'Friday' aeroplane but it did not enjoy being stalled. On the first occasion, after a single bump of warning buffet, the port wing dropped unexpectedly abruptly and I reflexively, and wrongly, responded with opposite aileron. Quick as a flash Ken neutralised the ailerons and applied opposite rudder to prevent the incipient spin. Some say that such a stall characteristic is unimportant as one never flies that slowly under normal conditions. That is true, but if there is airframe icing… and what about performing a circle to land in bad weather?

The Beechcraft is a strong aeroplane and felt safe even in the roughest weather. It had a high rate of roll and its handling was predictable and superb. It was back to the King's Arms at Woodstock, a stone's throw from Kidlington Aerodrome, for completion of the twin engine rating with matching upgrade of the I/R. The Oscar X-ray beacon was still radiating on 403 kHz and routes 14, 15, 16 and 17 were still leading to Stansted, Cranfield, Southend and Gatwick, though possibly not in that order, or even those destinations. Due to good fortune I passed first time.

REGULATORY
OVERTURE

Now landsmen all, whoever you may be,
If you want to rise to the top of the tree,
If your soul isn't fettered to an office stool,
Be careful to be guided by this golden rule—Stick close to your desks and
never so to sea
And you all may be Rulers of the Queen's Navee...

W. S. Gilbert (1836–1907) and Sir Arthur Sullivan (1842–1900)
HMS Pinafore, 1878

Whilst I was the neurological senior house officer at St Thomas's Hospital in 1967, the Edwards Committee had been set up to enquire into Britain's civil air transport. The committee's findings were published in 1969 in a report called *British Air Transport in the Seventies*. A principal recommendation was the establishment of a Civil Aviation Authority (CAA) whose functions would take over responsibilities previously held by the Air Transport Licensing Board, aspects of the Board of Trade and the Air Registration Board. The CAA was established in April 1972, under the terms of the Civil Aviation Act 1971; the main Acts of Parliament regulating aviation in the UK at present are the Civil Aviation Act 1982 and most recently the Civil Aviation Act 2012, concerned with the economic regulation of airports.

When the Civil Aviation Act was being drafted, the legal profession seems to have been unusually well intentioned. The enabling legislation allowed for the final decision on medical fitness of an individual to be the responsibility of the CMO alone, without scope for an appeal, apart from one against process (Regulation 6). This was in contrast to the Driver and Vehicle Licencing Agency (DVLA), which I advised for ten years, where a hapless lorry driver had to slug out an adverse medical fitness judgement in a magistrate's court before a lady in a hat. As an enlightened piece of legislation, the Civil Aviation Act was a fine example. As a rule, we do not go to lawyers to have our blood pressure checked (too expensive and too much argument).

For once the medical profession had the final say. But this enlightenment has had its comeuppance. Until recently the final fitness decision was taken by the CMO, usually with the consensus of the Medical Advisory Panel (MAP); now an appeal process has been introduced which has brought with it a more confrontational and less predictable format; this is a retrograde step. Furthermore the European Aviation Safety Agency (EASA) requires that the changes in its Implementing Rules and Acceptable Means of Compliance (IR and AMC) are passed through the legal department for expensive nit-picking; there is no reciprocity with the medical side when legal changes are made.

Before and immediately after the Second World War, the responsibility for the initial issue of the Class 1 medical certificate for the Commercial Pilot's Licence (CPL) was vested with the Royal Air Force. The medical examinations were normally carried out at the RAF Central Medical Establishment (CME) at Kelvin House in the West End of London. When cardiovascular anomalies needed resolution, investigation was either carried out by RAF specialists or by designated civilian specialists. Follow-up routine CPL examinations were carried out at any RAF station, of which there were many at that time. Medical Examination for the Private Pilot's Licence (PPL) was by a general practitioner. The Civil Aviation Act changed all this and created Authorised Medical Examiners (AMEs), who were separately accredited to carry out examinations for the CPL (Class 1 medical certificate) and the PPL (Class 3 medical certificate). Currently EASA compliant classes of medical certificate include Class 1 (commercial), Class 2 (private) and Class 3 (ATCO), which may be issued by an AME approved by the CAA.

The initial issue of a Class 1 or 3 medical certificate is by an Aeromedical Centre (AeMC) including the Gatwick centre at CAA Aviation House, presently being considered for closure and outsourcing. The AME (or AeMC in the case of an initial Class 1 or 3 applicant), following consideration of any additional information, is empowered to issue the certificate or assess the applicant as unfit. There is a further CAA medical certificate for the light aircraft pilot's licence (LAPL). This can be issued by a general practitioner and if there is denial, further assessment by an AME or an AeMC is required. All good, clean (European) bureaucratic fun.

My appointment to the CAA in 1974, two years following the *Papa India* disaster, involved initial attendance at Shell Mex House, No. 80, Strand, London, WC, where the newly founded CAA occupied some floor space. It is an Art Deco building constructed in 1930–1931 on the site of the old Hotel Cecil, next to the Savoy Hotel. It is topped by a large clock tower which used to be known as Big Benzine. The Royal Air Force had its first headquarters there, upon its formation on 1st April 1918. I had no office and usually visited in the evening until I moved to Surrey. There was a pub at ground floor level where many, excluding myself, went for a liquid lunch. From time to time it decanted rapidly when a briefcase was left behind – the IRA bombing campaign was active at the time. Shell Mex and BP (British Petroleum) split in 1975, and Shell Mex moved to the South Bank. The Shell building was said to have had the best view of London at the time, mainly because from it, you could not see the Shell Building.

Early the next year, in 1975, my time as a senior registrar at the London Hospital ended when I was appointed as Consultant Physician and Cardiologist to the South West Thames Regional Health Authority, based at St Peter's Hospital, Chertsey. The hospital is only a couple of miles as the crow leaves the circuit belonging to Fairoaks Airport. Following my early appointment to the CAA there had been a need for a definitive NHS consultant contract. I had not been successful in obtaining a post at the Radcliffe Hospital, Oxford and St Peter's Hospital was the next one to come up. Before the appointment committee met in London I stood on the perimeter track at Fairoaks. There in the summer of 1958, with no plan to pursue medicine at the time, I had looped a Tiger Moth to the consternation of the locally based skylarks. There was symmetry.

In 1976 the CAA moved to the speculatively built circular concrete building, called 'Space House' at that time, in Holborn, Kingsway. It was constructed in 1965, having been designed by Richard Siefert and built using high-alumina cement by Harry Highams. As a result it had an unwelcome tendency to shed slivers of concrete. In 1992 it moved to Aviation House, Gatwick South area, to a grey building known to the pilots as 'the Belgrano' after the Argentinian ex-US Navy light cruiser which was sunk in the Falklands war of 1982 by the Royal Navy. One purpose of the expanded Medical Department, which occupied the second floor, was for the initial issuance of the medical certificate for the CPL, this responsibility having been assumed from the Royal Air Force.

After two years, my appointment was extended to include assistance in the setting up of a clinic. This was intended to be a reference point for cardiovascular problems in aircrew. It was equipped, and staffed, as a hospital outpatient facility and had its own treadmill, electrocardiographs and later, Holter (ECG tape) and twenty-four hour ambulatory blood pressure recorders. There was a contracted-out echocardiographic service. Exercise electrocardiography was, and remains, a simple means of initiating the elucidation of borderline-abnormal routine resting electrocardiograms, and for the review of overall cardiovascular fitness. If a candidate can complete ten minutes of the Bruce treadmill protocol without symptoms or significant electrocardiographic change, it is likely that he/she is fit enough to fly an aeroplane, undergo surgery, climb mountains or explore the oceans. And maybe go with Richard Branson into space, if the risk is acceptable to you.

Prior to 1987 the CAA had been responsible for interpretation and application of the ICAO Standards. Subsequently this passed to the JAA (Joint Aviation Authorities) and later still to EASA, to which the UK is a signatory. It also contributes to the agency via the committee structures. The overarching regulator remains the International Civil Aviation Organisation (ICAO) in Montreal. After 1987 the national regulatory responsibility and development effort was progressively integrated with Europe as part of the European harmonisation process. In the same year, as part of that process, the JAA extended the work which had begun with the Joint Airworthiness Authorities in 1970. It was now to include the regulation of operations, licensing, certification and design. This included personnel certification and medical Standards. The CAA took the lead in several areas including medical certification. The JAA did not have full legal status, which EASA now has. It was created in 2002 and achieved full responsibility in 2008. It is a directorate of the European Union and employs more than seven hundred people. *Olé!*

★ ★ ★

The aviation medical environment in 1974 was not an easy one. The basis of cardiological assessment at the time relied upon a fusion of the ICAO International Standards and Recommended Practices (ISARPs), the chapter on cardiovascular medicine in the first edition of the ICAO *Manual of Civil Aviation Medicine*, which was discursive and not directly relevant, and the whims of consultant advisors to the Royal Air Force. There was also input from a small number of mainly London-based cardiologists. I had an early meeting with Dr Raymond Carré, head of medicine and cardiology at the French Direction Générale de l'Aviation Civile (DGAC) at his office in Orly Sud, together with Dr Franz de Tavel, CMO of the Swiss Office Fédéral de l'Aviation Civile (OFAC). We discussed high blood pressure and coronary artery disease.

The American College of Cardiology jumped in feet first in April 1975, when, uninvited by the US regulator (the FAA), it held a closed meeting on the subject of cardiovascular fitness of aircrew. This was published in the same year in the *Journal of the American College of Cardiology*. The Royal College of Physicians took much the same interest but over a much longer interval – three years; I gave written and oral evidence, twice. The UK ruminations at one point became politicised and there were dark observations at the college that the CMO, Dr Geoffrey Bennett, had lost the confidence of the unions. Both meetings recommended exercise electrocardiography as a routine, which I was to argue against at ICAO two years later. The first aviation medicine seminar organised by the CAA following the opening of the clinic was held on 15th October 1977.

The rate of professional licence loss in the UK in 1966, due to cardiovascular cause, had been 1.8 per one thousand licence holders per year, climbing to 3.9 in 1971, the year before the *Papa India* disaster. It peaked at 4.6 per one thousand per year in 1973/4/5 – the years immediately after it. By 1977 it had fallen back to 0.98 per one thousand a year. In the three years 2010–2012 it was of the order 0.08 per one thousand per year – a fifteen-fold reduction overall. This favourable trend was influenced by input from several directions. In part it was due to a significant fall in the pilot mean age and a 30–40% fall in the incidence of death from cardiovascular disease in the UK over the period. There had also been a thorough review of the commoner cardiological problems in the context of the flight deck by the Workshops in Aviation Cardiology.

Finally, ICAO had promulgated, and the UK adopted, the 'waiver (flexibility) clause' – now ICAO Annex 1-1.2.4.9. This provided the possibility of the application of an endorsement to a medical certificate to fly *as/with co-pilot*. This limitation to two-crew operation only permitted a slightly lower standard of medical fitness. Lastly there has been the development of a more scientific and enlightened approach to licence decision-making with a developing partnership between the regulator and the regulated. This is likely to be lost following the proposed contracting out of the AeMC, published by the CAA in *CAP 1214* (November 2014), but not yet adopted.

Routine pilot medical examination, then and now, involve an examination by largely generalist AMEs. Inevitably some may be better than others. A few may ignore significant observations, such as a raised blood pressure, to avoid an immediate regulatory complication, only to bestow a dismal legacy on future health. Such practice should be detected on audit by the regulator, and action taken. Routine resting electrocardiography was introduced in the UK for the initial medical examination of professional pilots in 1963 (implementing a new ICAO requirement), with the need for a routine follow-up recording being delayed until 1965. This was seven years before the *Papa India* disaster. Exercise electrocardiography (for which there is, and was, no requirement) was often performed, if indicated, by the poorly standardised Masters Two-step technique. Alternatively, my friend and mentor, Dr Aubrey Leatham, would send his patients up four flights of a Victorian staircase in Wimpole Street "taken fast". Nobody was reported to have expired on that test, which some wag suggested could have been useful in terms of aviation safety. Testing the airframe to destruction has a long history in aviation certification.

A component of licence attrition from cardiovascular cause in the 1970s was related to the mean age of the pilot population which, in 1974, was more than a decade higher than it is now. This was in part due to the significant number of war veterans coming up for retirement. Vascular risk is strongly age-skewed, and age is the most important of all the vascular risk factors. There was evidence that some regulatory judgements made in the aftermath of *Papa India* were too harsh and reflected anxiety at the time in the absence of sensibly balanced evidence. Such concern was expressed at a contemporary British Airline Pilots Association (BALPA) meeting at London, Heathrow in 1975, packed with a large number of disturbed and, in some cases justifiably, indignant pilots. There was a lot of talk about stress in the job at a time when British Airways pensions were predicated on a retirement age at fifty years. Then a hoary helicopter pilot stood up and said, "Some of you people do not know what you are talking about. Try flying a helicopter two hundred miles out to a North Sea oil rig, in winter, in a force six gale, in instrument conditions and you will know about stress."

Following that the mood eased somewhat. A subsequent edition of the BALPA journal *Log* was presented as *Cardiolog*, which rightly amplified their concerns. But 118 lives had been lost in a civil aircraft accident where a contributory cause had been the cardiovascular ill-health of the handling pilot. Resolution did not lie altogether in the direction of improved medical scrutiny. In 1974, ICAO promulgated the requirement for crew training for the possibility of medical incapacitation of one of their number. At the same time, the possibility of restriction of pilot duties to multi-crew operation was introduced. The importance of fatigue was also recognised. ICAO introduced Human Factors training requirements into Annex 1 in 1989, and Annex 6 in 1995. Crew resource management (CRM) – *vide infra*, was introduced by United Airlines in 1981, endorsement by the US National Transportation Safety Board (NTSB) following later. These initiatives have seen accidents attributable to cardiovascular cause in large passenger aircraft all but eliminated.

So does medical fitness matter, or is the envelope being stretched too far?

★ ★ ★

The earliest problem evident in the new aviation medical clinics was that there were no adequate ground rules for the definition of impaired fitness to fly; there was no methodology either. There were questions but no scientific basis for the answers. The Royal Air Force was familiar with some of the problems in a generally younger population, but had evolved fitness standards which did not have to be ICAO compliant. The attendance of Air Vice-Marshals John Cooke and Brian Kelly from the RAF Medical Services was helpful. There is nothing medically unique about a pilot. Sooner or later he/she will present, either for the initial issue or for the renewal of a medical certificate, with any of the multitude of congenital or acquired conditions that we see in hospital cardiological clinics all the time. It is true that pilots are healthier than their peers but in part this is the 'well worker effect' – those with ill health are taken out of the loop. In the early days even simple problems, such as hypertension (high blood pressure) had not been worked out. ICAO was clear – *the blood pressure shall be normal*. How was 'normal' to be defined, and could treatment be permitted provided it did not *interfere with the ability of the applicant to exercise safely the privileges of the relevant licence* (ICAO Annex 1-1.2.4.9; previously 1.2.4.8)? If so, how was that to be established with confidence?

It was at an Aerospace Medical Association convention in Miami that I had an early meeting with Dr Jon Jordan (see photo plate 25), then US Deputy Federal Air Surgeon (later Federal Air Surgeon), to discuss whether or not it was appropriate to use beta-blocking agents in the control of the blood pressure. At the time of the discussion, the USA had some 650,000 licence holders of all types (against 62,000 at the present time in the UK). As we taxied about the regulatory apron it transpired the US had been following what they thought was our lead in the matter, whilst we were doing the same with them. The worry was the possibility of side effects, including drowsiness, which it was felt might impair critical task performance. Unexpectedly, early investigation of the compounds had demonstrated enhanced performance of such activities as violin-playing and rifle-shooting. Perhaps they would improve adhesion to the ILS, if not at Stansted, where there was a bump on the ILS glide slope to trap the unwary. This was well known to the CAFU (Civil Aviation Flying Unit) in their Calibration Flight DH Dove.

Back in the UK it was agreed to trial propranolol as it was the first and best-studied beta-blocking agent of those available at the time. A precautionary check ride in a flight simulator was required after four (later two) weeks as a safeguard against side effects. No problems were found and the simulator checks were eventually discontinued. Subsequent detailing of the product demonstrated both that the propranolol is variably metabolised between individuals, and being lipophilic (fat soluble), crosses the blood-brain barrier. Atenolol, a polar non-lipid soluble analogue, does not. Atenolol became the industry standard, at least in the UK, for beta-blockade in aviation for many years. It has largely been replaced by bisoprolol.

A fresh look was required to manage those pilots whose medical fitness was on the borderline of the regulatory requirements. One short-lived approach was to place various operational endorsements on the medical certificate of those with a health deficit. Unintentionally these were arbitrary, potentially unsafe and cumbersome to apply. The holder of a Class 1 medical certificate might thus have had an endorsement restricting him/her to fly within thirty miles of his/her operating base, when carrying passengers for hire or reward. This was unworkable as there was a constant stream of requests for exemptions or extensions. Not until October 1977, in the UK, was the situation simplified to two standards for the Class 1 medical certificate – unrestricted (valid for single and multi-crew professional operations), or bearing an endorsement to fly *as/with a co-pilot* only. There were certain other endorsements at the time, later dropped, relating to the need for the second pilot to be a training captain. Recently there have been additional and bespoke licensing requirements in relation to insulin-requiring diabetic pilot applicants, and those receiving anticoagulants, which in some ways have turned the clock back forty years.

Endorsement of a medical certificate to multi-crew operation is enshrined in ICAO Annex 1-1.2.4.9 (c) (formerly 1.2.4.8) which allows for a degree of flexibility. This is subject to accredited medical conclusion which must consider that flight safety is not likely to be jeopardised. True to good regulatory form there is also an ICAO definition of 'likely' – in the context of the medical provisions in Chapter 6, likely means: *With a probability of occurring that is unacceptable to the medical assessor.*

In the USA until 1980, a Class 1 medical certificate could be 'waivered' by an as/with co-pilot endorsement. Following a legal challenge by the

NTSB, the special issuance of a licence with a functional limitation on the medical certificate was derogated two years later. Current UK CAA practice incorporates the EASA Part-MED Implementing Rules (IRs) and Acceptable Means of Compliance (AMCs), which in cardiology are recorded in Section 2 of AMC1 MED.B.010 Cardiovascular system. This is encompassed by: *Acceptable Means of Compliance (AMC) and Guidance Material to Commission Regulation EU 1178/2011 of 3 November 2011 which lays down technical requirements and administrative procedures related to civil aviation aircrew pursuant to Regulation EC No 216/2008 of the European Parliament and of the Council.* As will be seen later this has already been amended. No wonder EASA needs seven hundred employees, but in short, the waiver clause is applicable under AMC1 MED.B.001 at the discretion of the AeMC. It is for single case resolution, only, and not intended as a mechanism for rule change – as it evidently was, when the UK CAA decided, against the advice of many, to permit the certification of insulin-requiring diabetic pilots. When the JAA was in formative mode there was a plan to refer all doubtful decisions to a committee in Brussels or Cologne. We must be grateful for small mercies that that did not come about.

The unendorsed Class 1 medical certificate allows the pilot to fly as pilot-in-sole-command of an aircraft (less than 5,700 kg MTWA) as well as pilot-in-command/co-pilot of a heavier aircraft, depending on the rating(s) he/she bears. The difference between the two levels of operation is signal. Failure of the pilot in a single-crew operation almost always leads to disaster. In all but the most adverse circumstances, the consequences of medical incapacitation in the multi-crew environment should be the square of the individual risk. In practice it is not, for diverse reasons, including common mode failure. This will be discussed below.

There is a somewhat similar arrangement for private pilots in the UK who may have an Operational Safety Limitation (OSL) applied with restriction to fly with another pilot. The safety pilot will have received no training for the possibility of incapacitation of his/her colleague and there has no identifiable study of its efficacy (apart from my own: unpublished). There are sound reasons why this is not a good idea although it has been promulgated by EASA as the OSL (restricted to flying with a safety pilot). The OPL (operational passenger limitation), which prohibits the carriage of passengers, is more debatable. Contrary to the belief of some, collateral damage to people or buildings is very rare in the event of a light aircraft accident. And should an individual wish to risk his/her life with degraded medical status, no doubt some will argue that it is a human right to do so: *always provided the regulator has fully identified and communicated that risk*.

It seems needless, and potentially unsafe, to encourage private pilots to fly who are below the required medical standard for the PPL. The UK CAA accepts for the OSL a limit of 20% predicted annual mortality (at least twice the thirty day post-admission mortality following a heart attack). Solo flying may be permitted, or, if there is a passenger, he/she must be qualified on the same aircraft which must be fitted with dual controls. Any passenger can manipulate controls of a dual control aircraft, provided the pilot in command is trained on type and has a valid licence and medical certificate. What such a passenger cannot do is legally log the hours. Does this matter, and is the administration of (and responsibility for) the default justifiable in the absence of evidence that it is safe practice?

The Medical Advisory Panel (MAP) first met in July 1977 and was chaired by the CMO, Dr Geoffrey Bennett. Membership included representatives of BALPA and the airlines; certain CAA Medical Officers, Dr Richard Emmanuel, civilian consultant to the RAF; Professor Peter Sleight, civilian consultant to the Army; Dr Walter Somerville, civil consultant to the Army and the Royal Air Force; Professor Tony Dornhorst, civilian consultant to the Royal Air Force and some mainly London-based cardiologists about whom Geoffrey asked as to their suitability. It was to meet about three or four times a year. Almost without exception he and his successor, Dr Ken Edgington, used to accept the consensus views on fitness obtained as being the final (and therefore unchallengeable) decision of the CMO. This was to change.

The first meeting discussed the modus operandi, standards for the initial and renewal medical examination, medical standards for single-crew commercial operations, age limits and standard protocols of investigation. Later meetings included the discussion of problem cases. Following early meetings of the MAP, it became evident that there were sometimes windy opinions, but little in the way of evidence. One opinion to the Medical

Department by a London-based cardiologist, who also sat on the MAP, was expressed as follows: "On examination the pressure in the right arm was 180/120... later it was 200/80 and 210/90... There was a moderately loud systolic murmur... I am sure he should be taking a thiazide [diuretic] for his mild hypertension... His hypertension is not of the order which causes strokes." Rubbish.

I also recall a meeting at which another cardiologist patted his stomach and said, "This man is unfit, I feel it here..." Caesar in the Forum in Rome. Something had to be done in the interest not only of aviation safety and good health, but also in the cause of evenness, fairness and proportionality to the licence holders.

AVIATION RISK

Safety is no accident.
William H. 'Bill' Tench, 1987

No means of transportation is completely safe and the controlling legislation does not require that it should be so: it has to be safe enough.
John Chaplin, CAA Group Director, Safety Regulation 1988;
Second UK Workshop in Aviation Cardiology

Regulation of civil aviation in the UK began with the Aerial Navigation Act of 1911. This made civil aviation law the responsibility of the Home Office; protection of people on the ground was its sole interest. It also made the Board of Trade responsible for the registration and certification of aircraft and their pilots. Two years later, in 1913, the Act was extended and the onus placed on the Secretary of State for War. The Paris Convention of October 1919 came into force in 1922. It had been held under the auspices of the International Commission for Air Navigation (ICAN). It was based on the Air Navigation Regulations, drawn up for the control of civil flying in the UK at the end of the Great War. It was ratified by eleven states, including the UK, on 14th October 1919; twenty-six nations, including the 'British Empire' but not the USA, had been party to it.

Shortly after the end of hostilities, G. Holt Thomas (*Aerial Transport*; Hodder & Stoughton, 1920) wrote: *The argument that (civil) flying is inherently dangerous, cannot in fact be substantiated… since the Armistice, the Air Ministry's figures show that, for every fatal accident which takes place, more than 40,000 miles are flown in safety...* One fatal accident was occurring every five hundred flying hours or so at the time, whilst 4,886 people were killed in 124,000 accidents on the roads in the UK in 1926 (the first year during which data were collected). Perhaps Holt Thomas was adrift by only one order of magnitude in risk terms when flying was compared with the vicissitudes of vintage motoring. Post-war civil aviation had recommenced on 1st May 1919 under the supervision of the new Department of Civil Aviation formed by act of Parliament on February 12th 1919. The first Controller General of Civil Aviation was F. H. Sykes (later Sir Frederick), who was able to report that in the first six months of operation for every 5,200 passengers carried only one was injured.

★ ★ ★

James Reason is the Professor of Psychology at Manchester University who suggested the Swiss cheese model of accident causation. This has been used both in medicine and aviation for understanding and explaining how accidents happen. Mathematically it is called percolation theory. The hypothesis depends on failure in one or more domains which include, for example, organisation, supervision, predisposition and specific failure. In his packet of Gruyère, the slices represent the defence against adverse happenstance, and the holes the weakness in those defences. The holes change in size and position; if they all line up to allow a knitting needle to pass, there is *a trajectory of accident opportunity*, as Reason called it. The French variety has more holes than the Swiss variety. *Prenez garde.* The first known accident involving Gruyère cheese occurred in 161 AD when the Roman Emperor, Antonin the Pious, died of a surfeit.

There can be active and latent failures – a failed engine and a pilot poorly trained to manage this. In the *Papa India* disaster there was possible malfunction of the autopilot, failure to monitor the airspeed, withdrawal of the droop at too low an airspeed, failure of recognition of the change of configuration stall, probable loss of consciousness of Captain Key and the inexperience of S/O Keighley. There were several other issues as well of lesser importance. The air accidents in this book will be considered in terms of Reason's model.

Multi-crew scheduled jet air transportation is very safe indeed. In 2013 there were only 265 lives lost in fatal scheduled aircraft accidents, worldwide, for 3.1 billion passengers carried. In comparison, in 2014 two Boeing 777 aircraft of Malaysian Airlines were lost in exceptional circumstances within a few weeks of each other. One was from possible pilot suicide, the other from (presumably unintended) enemy action. A third hull loss occurred, to AirAsia, in December 2014 with the loss of 162 lives bringing the total for the year to 925. But this was also a year with twenty-one fatal accidents, the lowest number ever recorded. It should be recalled as a footnote that in the decade 1980–1989, attacks (by bombing or other hostile action) on aircraft accounted for more than 1,200 fatalities. Additional security has probably ameliorated this. By comparison, more than six times as many people were killed on the roads in the UK in 2013 (1,713) than were killed worldwide in scheduled jet air transport. And the UK is second only to Sweden as one of the safest driving environments in Europe.

One point one billion passengers were carried in UK-registered large aircraft (>5,700 kg) in the decade 1998–2007 (*CAP 780*, 2008) for the loss of eight lives in over twenty-five million hours flown – a fatal accident rate of 0.2 per million hours. Small (<5,700 kg) public transport aircraft flew some 415,000 hours over the same period and experienced thirteen fatalities. This represents a fatality rate 50% higher over the same time with <1/60 of the exposure in flying hours when compared with large aircraft. In the light of this exceptional performance by the airline industry, inexplicably the UK CAA is reorganising its approach to airline safety, presumably in the hope of improving on excellence, rather than attending to the safety of passengers in small aircraft. It is talking about safety 'entities'.

It seems of less concern to the national regulator that there were 163 lives lost over the 1998–2007 review period in the UK in non-public transport accidents, during which more than eight million hours were flown. This represents a fatal accident rate of 11.7 per million hours flown. Indeed there has been a tendency to discriminate between big accidents and small accidents in terms of licensing philosophy with increasing deregulation of the latter as they are less newsworthy. The government wants to reduce 'red tape'. Most passengers on an aircraft in the UK prefer not to be killed and do not know that the relative risk of dying in a non-public transport small aircraft accident is some thirty times greater than in a scheduled airliner, expressed in exposure per million hours. Such an attitude may reflect complacency on the part of the regulator which should be confronted. Enlightened regulation rather than regulation with a light touch is what is required; the latter is a political catchphrase and maybe the territory of the idle. Bad regulation is easy: good regulation is not. There is a difference between reduction of red tape under the Foster Economic Initiative and enlightened risk management.

Safety is a fragile flower and the metaphor of the iceberg is apt; there are far more safety-critical events occurring which, with a modicum of good fortune, do not end in disaster than those that do. Had the British Airways Boeing 777-200ER G-YMMM flight BA36 inbound from Beijing on 7th January 2008 been making its approach on Runway 27R instead of 27L, at London Heathrow, it would have crash landed in the car park. This could have resulted in a fireball and been disastrous in terms of loss of life. By good fortune, and good flying, there were no fatalities, and only forty-seven injuries when it landed short having lost power at 720 feet, two miles from touchdown. The cause, later established, was ice crystal formation in the fuel following a prolonged cold soak in the flight over Russia and Scandinavia. This obstructed the fuel flow when increased power was demanded during the final stages of the approach.

Thirty years before this event, a seminal accident occurred to the United Airlines McDonnell-Douglas DC-8-61 N8082U flight 173. It had departed from Stapleton International Airport, Denver, bound for Portland, Oregon on 28th December 1978. The crew of three (two pilots and a flight engineer) was highly experienced. When the undercarriage was lowered during the approach at Portland there was a loud thump associated with vibration and yawing of the aircraft. The cause, unknown to the crew, was failure of the right main gear retraction hydraulic cylinder due to corrosion which had allowed the leg to free fall, and lock down safely, as it happened. As it did so it damaged a micro-switch and the gear safe warning light failed to illuminate. During their preoccupation with the landing gear the crew failed to notice that the fuel was critically low and the aircraft crashed in suburban Portland, killing two of the crew and eight passengers. The accident which has been called one of the most important in aviation history, led the US National Transportation Safety Board (NTSB) in 1979 to issue: *an operations bulletin to all air carrier operations inspectors directing them to urge their assigned operators to ensure that their flight crews are indoctrinated in principles of flight deck resource management, with particular emphasis on the merits of participative management for captains and assertiveness training for other cockpit crewmembers. (Class II, Priority Action) (X-79-17).*

United Airlines ran the first Crew/Cockpit Resource Management (CRM) training programme in 1981; the process has now been adopted worldwide. It is based on interactive teamwork and is accepted in Western cultures. In more hierarchical Eastern societies the concept of a junior crew member challenging a senior one does not come easily. Australia has no worries – "Jeez, Captain, do you always fly that way or are you dead?"

There has been a tendency to regard the CRM-trained two-crew configuration in an aircraft as the ultimate safeguard. But that fails too. When the British Midland Boeing 737-400 G-OBME, flight BD 92, crashed short of the runway at East Midlands airport in January 1989, the event had been initiated by the shedding of a fan blade on number one engine near the top of climb. It had been passing Flight Level 283 – approximately 28,000 feet. This provoked a series of compressor stalls, and vibration and smoke in the cabin as well as on the flight deck. The crew had nearly twenty minutes to identify the failed engine and make fast the good engine. The most basic rule of all, and following engine failure, is to 'fly the aeroplane'.

With proper discipline and flight management, rather than wasting time reprogramming the FMS (Flight Management System), it should have been possible to land the aircraft and its passengers safely on the remaining engine. But the wrong engine was identified as having a problem and the good engine was shut down instead. When the mistake was recognised, late on the approach, there was insufficient time to restart the good engine. Forty-seven people died and seventy-four were seriously injured when the aircraft crashed and broke into three pieces. Most recently, the same problem – wrong identification of the failed engine – occurred to the TransAsia ATR 72-600 flight GE235 on take-off from Taipei Songshan Airport in February 2015. A flame-out occurred on one engine and the remaining intact engine was shut down. The flight had lasted two minutes and forty seconds; only fifteen of the fifty-eight people on board survived.

The CAA Global fatal accident review, *CAP1036*, covers the years 2002 to 2011 during which there were 250 fatal events worldwide, resulting in the loss of 7,148 lives; 70% of the total at risk. Thirty per cent survived and, by definition, only one fatality is required to enter that classification. This needs to be seen in the perspective of 100,000 departures a day and over three billion passengers carried in total, worldwide, in 2014. Fifty per cent of accidents occur in the approach, landing and go-around phase and two fifths in the take-off and climb-out phase. The American Airlines Boeing 757-223 N651AA flight 965 was a scheduled flight from Miami International Airport to Alfonso Bonilla Aragón International Airport in Cali, Colombia. It collided with a mountain in Buga, Colombia in December 1995 killing 151 passengers and eight crew members: there were four survivors. The crew were uncertain of their position and not helped by the radar system which had been disabled by FARC guerrillas two years previously. Controlled flight into terrain (CFIT) contributes to one quarter of all accidents, and, unbelievably, loss of control in flight (LCIF) accounts for at least two fifths of all *fatal* accidents. A similar value accounts for loss from airworthiness cause.

In the pantheon of seminal aircraft accidents AF 447 must claim some precedence. The Air France aircraft AF 447 A330-203 F-GZCP had departed Rio de Janeiro-Galeão International Airport on 31st May 2009 at 22.29 UTC (Co-ordinated Universal Time after a French fudge; it is the successor to Greenwich Mean Time (GMT) or 'Zulu'). There was no further R/T contact after 01.35 UTC when the pilot reported to Atlantico, the Brazilian Oceanic Control Centre, that he was passing waypoint INTOL en route to Paris Charles de Gaulle Airport. The aircraft was flying at 35,000 feet, two thousand feet below REC MAX, the service ceiling at which the aircraft would have been close to the Mach (high-speed) stall. The Aircraft Communication Addressing and Reporting System (ACARS) transcripts indicated that between 02.10 UTC and 02.14 UTC, six failure reports (FLR) and nineteen warnings (WRN) were automatically transmitted by the aircraft to its operating base in France. The first report detailed problems with one of the toilets. At 02.10.10 it reported that the autopilot and auto-thrust had disengaged: thirteen seconds later that the aircraft was in 'Alternate Law' – a mode closer to that of a basic flying machine. On the 2nd June debris was spotted on the surface of the ocean. It took twenty-one months to recover the greater part of the fuselage, and some bodies, from the seabed where they had been sitting, still strapped into their seats, at a depth of 3,800 to 4,000 metres (12,000 to 13,000 ft). It was the first hull loss in fifteen years of operation of over 1,100 of several variants of the aircraft.

The aircraft had been carrying a 'heavy' crew of three on account of the length of the flight. About four hours into the flight the Pilot Flying, Pierre-Cédric Bonin, aged thirty-two years, whose wife was in the main cabin, was sitting in the right-hand seat while the left-hand seat had been vacated by Captain Marc Dubois whilst he took a rest. He had been replaced by David Robert, the third pilot. Reportedly Captain Dubois needed some sleep as he had only enjoyed one hour the previous night, having spent the day touring Rio with his companion, an off-duty flight attendant and opera singer. She was also flying as a passenger. The French report did not feel this was relevant; other cultures might not share that view. As is commonly the case, there was a line of thunderstorms ahead embedded in the Inter Tropical Convergence Zone (ITCZ). This zone is caused by the surface level trade winds meeting as they converge in a westerly direction from the northeast and southeast, being pulled towards the equator by the Coriolis effect (a function of the rotation of the earth).

As the aircraft drew close to the weather the Pitot sensors (perceiving air speed) iced up making airspeed indications unreliable. This gave rise to a conflict in the Air Data Inertial Reference Unit (ARIDU). A recommended modification had been awaiting completion on the aircraft. This conflict caused the autopilot to drop out and the flight control system to change from 'Normal Law', where control inputs are modulated by ARIDU, into 'Alternate Law'. Stall protection was lost. The response of the Pilot Flying could not have been predicted – pulling back on the side stick and applying maximum thrust to the engines, possibly to climb above the prevailing cloud, and at times moderate turbulence.

The horizontal stabiliser reached its maximum upward deflection of +13 degrees after a minute or so and remained in that position for the four minutes twenty seconds of the flight that remained following the initial upset. This action increased the angle of attack of the wings and caused the aircraft to climb briefly at seven thousand feet per minute, eventually achieving its absolute altitude of 38,000 feet. The side stick was maintained in an extreme backward position and the airspeed fell to the (probably invalid) fifty-two knots indicated: the aircraft had stalled and the stall warning sounded continuously. The crew ignored the extreme angle of attack – up to +40 degrees, not helped by thrust – pitch coupling, the upward moment from the underslung engines, whilst descending at nearly 11,000 feet a minute. They also ignored the rapid loss of altitude. The stall remained unrecognised and the outcome was fatal as there was no corrective input.

Poor training and inexperience has been suggested as part of the explanation for the outcome, together with poor CRM between the Pilot Not Flying and the Pilot Flying. Some might have felt that Captain Dubois should have been on the flight deck in view of the relative lack of hands-on experience of the remaining crew members, and the predicted adverse weather. But weather can change and the Captain was on a designated rest period. Certainly when he eventually did return he made no useful input. But the 'flight' had only a minute or two left.

The stall should have been recognisable from the attitude of the aircraft on the EFIS (Electronic Flight Instrument System) and the rate of descent (from the altimeter), even under the circumstances of night, adverse weather and loss of IAS (indicated air speed). If the elevator control surfaces and trim had been moved forwards, and appropriate power – perhaps four fifths of N1 (design rpm) – been applied to reduce the nose-up effect of thrust from the underslung engines, tragedy might have been averted. The crew were disorientated and not flying the aeroplane. If one of them had had a medical condition, which was not believed to have been the case, how should that have been interpreted in the causation loop?

The accident suggested a revisit of the Airbus philosophy of the independent side stick rather than an easily visible, and connected, control yoke (as on Boeing and most other aircraft). In Normal Law this is coupled to the ARIDU computer protecting the aircraft, inter alia, from excessive pitch and bank angle, over-speed and airframe overloads. The side sticks can be moved independently giving no direct indication of control surface position (stick position is indicated on the EFIS), while the thrust lever position gives no analogue impression of engine thrust; it does not move. If there are different and competing side-stick inputs the ARIDU averages the input. With loss of two or more airspeed data inputs, pitch angle, bank angle and low energy protection will be lost, as well as high energy and high angle of attack protection. Thus there is consequential loss of stall protection. When the Pitot head iced up, Pierre-Cédric was obliged to hand-fly the aircraft under most difficult circumstances, close to the Mach stall in turbulence with invalid airspeed data. It is unlikely he would have had hands-on experience in this context although he should have flown the detail in the simulator.

There are general concerns that training has not remained abreast of the complexities of automation, particularly when there is a malfunction. And there is increasingly little opportunity for pilots to hand-fly an aircraft as it is less economical in terms of time en route, reflected in fuel burn. The loss of the AirAsia Airbus A320-200 QZ 8051 on 28th December 2014 was associated with a stall in the proximity of bad weather. It known that malfunction of the flight augmentation computer (FAC) was associated with the captain leaving his seat to pull its circuit-breaker There appear to be problems to confront – poor training, and lack of protection near the Mach stall to prevent a deep stall developing. It is not good enough if the autopilot shrugs off its responsibility at the limit of its envelope (as it is designed to do), if the pilot cannot interpret the problem and has insufficient training knowhow to rectify it. The upcoming generation of pilots may be computer savvy but a third of them may never have to shut an engine down in anger in the whole of their career. There is no substitute for hands-on flying to give confidence in the management of the aircraft as a flying machine, when the go-faster digital toys have departed the perambulator. Being spooked by adverse weather suggests the need for better forecasting, preparation and avoidance and/or penetration.

Over one hundred years ago, Yerkes and Dodson described fall-off in performance with over-arousal. Some might argue that in the circumstance of exceptional stress with concomitant loss of focus and of working memory, old-fashioned wooden toys may be best, even if the wheels have come off. L'Institut Supérieur de l'Aéronautique et de l'Espace in Toulouse is currently examining physiological and neurological reaction to stress in pilots in the hope of identification of early markers of its presence. These will vary between individuals, but the simplest solutions are likely to be the best in the search for amelioration of error. And these are likely to turn around training.

Human error is not confined to pilots. On 1st July 2002 Bashkirian Airlines Tupolev Tu-154M flight 2937, carrying sixty passengers (mainly children) and nine crew members, collided with the DHL Boeing 757-23APF flight 611 over Überlingen, Southern Germany. All seventy-one people on board died. The German Bundesstelle für Flugunfalluntersuchung (BFU) determined that the cause of the event was shortcomings on the part of the Swiss Air Traffic Control system – there was a single controller on duty at the time. There was also conflict between the commands of the relatively new TCAS (traffic collision avoidance system) and the Air Traffic Controller. A supplementary report from the Kingdom of Bahrain, where the DHL aircraft had been registered, added that CRM seemed to have been inadequate on the Russian aircraft. Two years later the ATCO, Peter Nielsen, was stabbed to death by Vitaly Kaloyeva who had lost his wife and two children in the accident.

Accidents are also caused by airworthiness issues. The investigation into the loss of USAir Boeing 737-3B7 N513AU flight 427 from Chicago O'Hare to Pittsburgh International Airport on 8th September 1994, killing all 132 on board, was one of the longest investigations into an aircraft crash. It continued for over four years. The aircraft was at six thousand feet on approach to land at Pittsburgh when it encountered wake vortices from a Delta Airlines Boeing 727 ahead. But the application of rudder input by the Pilot Flying to correct the roll: *brought about loss of control of the airplane resulting from the movement of the rudder surface to its blowdown limit. The rudder surface most likely deflected in a direction opposite to that commanded by the pilots as a result of a jam of the main rudder power control unit servo valve secondary slide to the servo valve housing offset from its neutral position and over-travel of the primary slide*, according to the NTSB.

Blowdown is a constant pressure applied to the rudder surface by, in this case, a single actuator unit, which reduces its deflection as the IAS increases, thereby maintaining even rudder authority throughout the speed range of the aircraft. Five other incidents were attributed to this cause with at least one other total loss – USAir Boeing 737-291 N999UA flight 427 inbound for Stapleton International, Denver on 3rd March 1991. Modifications were made to all applicable Boeing 737 aircraft subsequently.

★ ★ ★

Why then the obsession with aircraft accidents in a text whose strapline is cardiological? Four fifths of all aviation accidents are caused by human error – the term 'pilot error' should be avoided as pilots make errors because they are human beings. Some failure on the part of the pilot may account for three fifths of fatal accidents. The list of accident causes is endless and includes poor regulation, poorly planned deregulation, rapid expansion of an airline and/or its routes, poor scheduling, inadequate (procedural) training and checklists, inadequate regulation, poor adherence to checklists, lack of experience, excessive workload, time pressure, risk acceptance/taking, weather, warning systems disabled, over-reliance on automation, and FATIGUE. Rarely there is overt medical incapacitation but degraded critical task performance due to medical (cardiological) cause is a real possibility. Very rarely, there is the suicide of the pilot. Over one third of pilots report some incapacitating event during their duty lifetime. In two thirds or more, the cause is gastro-intestinal.

In the UK and Western Europe, although increasingly uncommon in the pilot age group, cardiovascular disease is one of the commonest causes of licence loss. Its manifestation is rare during the duty period in aircrew below the age of sixty years. When it does occur it is commonly incapacitating in some manner, as was the case with Captain Stanley Key in the *Papa India* disaster. It is human endeavour which keeps aircraft flying safely, and loss of performance (e.g. through illness) in non-specific ways will increase the risk that further failure will occur. In regulation both the systems engineer and the physician are responsible for the detection of potential problems, the prediction of likely outcomes and the definition of solutions. The mature regulator must resist the pressure for more medical fitness latitude if the evidence does not support it. Even if it saves a few pounds sterling. Some initiatives taken recently by the UK CAA in the relaxation of medical standards, some might feel are open to question from that point of view.

Flight Time Limitation legislation, reflecting as it does on the potential for fatigue, is a hot topic amongst aircrew. A recent BALPA survey of five hundred pilots found that three in five had fallen asleep on the flight deck at some time, one in three waking to find their colleague asleep too. On one recent occasion, an aircraft overflew its destination as both pilots were asleep. Half of all surveyed stated that they considered fatigue as the biggest threat to flight safety. The pilots I saw in my clinics over very many years were normally free of symptoms and exercised three times a week, but their commonest complaint (apart from deaf management – a congenital defect, especially in hospitals) was that at times flight safety had been impaired by their fatigue. Flight time limitation legislation is intended as a limit by the regulator but is employed as an operating standard by the airlines. Those who draft the rules need to bear this in mind.

Regulation 216/2008 (EASA Basic Regulation) includes Article 8 (6) which *Specifies that Air Operations regulations shall "be based on a risk assessment and shall be proportionate to the scale and scope of the operation* (EASA underscore). Whilst Article 5 specifies: *That the drafting of rules shall take into account risk assessments performed and available data.* Review of the EASA FTL (flight time limitation) Regulations promulgated in February 2014 as Commission Regulation (EU) No. 83/2014, amending Regulation (EU) No. 965/2012, applicable in February 2016, reveals complicated protocols but, unsurprisingly, no data (at least none that a non-Eurocratic cardiologist could find).

But there is plenty of urging of others to come up with it. There is a lot of jargon and emphasis on the need to comply with AMC1 ORO.FTL.120(b)(8) Fatigue Risk Management (FRM) FTL Schemes, and several paragraphs of ORO.FTL.125 Flight Time Specification Schemes which state: *Operators shall establish, implement and maintain flight time specification schemes that are appropriate for the type(s) of operation performed and that comply with Regulation (EC) No. 216/2008, this Subpart and other applicable legislation, including Directive 2000/79/EC,* without explaining how to do so. The reason is historic and relates to lack of agreement fifteen years ago, and lack of any prospect of one. Something for the Pilot Flying to bear in mind when his/her final trip of the day is a night leg to Barcelona with towering thunderstorms over the Pyrenees.

In the interest of European harmonisation, EASA appears to have been prepared to extend the duty hours of aircrew in response to commercial pressure, against the advice of the unions. This must be in the belief, presumably, that European aviation is safe enough and can contain a potential untested, negative effect from duty hours extension. Those concerned with identifying the risk and impact of a co-terminus cardiovascular event during duty hours will wonder at the effect of an additional quantum of fatigue, whether as a cause or a consequence. The saving in terms of direct operating cost (DOC) to the airline from the increased duty hours when fuel costs account for up to one quarter to one third of total cost of aircraft operation is likely to be minimal. It will certainly be less than the cost of a compound accident when the holes in Professor Reason's cheese line up with fatigue and/or medical event as one or two of the slices; especially if that cheese has come from France.

But now to consider the obligations of the UK to the International Civil Aviation Organisation, aviation being the only system of mass transportation controlled by international statute.

THE INTERNATIONAL
CIVIL AVIATION
ORGANISATION (ICAO)

Mission: To serve as the global forum of States for international civil aviation

ICAO, Montreal, Canada, 2014

In 1908, some German balloonists crossed the Franco-German border and landed in France. The occupants included some German officers. Showing prescience in the light of subsequent events, the French government proposed an international conference to plan the regulation of flights into and over foreign countries. The result was the Conférence Internationale de Navigation Aérienne, which was attended by twenty European states in 1910. This project had been anticipated by the International Commission for Air Navigation (ICAN) which first met as a group of eight countries in Berlin in 1903 – the year of the Wright Brothers' first flight. There was no agreement. Twenty-seven countries attended the second convention three years later, again in Berlin. The third ICAN convention, held in London in 1912, led to an agreement on aircraft call signs. ICAN was the forerunner of ICAO. The representatives of fifty-two ICAN states signed the Convention on International Civil Aviation (the Chicago Convention), in Chicago, Illinois, on 7th December 1944. This agreement was ratified by the Council of the International Civil Aviation Organisation – ICAO, as it became – in 1947.

ICAO is a specialised agency of the United Nations Economic and Social Council, created to promote the safe and efficient development of aviation. As it is a safety organisation no veto is allowed. When on 1st September 1983 the USSR, as it then was, shot down the Korean Air Lines Boeing 747 flight KAL 007 airliner over the Sea of Japan and vetoed its censure at United Nations Organisation (UNO), it could not do the same at ICAO. Malaysian MH17, a Boeing 777-200ER, was also shot down on 17th July 2014 by a Russian-made SA11 Buk missile fired from the Ukraine, killing all 283 people on board. Such events are not new; sabotage or enemy action accounted for up to 25% of lives lost each year in airline operations a generation ago.

The agreed ICAO International Standards and Recommended Practices (ISARPs) for medical assessment in personnel licencing are enshrined in Annex 1, Chapter 6. These Standards are binding on all national signatories, currently 191, including the UK. They are general statements and are not in a particularly logical sequence. Sub-chapter 1 includes the important administrative clause 1.2.4.9 which permits certification outside the stated ICAO Standard *subject to accredited medical conclusion*. This enabling statement places the onus for a fitness decision on the individual state and their medical advisers. The UK CAA is planning to contract out these advisors *to reduce the cost burden on industry*. The requirements for medical assessments are included within Sub-chapter 6.2, with the Hearing Test Requirements separately disposed in 6.2.5. The Class 1 Medical Assessment is covered in Sub-chapter 3 with the Physical and Mental Requirements being contained in 6.3.2.; commencing with psychiatry and followed by neurology.

It is an international requirement for a pilot to be ICAO medically compliant, and a European one for him/her to be EASA compliant. The European JAR-FCL and JAR-Med guidance material, succeeded in 2012 by the EASA Part-FCL AMC/GM, is explained in CAA *CAP 804*. The earlier JAA 'red book' was to be found on desks as far apart as the Arabian Gulf, Singapore and New Zealand. The ICAO Standard cardiovascular paragraphs are to be found in Annex 1 6.3.2.5–6.3.2.8 and contain 256 words with frequent reference to Doc 8984, the cardiovascular chapter in the *Manual of Civil Aviation Medicine*, written by the author in 2010. The controlling legislation, national, supra-national (i.e. European) or international does not require that aviation should be completely safe – it has to be safe enough. A state may enhance, but not diminish, the ICAO Standards which are minimum requirements. Under Resolution 5 of 1999, the Council of ICAO cautioned restraint against individual national increase of the promulgated Standards. The evolution of a methodology to help make the regulatory process safer, more scientific and fair was the substance of many years' work by many people and is related in the following chapters in this book.

★ ★ ★

One of the first requests I received from the newly fledged CAA was to represent the UK at the first Cardiovascular Study Group meeting at ICAO headquarters, Montreal in June 1980. This had been requested by the Air Navigation Commission the previous year. I was invited as cardiologist to the UK CAA with Dr James Alexander, deputy CMO. At that time the ICAO building was at No. 1,000, Sherbrooke Street, Montreal, Quebec, later moving to No. 999, University Street, Montreal, which is its present address. The invitation had come through the Department of Trade and Industry (DTI). In Civil Service terms this entitled me to first class travel which seemed to be unwelcome to my local Member of Parliament, Geoffrey, later the Right Honourable Sir Geoffrey, Pattie, MP.

The meeting lasted three days and was chaired by the Chief of Medicine at ICAO, Dr Silvio Finkelstein. Silvio, who became a friend of many years' standing, is a remarkable man. An Argentinian, he qualified as a doctor in Buenos Aires and gained his MSc in aviation medicine at Ohio State University. He moved to ICAO in 1971 and was domiciled in Canada, being Chief of Medicine at ICAO from 1975–1994. He speaks several languages fluently and his personal charm, diplomatic skills and great knowledge of his subject have afforded him much influence on the medical aspects of aviation safety over several decades. He received the Warner medal, the highest honour in civil aviation, from the Council of ICAO in 2007. He is still a leading light in the International Academy of Aviation and Space Medicine; this fosters teaching, collegiality, exchange of ideas and foreign travel at its meetings around the globe. (See photo plate 20.)

Montreal is situated on an island in southern Quebec at the confluence of the St Lawrence and Ottawa rivers. For the three winter months the temperatures are of the order of –10 degrees C and much of the pedestrian traffic is out of the snow, below street level. We were there in June and walking on Mount Royal was still chilly. Originally settled by the French in the early 17th century as a fur trading post, it developed to the point that it was the capital of the province of Canada for the five years 1844–1849. At this point the Parliament building was burnt down in a riot and it was felt sensible to move the capital city to Ottawa which was nearer the centre of the country. Charles de Gaulle was unhelpful in supporting the Parti Québécois in the 1970s – *"Vive le Quebec libre!"* he exclaimed when the pressure for separation was at its height.

The French connection is evident on getting into a cab at the airport. Once the driver has established that one is English, he/she will only speak loud French with a broad Canadian accent. The North American connection is also evident in that no car can leaves the traffic lights without a squeal of tyres and puffs of smoke; but there is not that sense of threat sometimes felt in cities in the USA. The restaurants are excellent and the atmosphere very different from that south of the forty-fifth parallel. We paid an official visit to the Canadian Civil Aviation Headquarters, dozing in Ottawa, travelling on one of those ponderous North American trains. It had a cow-catcher and a bell which dinged continuously as we lurched along our way at 20 mph. Each newly appointed medical officer is obliged to take some months off to learn French (or English).

The first surprise was the brevity of the index meeting at ICAO as a whole. It was to last three days and consisted of two two-hour sessions each day. When I suggested that we would not cover much ground in the time, particularly as we were using interpreters (mainly Silvio himself), he said, "Ah, you see, Michael, some of these people are not used to working like you and me…" and burst out laughing.

The advisory group that Finkelstein had put together had been, as would have been anticipated, politically based. The major players at the time were represented – the USA by Dr Ed Westura, Canada by Dr John Catching, Australia by Dr John Lane, France by Dr Raymond Carré, the USSR by Professor Vladimir Todarev, Finland by Dr Kari Antilla, Mexico by Dr Luis

Amescua and Dr Jesúus Lópes Reyes, Yugoslavia by Dr Rade Podjanin, and finally the UK by Dr James Alexander and myself. The International Air Transport Association (IATA) was represented by Dr Peter Vaughn and the International Federation of Airline Pilots Association (IFALPA) by Captain G. R. Richardson. The Chinese did not attend although they had been invited. Poor Vladimir, who was devoted to the intrigues of Sherlock Holmes, was later reported to have been murdered in Moscow. (See photo plate 21.)

The languages of the meeting were English, French, Spanish and Russian. It took much of the first morning to be certain that the Russian interpreter, Viktor, was not an American as he made those syntactical errors that tend to occur when the speaker is not using their first language. "Ah, you see Michael, Viktor is the KGB station chief accredited to ICAO," said Silvio when I asked about Viktor's provenance.

The agenda covered a number of cardiovascular subjects – at that time amongst the Western nations, cardiovascular disease was, and still is, an important cause both of mortality and of professional licence attrition. One of the most helpful aspects of the meeting, from the UK perspective, was an appraisal of how other states were managing the rapid advances in cardiology which had been made in the preceding decade or so. Looking back it is worth recalling how far we have come in the regulatory process. At that time (1980) the UK had not yet permitted any Class I certificate holder to return to flying following coronary surgery. The USA had had only one which the FAA had originally denied, but which was overturned on appeal to the National Transportation Safety Board (NTSB). A handful of US Class II pilots had been made fit – there is no EASA equivalent. It includes air cargo and air taxi pilots, and flight engineers on passenger flights. Canada and Mexico had one each.

Some private pilots (Class III) in the USA had recovered their medical certificates following myocardial infarction (heart attack). The fitness requirements included a wait of two years and the successful completion of an exercise electrocardiogram to 85% of maximum heart rate, only. Not an adequate assessment by any means – furthermore the risk of further event increases, rather than decreases, with age. The FAA had also issued about three hundred Class I certificates restricted to fly as/with a co-pilot

1. Great Uncle Jack Gough, in aquatint, died on 18th March 1918. He is buried in the cemetery at Ste Emilie Valley, Villers-Faucon, near Peronne. A soldier of the Great War.

2. David Joy (1910 – 2004). My father as a house surgeon at the Salisbury Royal Infirmary in 1937. He raced his Roesch Talbot 90, GO 99, until he met my mother whom he married in 1939. The car was written off on the Barnet bypass, but not by him.

3. Sir Hiram Stevens Maxim (1840 – 1916) was born in Maine and moved to England in 1881. He was a prolific inventor and designed the Maxim gun, later the Vickers Machine Gun. This made him deaf, but brought him a knighthood. With his 'captive flying machine', driven by steam and running on rails, he can probably claim to have been the first man to have been lifted by power into the air.

4. Samuel Franklin Cody (1867 – 1913), born in Iowa, was the first man to fly a free, heavier than air machine in England. This was on Laffan's Plain – now Farnborough Airport – on 16th October 1908. It was a home-built - British Army Aeroplane No 1. After his success, somewhat as today, the War Office saw no future for flying machines. He became a British subject at a ceremony on Doncaster racecourse two years before his death. This followed the in-flight break up of his aircraft. About 100,000 people attended his funeral.

5. Claude Grahame-White (1879 – 1959) was an engineer and one of the earliest pupils of Louis Bleriot. He made the first night flight - during the Daily Mail London to Manchester air race, in 1910. He won the Gordon-Bennett trophy for England in New York, in a Bleriot XI aircraft, in the same year.

6. DHC Chipmunk powered by a DH Gipsy Major 8 inverted air cooled engine. It was the basic trainer for the RAF when it replaced the DH Tiger Moth in 1952; 725 were supplied. It persisted with the Air Experience Squadrons of the RAF until 1996. The author received his early flying training on the aircraft at Kidlington, Oxford, in 1956.

7. G-ACDA - the first prototype Gipsy Major III powered DH82A Tiger Moth; it joined the de Havilland School of Flying at Stag Lane in February 1933, later serving with the RAF as BB724 before disposal in 1943. The marque was a primary trainer with the RAF from the early 1930's until it was superseded by the DHC Chipmunk in 1952. Over 7,000 were built in the UK. The author gained his PPL in 1958 on one through an RAF flying scholarship. It is said to be easy to fly, but difficult to fly well, demonstrating adverse yaw requiring both rudder and stick-back in the turn.

8. Ken and Heather Edgington. Dr Ken Edgington was CMO of the UK CAA 1992 – 1999. He is a consultant in occcupational and aviation medicine, and a current helicopter pilot. We went deer stalking on Salisbury Plain together in an Aérospatiale Gazelle. © James Millar.

9. The author and Geoffrey Marlow, Chair of the Surrey County Council, 2009 – 2011; at RAF Odiham in search of facts - summer 2010. The ride in the Chinook helicopter resembles that on an elephant though the elephant does not vibrate and neither does it have a yaw damper.

10. *The tail section of the HS Trident 1, G-ARPI (Papa India) which crashed in a deep stall, at Staines 150 seconds after brake release: London Heathrow, 18th June 1972. All 118 people on board were killed. Mismanagement of the droop, a leading edge lift device, and cardiovascular ill-health of the fifty-one year old pilot were contributory factors. © Getty Images.*

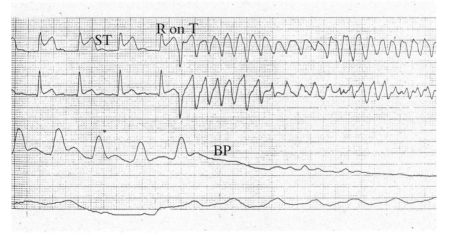

11. *Electrocardiogram at the point of a 'cardiac arrest'. ST reflects the injury current following obstruction of the (right) coronary artery. R on T is the premature (ventricular) contraction, which provokes ventricular tachycardia, then fibrillation. The blood pressure, BP, drops to zero and the subject is unconscious in ten seconds, and brain dead - without resuscitation - in three minutes. The patient – who was in the cardiac care unit – was successfully resuscitated.*

12. Dr Geoffrey Bennett (1926 – 2008) whilst with BOAC in the 1960s. In 1964 he was appointed CMO to the Ministries of Aviation and Technology. He became CMO to the newly created CAA in 1972, a post which he held until he retired in 1991. He had joined the RAF as a pilot in 1945, later gaining the Theodore Williams scholarship to Oxford University to study medicine. At BOAC he retrained as a part-time airline pilot, later flying the McDonnell Douglas DC10-30 with Freddie Laker.

13. Diana Barnato-Walker (1918 – 2008) with the author. She flew eighty different types of aircraft for the ATA during the war, delivering 260 Spitfires. Brooklands: 2005.

14. Patrick Forman (1924 – 2014). Sometime Air safety correspondent to the Sunday Times and member of the Insight Team. He shared the Piper Arrow PA 28R-180 - G-AVWU, with the author. He also came on the ill-fated trip to Monaco and returned the aircraft to Elstree.

15. Haggis, Patrick Forman's kitten. She was given him by a night nurse during the first of two years spent in St Thomas's Hospital, London, in 1944 – 45. He was being treated for tuberculosis. She used to be let out in her harness to answer calls of nature. One day she escaped and was returned by the matron, Miss G V L Hillyers.

16. Mandy

17. Philip Keyte (1935 – 2014) from an oil painting by Peter Walbourn (1910 – 2002). We explored the Greek Islands in sybriatic days, at one time living above Yannis' shoe shop in Lindos, on the Isle of Rhodes. Later we travelled hopefully to Monaco in G-AVWU but had to make a weather diversion to Reims. I went on alone, courtesy of SNCF and Air Inter.

18. WHISKY UNIFORM stuck at Reims by defective VOR receivers, and cloud which remained 8/8 at 300 feet for several days. I left Patrick Forman and Philip Keyte, flying to Nice on an Air Inter Mercure, en route for Monaco and a villa at La Croix-Valmer…

19. Cessna 340 IIA G-LIZA, somewhere in Europe, probably Belgium. For once it is VMC (Visual Meteorological Conditions). The logo of the European Society of Cardiology on the tail surprised Professor Paul Hugenholtz, the president, at a meeting in Santiago de Compostela. Shortly after the photograph was taken we were admonished for admiring a large Russian transport aircraft surrounded by lantern jawed guards armed with Kalashnikov AK 47s.

20. Dr Silvio Finkelstein at his award of the ICAO Edward Warner Gold Medal, in 2007. It is the highest honour in the world of civil aviation. He was Chief of Medicine at ICAO, Montreal, from 1975 – 1994.

21. Members of the Cardiovascular Studies Group Meeting at ICAO, Montreal, in 1980. One of the two UK delegates, Dr James Alexander - deputy CMO of the UK CAA - is standing in the centre. Dr Silvio Finkelstein, Chief of Medicine at ICAO, is seated on his right. Standing next to James, on his right, is Dr John Lane - Chief Medical Officer of the Australian Civil Aviation Safety Authority (CASA) whilst on his left, is Victor, reputedly the KGB station chief. I was the second UK delegate and took the photograph.

22. *Dr Claus Curdt-Christiansen, Chief of the Aviation Medicine Section, ICAO, Montreal, 1994-2005. We went to numerous meetings together. A harmonisation event planned in Mauritius did not get airborne due to unhelpfulness on the part of the French. I had been shadowed by representatives of the DGAC during a preliminary recce. We flew on a Boeing 747SP on the way out and were obliged to penetrate a Napoleonic thunderstorm in the ITCZ.*

23. *The author, Dr Anthony Evans and Dr Claus Curdt-Christiansen at an ICASM meeting in Bangalore in 2006. Tony is the Chief of Medicine at ICAO, Montreal, and Claus was his immediate predecessor. Tony later won the Tuk-Tuk race across the city.*

24. *Air Vice-Marshal John Cooke, OBE, CB, FRCP, RAF (1922 -2011). Whittingham Professor of Aviation Medicine from 1974 to 1979; Dean of Air Force Medicine and chair of the Defence Medical Service Postgraduate Council until 1982. We served as consultants to the CAA for many years. As a general physician and lecturer in a Wesleyan revivalist mode he had few equals.©Graham Pitchfork.*

25. *The author, Jackie and Jon Jordon at an ICAO meeting in Budapest, Hungary in 1999. Jon was appointed Deputy Federal Air Surgeon to the Federal Aviation Administration (FAA), in the USA, in 1979. In 1991 he was appointed Federal Air Surgeon; he retired in 2006. A very steady pair of hands.*

26. Hugh Tunstall-Pedoe has been Professor of Cardiovascular Epidemiology at Dundee University since 1981. He chaired the sessions on epidemiology and risk at the aviation cardiology workshops. He was the architect of the "1% rule" - the first attempt to place medical regulatory decisions on a scientific basis.

27. Professor Ronnie Campbell (1947 – 1998) who died shortly before chairing the electrophysiology session of the Second European Workshop. He had contributed much to the three earlier workshops, saying that the problems of cardiology in aviation were some of the most interesting which he had encountered. His research, teaching and pastoral care of his patients, were exemplary; his humour was unsurpassed. Sadly, sudden death stalks us all.

28. Dr Michael O'Brien, Emeritus consultant neurologist at Guy's Hospital, London, and was my colleague as neurologist to the UK CAA. Michael is an authority on Khmer Art and Architecture. Like most of his ilk, he enjoys arcane argument. He also flies a French Wassmer.

29. Hurricane 1 R4118 – UP-W had flown in the Battle of Britain, in which it was shot down. It was exported to India where it was found by Peter Vacher and repatriated in a delapidated state in 2001. It flew at my garden party at Brooklands Museum in June 2011.

30. Peter Teichman in his Spitfire Mk XI PL 965, which forms part of his Hangar 11 collection. The aircraft flew in combat in 1945, and flew at my Garden Party at Brooklands Museum in June 2011. Peter purchased G-BDXW, and later, G-SUZI from the author. ©John M Dibbs.

31. *David, possibly uncertain of position; with the Cessna 340 IIA G-LIZA, at le Touquet: March 1994. The logo of the European Society of Cardiology is visible on the tail. Eliza-Jane was one of our Labradors.*

32. *Toby scanning his passengers rather than his instruments at 2,000 feet, somewhere over England. He is sitting in the left-hand seat of the 1972 Navajo PA31 310B G-BJLO, co-owned with Nigel Reynolds. Sometime in 2001.*

33. BAC / Sud Aviation Concorde taking off from London Heathrow in 2001. The cloud over the upper surface of the wings is due to super-saturated air at higher velocity, and lower pressure, caused by incident flow over the trapped vortices behind the leading edge of the wing. These are seen on the right. On rotation the aircraft is also pushed up upon a wedge of air. The trailing edge has elevons which act together as elevators, and differentially as ailerons. The shock diamonds of the after-burners are not visible from this angle. © Getty Images.

for various reasons, but following a challenge from Delta Airlines, this was declared invalid by a Federal Judge and the practice was discontinued in 1982. Now the FAA relies on discretionary 'special issuance' of medical certificates when the ICAO requirements cannot be met in full. Neither the USSR, nor France, nor the UK permitted recertification after a heart attack at that time.

High blood pressure (hypertension) is a major health issue worldwide. It was described by W. B. Kannel, who was responsible for the Framingham, Massachusetts community study which was launched in 1947, as *the most powerful and prevalent of all the vascular risk factors*. He had overlooked age. The only products permitted by most states at that time for the treatment of hypertension were the thiazide diuretic agents with occasional use of propranolol (which blocks the effects of adrenalin on the heart, *inter alia*). The UK was requiring a flight simulator check ride in an attempt to determine whether there was decrement of performance as a consequence of its administration. At the present time (2015) most anti-hypertensive agents are permitted after a two-week delay to determine whether there are any side effects; there is no requirement for a flight simulator check.

Muscle disorders of the heart (cardiomyopathies) were discussed but experience was limited. In Canada the hypertrophic form was disallowed in the event of first-degree relative involvement – presumably with a history of sudden cardiac death (SCD). France was concerned about the prevalence of EMF (endomyocardial fibrosis), which stiffens and obliterates the cavities of the heart, in what had been its tropical and equatorial African colonies. Conduction disturbances in the heart were considered. Bundle branch block on the right (RBBB) was permitted by most states in the absence of other abnormality, but Australia, Canada, the USA, Mexico and Finland would not accept it on the left (LBBB) due to its frequent association with coronary artery disease. The UK took a more enlightened view (at that time about 50% of LBBB was attributable to coronary artery disease).

France was concerned about isolated left axis deviation in the ECG, which usually runs a benign course when associated with fine fibrosis (scarring) of the conducting tissue. It can be also slowly progressive and later, as Lenègre's disease, may progress to complete atrio-ventricular block (heart block in the vernacular). Finally aspects of congenital heart disease, valvular heart disease, mitral leaflet prolapse and the Wolff-Parkinson-White pattern/ syndrome (associated with an anomalous conducting pathway in the heart muscle) were also considered.

It fell to myself to lead a review of exercise electrocardiography and its role in the routine investigation of professional aircrew. Exercise electrocardiography is carried out to a standard protocol, usually that of Robert Bruce, first published nearly fifty years ago (fifteen years before the ICAO meeting). The subject walks on a treadmill at an initial speed of 1.7 mph and at an initial gradient of ten degrees. Every three minutes both are increased. The test should be continued until symptom limitation or exhaustion. Sometimes it is taken to 100% of the age-predicted maximum heart rate (220 – age in years) although it is less sensitive in that context. Tests carried out to an endpoint at 80% or 85% of age-predicted maximum, sometimes used, are pretty useless.

Fortunately the argument, based on the Bayesian theory of conditional probability, won the day and had it not been, there would have been a lot of unnecessary investigation performed on aircrew worldwide. Thomas Bayes (1701–1761) was a mathematician, philosopher and Presbyterian minister who examined the theory of probability. His major work *An Essay Towards Solving a Problem in the Doctrine of Chances* was read to the Royal Society and published in the *Philosophical Transactions of the Royal Society of London* two years after his death in Tunbridge Wells. Five years later William Heberden published his classical description of angina in the *Transactions of the Royal College of Physicians of London*. The argument put forward to ICAO was as follows:

The exercise ECG is not completely sensitive (failing sometimes to detect coronary disease which is present), nor is it completely specific (giving the wrong answer in either a positive or negative sense); thus there are the following scenarios (without defining the boundaries of 'significance' in terms of coronary artery disease):

- Significant coronary artery disease may or may not be present in a subject and
- The exercise ECG may or may not be normal.

This makes for four possibilities following investigation:

- Significant coronary artery disease + an abnormal exercise ECG (true positive)
- Significant coronary artery disease + a normal exercise ECG (false negative)
- No coronary artery disease + an abnormal exercise ECG (false positive)
- No coronary artery disease + a normal exercise ECG (true negative)

In twenty-year-old recruits, where coronary artery disease will be very rare, the false positive rate will be significantly higher than the true positive rate, which itself will be close to zero; there will also be a large number of true negatives. In a cardiological clinic where coronary artery disease is common, true positives will be frequent, but there will be some false negatives and a few false positives. If the prevalence of significant coronary artery disease in a population of sixty-year-old Western pilots is of the order of 1% with a sensitivity of the test of 70% (the ECG is abnormal in the presence of disease in 70% and wrongly negative in 30%), coronary artery disease will be detected <1% and missed in a small fraction.

But if the test is only 93–95% specific (in 5–7% no coronary artery disease is present but there is an abnormal test) there will be perhaps seven false positive results for every true positive one. Further investigation is usually demanded in the presence of an abnormal finding. This may involve potentially harmful radiation – nuclear angiography – and/or invasive investigation (arterial puncture and cardiac catheterisation), which should be avoided if possible. Increasingly stress echocardiography, being non-invasive, and carrying no raditation burden is being employed in this role. From the foregoing it will be seen that the usefulness of the test will depend both on the prevalence of the disease and its predictive accuracy. Bayes theorem expresses the conditional probability of the presence of disease in the context of a test with limited sensitivity and specificity.

In the end the solution did not lie with the cardiologists, but with the regulators and specific pilot training requirements. As has been seen, two fifths of accidents occur in the take-off and initial climb-out phase, lasting perhaps five to ten minutes; half occur between the top of descent through the approach to the landing and roll-out, which lasts rather longer. Provided there are two crew members and they are trained to recognise incapacitation in their colleague, the truly vulnerable period of flight should be of short duration. Vigilance, avoidance of complacency, and training for the containment of an event are required. It should not be claimed (as it sometimes is) that operation with a disabled or dead crew member is as safe as two fully functioning pilots, any more than engine-out operation is as safe as having two engines online.

The evidence that this model was not always fail-safe was demonstrated soon after *Papa India* by the Air New England DHC-6 flight 248 accident at Hyannis, Massachusetts on 17th June 1979. The aircraft crashed 1.5 miles short of the airfield due to incapacitation of the pilot who was also killed in the accident. Likewise, on November 22nd 1987, the captain of an American Airlines DC10 flight 612 from Chicago O'Hare, due at Newark, NJ, just before midnight died, unnoticed, on the final approach from a heart attack. He had not responded to challenges from the first officer below one thousand feet. The initial approach had been 20–40 kts too fast but the co-pilot thought his captain was acting appropriately. Below one hundred feet there was no further input from the crew and the aircraft hit the runway hard. As the power remained on and the aircraft was drifting off the runway the co-pilot took over and brought it into dock. Remarkably the senior airline medical officer who first drew my attention to the event said, *So, you can see that the two crew configuration* (three in this case) *works – nobody died*.

I wrote back saying that I thought it had failed spectacularly. It is not safe to assume that in the event of an older captain being taken unwell a young and inexperienced co-pilot will always have the emotional maturity to manage the situation optimally in an adverse situation. It takes nerve to fly an approach in difficult weather sitting next to a dead pilot. S/O Keighley in the *Papa India* disaster was inexperienced and untrained in managing the incapacitation of his colleague.

$\star\,\star\,\star$

There was a hidden agenda at the ICAO meeting. Following conclusion of the proceedings, John Catching (who said he was avoiding the draft in the

US from the Vietnam War) and I sat in the library at McGill University and wrote the cardiovascular chapter for the second edition of the *Manual of Civil Aviation Medicine*. He recounted that his mother had said that she would rather that he avoided the draft in Canada than died in Saigon. As a spectator, then and now, of US foreign policy, one could but sympathise. But anyone who has written a chapter in a scientific book will know that that is not the way to set about it. It was not until 1985 that the finished product emerged, having weathered the doldrums (confer ITCZ) of international bureaucracy. In 2008 I was requested to write the third edition of the same cardiovascular chapter. It was completed in 2010 and published in 2012.

One evening Silvio asked us over to his home and I fell into conversation with Viktor. He wore Nina Ricci ties and a sharp-cut suit. He had the aggressive conviction of a well-programmed senior Communist apparatchik and was a true believer in his cause. This was notwithstanding that its implementation had involved the wholesale murder of peasants, kulaks, intellectuals, party officials and high-ranking officers. Eventually the Communist Revolution, like the French Revolution before it, had devoured its protagonists. He started to talk about the great patriotic war, as the Russians call the Second World War, and how the Russians, or as Hollywood likes to claim, the Americans, had fought and won it single-handed. He elaborated saying that Britain had ignored the plight of the Russians following Operation Barbarossa on 22nd June 1941 when four million troops of the Axis powers invaded the Soviet Union on a 1,800 mile front. I forwent a prod about the Molotov-Ribbentrop pact.

It had been the largest invasion in the history of any war and would ultimately fail; up to three million Soviet soldiers were taken prisoner, the majority of whom perished. I reminded him of the 78 PQ/QP Arctic Convoys to Russia, and of the sacrifice in men and the tonnage of stores sent when we were standing alone before 7th December 1941 – the Japanese attack on the US navy base at Pearl Harbor. One third of the tanks used in the defence of Moscow were British, I said. He was unconvinced. To lighten things I asked him how many private fliers there were in the USSR. He went pink (it should have been red) in the face and said that there was none, only personal fliers, whatever that meant. One wonders where he is now and whether he survived the upheavals of the collapse of Communism. I should not have asked Vladimir Todarev, in the meeting, how many aircraft belonged to Aeroflot. Victor silenced him abruptly and spluttered in a circuitous statement that that was unknown (it was a military secret). This was the permafrost of the Cold War.

On the return home on a DC10, leased from Air New Zealand, the cabin stewards and stewardesses seemed unusually courteous and friendly. Anyone who has flown a few miles will recognise the syndrome. The Captain came over the public address system with the warning that severe weather was forecast for our arrival in the UK. We were to be fed early, following which we would be strapped in and everything tied down. Not a good aperitif, even in first class. As we came over Prestwick the hail on the front of the aircraft sounded like the blitz and there was near-continuous lightning. Surprisingly there was not a lot of turbulence, but although the atmospheric unease was disturbing, the big GE CF6 engines ingested it all without demur. London Gatwick was shut by weather and the tunnel under the runway at Heathrow flooded. The weather was too bad for the baggage handlers who refused to unload the aircraft. It was good to be back. *If you have time to spare, go by air*, as they say.

★ ★ ★

Silvio Finklestein was succeeded as Chief of Medicine at ICAO by Dr Claus Curdt-Christiansen in 1994. Claus had gained his MD at Copenhagen University in 1968, and his PPL three years later. He attended the diploma in aviation medicine (DAvMed) course at Farnborough in 1977, and worked in the Clinic of Aviation Medicine at the University Hospital of Copenhagen (1973–1979). After appointments in Sweden and with the Swedish Air Force, he served for several years with the Royal Saudi Air Force in Jeddah, Saudi Arabia. He held the post of Chief Medical Officer in the Danish Civil Aviation Administration, Copenhagen between 1988 and 1994. He was appointed Chief of Aviation Medicine Section, ICAO, Montreal in 1994, serving until 2005. His accomplishments in those years included revision of the *Manual of Civil Aviation Medicine*; elevation, against opposition, of the retirement age for professional aircrew to sixty-five years; and, from the cardiological point of view, making smoking illegal on international flights. (See photo plate 22.)

Claus was in contention for the post to succeed Silvio when we attended a meeting of the Aerospace Medical Association in Miami together. We took a trip to the Everglades, the tropical wetland in southern Florida where the Valujet McDonnell-Douglas DC9 flight 592 was to crash and more or less disappear into the swamp two years later in May 1996. This was caused by an on-board fire. All 110 people on board lost their lives. There had been a precedent when Eastern flight 401, a Lockheed L-1011 Tristar, had crash landed there in December 1972; there had been 101 fatalities and seventy-five survivors. No-one on the flight deck noticed that the autopilot had become disconnected whilst all three flight crew members had been distracted whilst attempting to rectify a blown indicator bulb. *Please fly the aeroplane.*

We discussed aero-politics, and his hoped-for appointment. We visited the Everglades alligator farm by way of CPD (continuing professional development) in international aviation medicine. Two old crocks together. The air boat (hovercraft) noise in the swamp was ear-splitting. He has a holiday home in the Dordogne which he shares with his second wife, Xiao Lan, his first wife having died in 1992. There are two children by his first marriage and his daughter, Amanda, with Xiao Lan, who produced for us a superb Chinese meal. It may take five minutes to cook and eat but it takes all day to prepare. For novices in Chinese cuisine, chicken feet are a delicacy.

He was succeeded in 2005 by Dr Anthony Evans who had been a senior medical officer colleague at in the Medical Department of the CAA and, for six months before taking up his post with ICAO, briefly the CMO of the UK CAA. Tony has ably extended the influence and scope of the organisation as well as winning our tuk-tuk race in Bangalore. (See photo plate 23.)

REGULATORY DAYS

Bureaucracy is the death of all sound work.

Albert Einstein (1879–1955)

Initially my responsibilities at the UK CAA Medical Division were limited to interpretation of aircrew routine ECGs. Previously the recordings performed by the AMEs had been scrutinised by local cardiologists and were now to be repatriated to the department in stages. They were submitted on festoons of thermal recording paper wound into tight rolls originating from first generation portable electrocardiographs. These included the heavily damped Hewlett Packard machine, the Cambridge VS4 or its battery-driven smaller brother. Technical shortcomings abounded and this hampered interpretation. The routine resting electrocardiogram in fit, symptom-free individuals shows up relatively few anomalies; perhaps 3–5 % will have a point of comment. It is not displacement activity in diagnostic terms, as Tan and Sungar (2009) have recently confirmed. Important changes are scarce but with experience there is often something to comment upon. Those which are present can be distorted or concealed by recording artefacts.

The first task was to raise the quality of the recordings with the objective of reducing the number of queries. This involved specifying that recordings be made on machines satisfying the American Heart Association (AHA) standard. As the workload grew a second consultant was appointed – Air Commodore (later Air Vice-Marshal) John Nigel Carlyle Cooke, OBE, CB, FRCP, RAF (see photo plate 24).

John Cooke came from a Service family. His father was Air Marshal Sir Cyril Bertram Cooke, CB, RAF. John spent some of his childhood on the northwest frontier of India, now Pakistan, which I was to visit years later on behalf of the CAA. He had hoped to become a pilot but failed on grounds of his eyesight; he decided to become a doctor instead. He later recalled that at his interview for St Mary's Hospital Medical School he was chosen on morphological grounds as he had the appearance of, and indeed was, a fine rugby football player. On qualification in 1945 he joined the RAF. He initially served at the RAF Central Medical Establishment in Cleveland Street, W1, specialising in Miniature Mass Radiography (MMR). At one point when stationed at RAF Cosford in 1952, he was conducting the sick parade one morning when to his surprise a Flight Sergeant presented in tears.

"Brace up, Flight, get a grip on yourself."

"I have a sore throat, sir, I think it is a quinsy [peri-tonsillar abscess] – I have had one before."

"That's no reason to blub like a schoolgirl."

"It's not the pain, sir, but I have two tickets for the cup final and I know you will not let me leave the station if I am on the sick list."

"Too right, Flight, but I can buy them off you if that would help. Would 15/–d [75p] each do the trick?"

But there was no suitable transport from Wolverhampton so he approached the duty pilot. For the price of the second ticket, a four-engine Handley Page Halifax bomber was placed at their disposal for the trip to RAF Northolt, from whence they made their way to the match. They came back the next day having been too hung over to return the same night.

At the time I first met him, John was commanding the medical division at the RAF Hospital, Halton. He was Whittingham Professor of Aviation Medicine from 1974 to 1979. He subsequently became Air Vice-Marshal and Dean of Air Force Medicine, chairing the Defence Medical Service Postgraduate Council until 1982. He retired in 1985. He obtained dispensation from the RAF to attend the CAA and together we looked at increasing numbers of aircrew and their ECGs. Later we were joined by Air Vice-Marshal Brian Kelly who was the Commandant of the RAF Central Medical Establishment in Cleveland Street for a time. John (and Brian) also sat on the Medical Advisory Panel (MAP) to the CAA. As a very sound, pragmatic all-round physician, like many of his RAF medical colleagues, John had few equals. His tub-thumping Wesleyan revivalist style of lecturing was unequalled too. Air Commodores David Rainford and Anthony Batchelor, and Group Captain Andrew Hopkirk, also attended later and contributed significantly to the Clinic and the MAP.

From 1977 onwards the MAP meetings attempted to gain consensus in the management of aircrew with cardiovascular problems. One of the early subjects considered was Group Captain Sir Douglas Bader, KB, CBE, DSO and Bar, DFC and Bar, FRAeS, DL (1910–1982). Educated at St Edwards School, Oxford, he entered the Royal Air Force College, Cranwell in 1928. He just missed the Sword of Honour and excelled at sport. In 1930 he was commissioned into the Royal Air Force and joined No. 23 Squadron at Kenley, flying the Bristol Bulldog. Whilst practising for the 1932 Hendon Air Show at Woodley, in December 1931, he carried out a slow roll at low level and crashed, losing both his legs. It was claimed that it was for a dare. He was taken to the Royal Berkshire Hospital in Reading and not expected to survive. *Crashed slow-rolling near ground. Bad show,* was the entry in his log book when he was well enough to record it.

After convalescence he attempted to rejoin his old squadron, having proved that he was physically fit and able to fly with his artificial legs. He was denied a return to general duties (flying) and invalided out of the service as there was no precedent in King's Regulations. He joined what became Shell Royal Dutch, and later, after the war, rejoined the company to become chairman of Shell Aviation Ltd. In 1939 he persuaded the Air Ministry to accept him back and was posted to No. 19 Squadron at Duxford, later transferring to No. 222 Squadron with which he was involved in Operation Dynamo – the evacuation of Dunkirk. He moved again to command No. 242 Squadron, made up mostly of Canadians who had had a rough time during the Battle of France. This became part of the Duxford 12 Group commanded by Air Vice-Marshal Trafford Leigh-Mallory, who became his friend and with whom he was a proponent of the 'Big Wing' theory.

12. Group Captain Sir Douglas Bader (1910 – 1982), from the bronze statue by Kenneth Potts (2001). It stands facing the airfield at RAF West Hampnett, now Goodwood airfield and motor racing circuit. It is inscribed:

WING COMMANDER DOUGLAS BADER, DSO & BAR, DFC, RAF, FLEW HIS LAST MISSION FROM THIS AIRFIELD, 9TH AUGUST 1941

Bader was a critic of Air Vice-Marshal Keith Park, commander of 11 Group, in the thick of it to the south, although Park himself was supported by the head of Fighter Command, Air Chief Marshal Sir Hugh 'Stuffy' Dowding (later 1st Baron Dowding), GCB, GCVO, CMG (1882–1970). The controversy between Bader and Leigh-Mallory, who wanted to launch large formations of fighters north of the capital, and Keith Park, supported by Dowding, who favoured a more pragmatic approach, was unfortunate. The disagreement contributed to the departure of Park, who was replaced by Leigh-Mallory in November 1940. Dowding, who more than any other single man had led to victory in the Battle of Britain, was sidelined and sent to the USA in the same month.

In early 1941, Bader moved to RAF Tangmere as acting Wing Commander to lead squadrons which included Nos. 145 and 616. He took part in offensive operations – fighter sweeps – over Northern Europe in 1941 and was credited with twenty 'kills'. On the 9th August he departed from RAF Westhampnett – now returned to the Goodwood Estate. Goodwood is the home of Charles Gordon-Lennox, Earl of March and Kinrara, the elder son and heir of the Duke of Richmond. It is also home to the Festival of Speed and of the Revival meetings which celebrate the pre-war years in motoring and aviation in memory of Freddie March, the 9th Duke.

Bader was shot down, possibly by friendly fire, or suffered a mid-air collision, over St Omer. Having been trapped in the cockpit, he deployed his parachute and was hauled out of the aircraft, losing one of his artificial legs in the process. A replacement was dropped from a Bristol Blenheim during a routine bombing raid on Bethune. This was at the suggestion of General Adolf Galland with the agreement of Hermann Göring. Understandably a dim view was taken, when, after the drop, the Blenheims continued with their bombing raid. A few days later he escaped, only to be recaptured. He was to escape several times more before being incarcerated in Colditz Castle, Oflag IV-C, where he remained for the rest of the war – nearly three years. In June 1945 he led the three hundred aircraft flypast up the Mall in celebration of victory in Europe.

Bader was a strong-minded, outspoken man, never a stranger to controversy. Whilst in Colditz he used to 'goon bait', which led to privileges being withdrawn. This did not always please his contemporaries. After the war, and following the loss of his friend and comrade Trafford Leigh-Mallory, he left the RAF. He did much inspirational work to encourage interest in, and acceptance of, disability, for which he was knighted in 1976. He served on the Board of the CAA and chaired the Bader Committee which published, in 1975, its recommendations as CAP371 (*The Avoidance of Fatigue in Aircrews – Guide to Requirements*). It has been updated many times since. In his role at Shell after the war, he flew the company Percival Proctor and later a Beechcraft Bonanza. It was at this point that I got to know him on account of medical issues. He had sought the advice of various specialists, including myself in my role at the CAA. He came down to St Peter's Hospital for an ultrasound investigation. When this was explained to him he exclaimed, "Have never minded lying on a bed with a pretty girl, old bean."

13. *Warbirds at Goodwood during the 'Revival' meeting held each year in September by Charles, the Earl of March. Goodwood - formerly RAF West Hampnett - from which Douglas Bader flew on his last wartime mission, is the only motor racing circuit in the world devoted to historic motors.*

Eventually the consensus was against him continuing flying and he would say, "Look, old chap/boy/man/bean, could I not just go on flying until the anniversary of my first flight/first solo/wings?" And so on. When that failed he appealed to the board of the CAA who sent down a note to the Medical Department stating: *This pilot is a national hero. You will make him fit to fly.* Which led to the response: *If you think he is fit, you are the Executive – you issue him with a medical certificate.*

It was not the only time in my experience that a regulator invited a bending of the rules for a highly placed staff member. Nor indeed that ranks have been closed to protect the high and mighty. Bader stopped flying in June 1979, dying suddenly in September 1982 on his way home from making a speech at the Guildhall. Each time I saw him I recommended the withdrawal of his medical certificate, but he was unfailingly polite and friendly in spite of my youth and inexperience. He even found time off from his international lecturing activities to come and talk to the St Thomas's Hospital Medical and Physical Society, having dinner with us afterwards. I asked him which of the two Battle of Britain combat aircraft, the Supermarine Spitfire or the more heavily armed Messerschmitt Bf 109, was superior in combat. Perhaps surprisingly, he did not have much to say about their comparative performance.

★ ★ ★

One of Geoffrey Bennett's objectives as Chief Medical Officer (CMO) was for the medical clinic at Space House to centralise and standardise the investigation of pilots who needed further cardiovascular evaluation. He also saw its potential as a centre of excellence, which after many years it was to become; its advice was sought internationally. We reviewed six or more airmen and/or ATCOs over two sessions of three or four hours each. Most underwent exercise electrocardiography which effectively doubled the number of consultations. There were also case notes which required an opinion, and routine resting ECG recordings to scrutinise. Most of the ECGs were within normal limits (in electrocardiography, it is said, the report may state absolutely normal, normal or within normal limits). The doubtful ones needed to have the previous records pulled, which was cumbersome, as the recordings were for the most part unmounted. Later on they were photocopied and microfilmed and later still, digitised.

In order to encourage the pilots to attend the CAA clinic there was no charge to the individual. Over the years the aeromedical clinic built up a significant expertise across several specialities, to the advantage of both of the pilots whom it was serving, their employers and the authority itself. It also assisted the education of the non-clinical CAA medical staff. The CAA at that time was a world leader in engineering, type and line certification, and aviation medicine. It was also, as a centre of excellence, of assistance to less experienced states. The benefit of such assets did more for the brand of the authority, and of the UK, than the relatively small cost involved would suggest. Individual pilots were still allowed to seek a different cardiological opinion, if they wished, although some of them were not well versed in the prevailing ICAO/CAA requirements. Reasons for so doing may have reflected lack of trust, or the hope of more sympathetic treatment elsewhere.

From the oversight viewpoint it is surprising how variable such opinions can be. The downside for the pilot includes incomplete, or worse, extensive and unnecessary investigation. This is still seen today in spite of the publication of investigative algorithms on the CAA website. These algorithms helped systematise the investigation of common cardiological and other medical conditions following a proposal I made to the then-CMO, Dr Ken Edgington. They were developed by both him and his successor, Dr Simon Janvrin, and now form part of the EASA process.

Inevitably in the UK, when a system works well (increasingly infrequently in public life, mainly due to political interference), there is meddling. Often this is due to under-employment of an excessive number of managers with career or other agendas running. Everything is cost-driven, often in the naïve presumption that the private sector can deliver that which, by popular prejudice, a turgid and incompetent public sector cannot. And at a lower cost whilst still making a profit. The private sector, as Lord Darlington might have suggested (confer Oscar Wilde – *Lady Windermere's Fan*), knows the cost of everything but the value of nothing.

An early change to Bennett's protocol was to pursue a cost recovery policy, unlike some similar entities in Europe. In practice this required attending aircrew to reimburse the authority for the services rendered. Inevitably this was at well below market rate, and equally inevitably, it was forbidden to raise charges by more than the rate of inflation. Just how damaging this was to prove to be will emerge later as the strategy was to lead the CAA to propose outsourcing what was to become the Aeromedical Clinic (AeMC) under EASA. The situation was also made worse when the fees for the central scrutiny of the ECGs were repatriated to the AMEs. For the onerous task of a five-second glance at the computerised ECG report, a princely reward adjacent to £30 was made. It was to cost the Medical Department 10% of its annual budget.

Previously the ECGs had been individually scrutinised by specialists at the CAA, which pretty much paid for the cost of the specialist clinic. The reason for the free good was not clear, although it was claimed to have been a bribe (sic) to encourage the AMEs to computerise their records. Some might have told them to get on with it. The loss of revenue was made up by an additional levy on each medical examination: a further cost burden to the industry. Pointing out this strange move in a Public Interest Disclosure

Act (PIDA: 1998) statement made no difference. Someone mentioned hypothecation, a form of faux transparency loved by accountants. I was told that the CAA "did not account like that" and was reminded not to confuse with the facts once minds had been made up.

There was to be a further change, this time in the review procedure. It involved the introduction of another tier of appeal against an adverse medical decision. The 'final' medical fitness decision under the Air Navigation Order had been lodged with the CMO, who chaired the meeting of specialists forming the MAP. Now, apparently for presentational purposes, this defining piece of legislation was to be burdened with an appeal process. This was usually chaired by the CMO, at which the pilot and his/her (cardiological) specialist representative were in contention with one or more specialist advisers appointed by the CMO. This was not part of the administrative appeal process (Regulation 6). Initially no CAA clinical specialist was in attendance and appeals were allowed against the advice of the Cardiovascular Review Panel (CVRP) which replaced the MAP. This was in spite of attendance at the MAP by half a dozen cardiologists with special expertise in aviation medicine and its regulation. This change is only justifiable if difficult medical certificatory decisions are better made by advocacy between one or two specialists, instead of with the input of a consensus of a panel of experts.

Career-critical fitness decisions are as important to the individual pilot as they are to flight safety. The resolution of fitness issues demand involvement of the pilot, relevant clinical specialists experienced in aviation, and the regulator. In the interest of fairness and good judgement, the approach should be conciliatory rather than adversarial in an environment where outcomes vary and may lack certainty.

★ ★ ★

In the years following the Great War, fitness assessment had centred round the special senses. There was a requirement that the blood pressure should be normal and the heart free of 'significant' murmurs. As specialist medicine developed with the increasing availability of diagnostic, interventional and therapeutic procedures, it was incumbent on the regulator to update the medical standards continuously. This was in the interest of the retention of highly qualified and experienced professional pilots, both for their benefit as well as that of the industry. Increased aircrew age and experience is associated with a lower accident rate until the second half of the seventh decade, and mitigates the increasing risk of a medical (cardiovascular) event.

Age is the wild child both in terms of performance and risk of pathological event; its effect is expressed at different rates in different individuals. Index events such as a heart attack may carry such an adverse prognosis (outlook) that the inferred risk of a further event provoking pilot incapacitation will be unacceptable. On the other hand intervention with coronary artery surgery, or angioplasty/stenting (ballooning with the deployment of a small deformable wire basket into the coronary artery), and optimum medical management (lowering the blood pressure and plasma cholesterol level), may improve the outcome sufficiently, in the short to intermediate term, to permit recertification with increased scrutiny.

Risk of cardiovascular event (heart attack, rhythm disturbance, stroke) has a number of contributory factors and increases in a curvilinear fashion with age. The level, or presence or absence of such factors – high blood pressure, high plasma cholesterol, family history, smoking, diabetes mellitus and indolence – has a profound effect on the event rate. Risk is a continuum whilst fitness certification, almost by definition, is binary – the applicant is either fit or unfit. There is a détente for limitation of the airman to multi-crew operation. At some point, the day after the day before, the pilot is deemed no longer fit and the reason has to be transparent, demonstrably secure, scientifically based, fair and proportional. It must not be the property of the legal profession any more than gynaecologists should dominate the High Court.

It was to enhance the database and facilitate sound judgement that the Workshops in Aviation Cardiology were conceived.

TOWARDS THE
WORKSHOPS

*There is no expedient to which a man will not resort to avoid the real labour
of thinking*

Sir Joshua Reynolds (1723-1792)

The first meeting of the MAP to the CAA was held on 22nd July 1977. It
was clear that there was a requirement for an appropriate and accessible
database on the epidemiology, natural history, effect of intervention and
outcome of commonly encountered cardiological problems. Such an
asset would facilitate the making of regulatory judgement more scientific,
consistent and fair within the ICAO ISARPs. On reflection at the time
it seemed that the best format was likely to be a workshop. I ran the idea
before the CMO and some colleagues who were generally supportive.
One or two were discouraging, perhaps because they had not thought of
it themselves. We were breaking new ground. Cardiovascular problems
were, and remain, an important cause of licence loss in pilots, particularly
in the Western world. This is related to their propensity for abrupt,
unheralded presentation at times associated with partial or complete
incapacitation.

The workshops were conceived as a series of interactive seminars involving
some two dozen cardiologists each time, and running over three days. The
moderators and participants were chosen for their expertise in the aspects
of cardiology chosen for examination. It seemed common sense to invite

submission of scientific position papers, annotated from the literature, beforehand. The intention was to publish after the meeting. This worked well and the standard was high. Some needed little tweaking, a few, revision. It transpired that this approach was standard for working groups of the World Health Organisation (WHO). Following publication of the first workshop as a supplement of the *European Heart Journal*, similar exercises were carried out by the USA, Canada and Australia.

There were four or five sessions in each workshop, following each one of which there were recorded discussions. The conclusions and recommendations were edited and all were published as supplements of the *European Heart Journal*. With its novel approach, the First UK Workshop in Aviation Cardiology proved to be the most popular supplement the journal had produced at that time. The first UK workshop was held at the Copthorne Hotel, Gatwick Airport, in 1982. It suffered the disadvantage that there tended to be a noise of tearing calico every so often as one or other of the discussants headed back to London, prematurely, in a Porsche, or some other such arriviste contraption.

To circumvent this, the Second (UK) Workshop was held at Leeds Castle in Kent in 1987. It has been called the loveliest castle in the world. It originates from the 12th century but was adapted and underwent a major upgrade in the 19th century. Lady Baillie, daughter of Almeric Paget, 1st Baron Queenborough, was the last owner and bequeathed it to a charitable trust on her death in 1974. She extensively refurbished it, inside, during the 1920s and 1930s, and the facility was available for medical meetings at a discount, if you knew the right people. A plan to avoid a premature cardiological diaspora by raising the drawbridge was thwarted because there was none, but the beauty of the place kept everyone there for the entirety of the proceedings. Early one morning I watched a mother blackbird giving her offspring flying lessons. She was heartbroken when a magpie caught and killed one on the wing. We are wrecking her environment too.

The First (European) Workshop was held at Brocket Hall in Hertfordshire in 1991. It has a magnificent collection of paintings, including by van Dyck and Reynolds. Charles (the noble Lord) Brocket gave an amusing speech

14. *Leeds Castle, Kent. It has been called 'the loveliest castle in the world'. It was the venue for the Second UK Workshop in Aviation Cardiology, May 1987. No-one left early in spite of the lack of a drawbridge.*

at the conference dinner in the dining room in which Lady Caroline Lamb had sprung naked from a silver dish in front of the Prime Minister Lord Melbourne (1779–1848; Eton and Trinity College, Cambridge) was also her husband. It was his birthday. Maybe it was to make up for her affair with Lord Byron ("mad, bad and dangerous to know"). There is also a tale that Lord Palmerston (1784–1865; Harrow and St John's College, Cambridge), suffered SCD (sudden cardiac death) whilst ravishing a chambermaid on the billiard table – not very comfortable. ("Pot red in one, eh, what, what, m'dear?")

Other sources say that he died of a chill – "Die, my dear doctor, that's the last thing I shall do!" were claimed to be his last words. Voltaire was invited to renounce the Devil on his deathbed but refused, saying, "This is no time for making new enemies."

Brocket recounted that two or three of his forebears had had their heads cut off for some misdemeanour or other in the past. This caused my friend

Joachim Wurster, CMO of the Luftfahrt-Bundesamt (LBA) of the Federal Republic of Germany, to go puce in the face and explode that "In my country we do not boast if our relatives have had their heads cut off."

It was just as well that the practice had been discontinued in the UK as the noble lord in question was at about that time cutting up some of his Ferrari collection to perpetrate a fraud on the General Accident Insurance Company. They refused to pay out on his claim for the 'stolen' cars – "If you do not pay up, I will sue you," he was reported to have said.

"Go ahead," they said, mindful of the fact that the cars had vanished from a venue which presented itself as one of the most secure conference environments in Europe. Eventually he went to jail for five years, serving two and a half; some Ferrari aficionados felt it should have been longer.

★ ★ ★

The last of the workshops (the Second European) was held at Hanbury Manor in Hertfordshire in 1998. It was unexceptional as a venue although it had originally been a convent. There were no residual nuns, or their shades, and thus there was no opportunity to put the hairy leg hypothesis to the test. Mandy turned up for a few minutes, which was the first time we had met for many years. Four of the moderators, all Professors of cardiology – Hugh Tunstall-Pedoe (see photo plate 26), John Camm, Douglas Chamberlain and Michael Webb-Peploe, ably supported by Howard Swanton (who also chaired the DVLA committee) – provided continuity, having led sessions in all the previous workshops; there were many other outstanding contributors. Professor Ronnie Campbell, who had contributed magnificently to the first three workshops, sadly died suddenly before the final one, at the age of fifty-one years (see photo plate 27).

The last two meetings were enhanced by an excellent representation of European colleagues, both cardiological and regulatory. For the final (Second European) Workshop, both Jon Jordan, US Federal Air Surgeon (see photo plate 25), and Claus Curdt-Christiansen, Chief of Medicine at ICAO (see photo plate 22), flew over from North America on the Concorde, a visit arranged by my friend Ron Scobling, at that time the director of Corporate Affairs at British Airways. Paulo Manfroni (Italy) and Ken Edgington opened the first session on regulatory issues, followed by Suzanne Panton (Denmark) and Hugh Tunstall-Pedoe, who reviewed prediction of vascular risk. Michael Webb-Peploe and Per Årva (Norway) covered the session on coronary artery disease; Kari Antilla (Finland; whom I had first met at ICAO, Montreal in 1980) and John Camm looked after rhythm and conduction disease. Finally Jean-Paul Broustet (France) and Kurt Bachmann (Germany) gave an overview of cerebrovascular disease.

Annetje Roodenburgh, CMO of the Netherlands Inspectie Leefomgeving en Transport (ILT) suggested at the meeting of the moderators that the frequency of the medical examination – six-monthly at that time for the airline transport pilot's licence (ATPL) – could be reduced to twelve months below age fifty, and thereafter. This was conditional on the licence holder being denied single-crew commercial operations, without additional review. The proposed reduction in the burden of scrutiny bore the authority of the workshop participants without being binding on the authorities concerned. Soon that would change with the arrival of the JAA, and later EASA.

Funding for the workshops was obtained from a variety of sources. The CAA contributed financially to some extent, but there was an advantage in maintaining a distance to avoid the potential for sponsoring a 'blue skies' review of standards which it was unable to endorse subsequently. This had been the case in the uninvited (from the regulatory point of view) reports of the American Heart Association and the Royal College of Physicians following the *Papa India* disaster. Major sponsorship came from educational grants from the pharmaceutical industry, notably with the help of Michael Gatenby, CEO of Stuart Pharmaceuticals, and an offshoot of ICI, later Zeneca and now Astra-Zeneca. This form of funding has fallen into disfavour for reasons of governance but at the time it was widespread, and, it has to be said, very helpful. It was part of the agreement that there was to be no commercialism and the company profile was minimal. Publication was supported by the *European Heart Journal*.

Attention was given to background briefing. Between one sixth and one quarter of passengers admit to anxiety/flight phobia in an aircraft. This colours judgement on fitness to fly. To familiarise the participants with the flight deck and demonstrate the inherent safety of incapacitation training in the two-crew configuration, sessions were provided in the flight simulators at Crawley. Likewise arrangements were made for a visit to the air traffic control tower at London, Gatwick Airport. But first the participants were sent briefing documents on the operational environment and given some insight into accident causation.

One of the issues which emerged in the later workshops was the change in attitude to authority which had occurred in the generation following the Second World War. There was a meeting, in which I was involved, of the American Heart Association and North American Society of Pacing and Electrophysiology (NASPE): Personal and Public Safety Issues Related to Arrhythmias That May Affect Consciousness: Implications for Regulation and Physician Recommendations – held in January 1995, in Washington, DC. It was published the following year. The session on ethics considered the rights and responsibilities of the individual and of society. In the UK this has become distorted. Now the rights of the miscreant overwhelm the rights of the victim or society, espoused by a legal professional which has access to vastly more treasure than other comparable European states in terms of legal aid. At this meeting I met Dr Mark Anderson who was to join both the DVLA and CAA medical advisory processes.

In the context of transportation, the rights of the individual, including the right to accept personal risk, may conflict with the right of society to set a legal level of risk where individuals are in a position to cause harm to others. Any constraint must be fair, recognising that personal freedom, job security and sense of wellbeing may be impaired. Attitudes have changed. A generation or more ago an airman might have accepted, without question, that the physician could be relied upon to make a sound and fair judgement. Now there is an appropriate challenge for proper explanation and justification. This has been extended into the acceptability of age-related restriction of the licence, which, whilst potentially unfair to some, is from the administrative point of view easy to apply. Retirement on the basis of slowly deteriorating performance and increased risk of ill-health is more difficult to define and demonstrate.

The Joint Aviation Authorities (JAA) directorate was born as the Joint Airworthiness Authorities in 1970. Originally, its responsibilities were restricted to the certification of large aeroplanes and engines in support of the European industry, and consortia such as Airbus. Its role was extended in 1987 to include operations, maintenance, licensing and certification/ design standards for all classes of aircraft. It was the European uber-regulator between 1999 and 2007. The Cyprus Arrangements were signed in 1990 by nine states including the UK, to harmonise safety standards and procedures in civil aviation in Europe.

During 1991 the JAR (Joint Aviation Requirements) Flight Crew Licencing (FCL3) sub-committee started the work of harmonisation of the medical standards for flight crew licences. This was initiated on 1st January 1993 for completion by the 1st January 1996. The European Union was created in the same year (1993). At the time, shortly before his retirement from the CAA in 1992, the CMO, Geoffrey Bennett, was unwell and I was asked to represent him at two of the European Civil Aviation Conference (ECAC) Flight Crew Licencing (FCL) meetings held in 1990. One was in Neuilly-sur-Seine, Paris, and supported by Médecin-Général, Robert Auffret; the other in Geneva under the chairmanship of M. J-R Willi (Switzerland). The new European Cardiological Standards were to be discussed. There was no preparation beforehand and only limited pre-circulation of the agenda for discussion. There were representatives of many European states; Silvio Finkelstein represented ICAO and M. Kuntz – IFALPA (the International Federation of Air Line Pilot's Associations).

Age limitations were discussed, the minutes rather quaintly remarking that *mental weakness* as well as *heart incapacitation* had to be taken into account as potentially incapacitating events in the air. There is a lot of the former about. It was proposed that the age limit for multi-crew operation *could* be raised to sixty-five but the sixty-year age limit should still apply for single-crew professional operations. There were no other cardiological specialists apart from myself and Dr Harald Eliasch (Sweden). The meetings were not a success from the drafting point of view., Médecin-Général Robert Auffret, CMO of the French DGAC (Direction Générale de l'Aviation Civile), *un cher collègue, un bon ami, mais un vieux renard à certains égards*, did not turn up to one meeting because he had not been told about it. On one occasion Joachim Wurster exploded into the conference room two hours late, spluttering that although he came from the richest country in Europe, he still had to take public transport. It has always been tough at the top.

As we were getting nowhere in terms of drafting the Standards, a new approach was needed. In May of 1992, shortly after Ken Edgington had taken over as CMO of the CAA, the annual meeting of the Aerospace Medical Association was again held in Miami. After some consultation I hired an upstairs room (Acts 1:13) and assembled the CMOs of all the European nations attending the meeting. They were tasked, collectively, to help draft the cardiological standards that day. Furthermore we finished the job, which was greatly to their credit, although it did take five hours. I fettled the text on the way home on the Boeing 747.

This informal meeting, together with the workshop output, formed for the basis of the cardiovascular section of the JAR FCL, including the Standards, Appendices and Guidance Material. It was planned that the material would be regularly updated after its promulgation in 1997. But Ken Edgington retired in 1999 and his successor was anxious to reduce specialist advice and repatriate input back to the AMS. Subsequent updating of the Standards and Appendices was to be carried out by non-experts in the subject. I continued to review and rewrite the Guidance Material until the JAA was overtaken by EASA in 2007. It was last published in 2009.

Further workshops were embargoed in 2000 and they have not been repeated. The JAA was superseded by EASA in 2007 in the interest of the expansion of European bureaucracy. Endless political churning has wrecked the NHS in the UK and is always a risk to similar institutions. *Facet aliquid operis, ut semper te diabolus inveniat occupatum*; confer Chaucer, *The Tale of Melibee*, 1386 – the devil indeed finds work for idle hands. Increased bureaucracy is a side-effect (or the centrepiece, some might echo) of European harmonisation but is difficult to justify on safety grounds in the context of the prevailing accident rate. But as progress is made towards the SES (single European sky), common policies for personnel (including medical) certification will evolve and further change is inevitable. The main beneficiaries are the smaller and less experienced states but a common (high) standard is in the interest of all. When I asked at a CAA briefing meeting what the new EASA process, per se, could be expected to deliver in terms of aviation safety, it was an H. M. Bateman moment. Everyone was aghast.

The European Aviation Safety Agency publishes the Basic Regulation which has been adopted by the European Parliament and Council; it is binding in all its elements. The Implementing Rules (IR) to the Basic Regulation have been adopted by the European Commission (and are pretty much non-negotiable), whilst the Acceptable Means of Compliance (AMC) is so-called soft law. It is not legislative but there is a presumption of legal compliance; it is an India rubber standard (for bending rather than stamping). What a sunlit playground for the lawyers. There is also an Alternative Means of Compliance (AltMOC) which may be filed as a difference by individual states. These are pondered upon by non-specialist committees in Cologne, the output of which is relayed back to the national regulators, and their advisers, for comment. It is a bit like trying to design a camel on a bad telephone line and then selling it, unseen. Changes in the AMC have to go through the legal department, although lack of reciprocity denies a requirement for legal issues to be passed through the medical department. These problems are pursued in the last two chapters.

Once again, risk is a continuum whilst the fitness decision is binary – pass or fail.

MODUS OPERANDI OF THE WORKSHOPS

"A slow sort of country!" said the Queen. "Now, here, you see, it takes all the running you can do, to keep in the same place. If you want to get somewhere else, you must run at least twice as fast as that!"

Charles Lutwidge Dodgson (Lewis Carroll)
Alice in Wonderland, 1865

The regulator (e.g. the CAA) and the specialist adviser (e.g. in cardiology) have different but complimentary responsibilities. The cardiologist is required to diagnose the presence, or the likelihood, of a cardiovascular event over a defined period. He/she also has to predict the short and longer term consequences and possible outcomes. The regulator is tasked to determine at what point the cursor of judgement denies, or restricts, certification of the individual to fly because the risk of a disabling event is unacceptable. In general terms, the following briefing questions, updated, were put to the workshop participants:

1. What are the different levels of operation and do they have different safety targets?

The ICAO ISARPS recognise three levels of Medical Assessment: Class 1 – commercial pilots; Class 2 – private pilots (including glider and balloon pilots) and Class 3 – air traffic controllers (ATC). No international standard has been established for micro-light pilots. They are general medical assessments only. In ICAO Annex 1, 1.2.4.9, is a Standard often incorrectly called a waiver. It is the 'flexibility clause'. Legally waiver means "an act of dispensing with a requirement". In the UK the terms 'full' or 'unrestricted' Class 1 Medical Assessment and 'restricted' Class 1 Medical Assessment are in use – with the latter the licence bears an Operational Multi-Crew Limitation (OML). In this case flying is restricted to multi-crew operation and single-crew commercial operation is denied. Not all states endorse this approach (such as the USA). EASA promulgates the three classes of medical assessment and adds a fourth – the LAPL (Light Aircraft Pilot's Licence) which is a non-expiring 'sport flying' licence. This was developed at a meeting to which I was invited by Dr René Maire, a Swiss cardiological colleague, who was president at the time of the Medico-Physiological Commission (CIMP) of the Fédération Aéronautique Internationale (FAI). We met in Lausanne in 1999.

In the UK there is also an Operational Safety-pilot Limitation (OSL) which can be applied to a UK Class 2 (private pilot) assessment and is equivalent to the proposed EASA ORL; (Operating-pilot Restriction Limitation) which may replace it. Finally there is an EASA OPL which would restrict the pilot to fly solo, although at the time of writing (April 2015), this privilege may be included in the forthcoming EASA ORL. The OSL/ORL requires/ will require a second pilot, rated on the same (dual control) aircraft to be available for the management of a potential incapacitating event.

That he/she has had no training for this eventuality and its consequences, and has not been the subject of objective assessment by the regulator, appears to have been overlooked. There is, however, a leaflet. This is not satisfactory from the safety point of view, and a questionable exercise for the regulator. Anyone can handle a dual control aircraft provided the pilot in command remains in control. There was also an equivalent 'proximity endorsement' to a Class 3 (ATCO) Medical Assessment in the presence of a health issue but this is being phased out.

Different jurisdictions may have different licence categories and an ICAO/ EASA Medical Class number may not reflect the same privileges in all states. The classes vary in terms of frequency of examination with small differences in, for example, visual requirements.

2. *What is the operational exposure – how much flying is going on and at what level?*

This may be expressed in terms of number of hours flown, number of departures or number of passenger-kilometres travelled. It is can be sub-divided into scheduled passenger (jet turbine, turbo-prop or piston aircraft) operation; non-scheduled (inclusive tour or IT) and cargo operation; and private operation although the system is blurred as a jet airliner may be operated as a private flight. There are also rotary (helicopter) and fixed wing sub-divisions. Globally, there were some 550 million passenger and air cargo hours flown in 320 million sectors in the decade 2002–2011 (CAA – *CAP 1036*, 2013).

Over three billion passengers and fifty million metric tons of cargo were carried by air in 2013 in some 25,000 jet turbine and turboprop multi-crew aircraft, worldwide. This effort supported fifty-seven million jobs and produced about 3.5% of global Gross Domestic Product (GDP) (IATA, 2013). There has been a 50% growth in passenger carriage in the past five years following the recessional downturn, supported by the tiger economies of the Asia-Pacific and South American regions. During the decade ending 2007, 25.5 million hours were flown in 11.2 million flights by the UK airlines and air taxi operators, 91% involving jet aircraft, 8% turboprop aircraft, 0.47% business jets and 0.01% piston aeroplanes (CAA – *CAP 763*). This reflected a significant increase on the decade ending 1975 which covered the birth of the CAA. During that period 7.4 million passengers were carried in UK-registered scheduled and non-scheduled passenger aircraft (CAA – *CAP 386*).

The US FAA Part 135 commuter and 'on demand' (air taxi) operations with thirty seats or fewer, and general aviation fleet, is vast by world standards involving an estimated 220,670 aircraft of all types in 2012 (FAA, 2014), flown by over 500,000 pilots (excluding air transport pilots) in 24.6 million hours. An estimated 8.1 million hours were flown during 1998–2007 in the UK in a non-public transport capacity. Small fixed wing (generally single-pilot) aircraft commercial flights in the UK in the ten-year period 1998–2007 flew 415,000 hours (CAA – *CAP 763*).

3. What is the fatal/non-fatal accident rate expressed in the same units?

Accidents are often expressed per million hours flown or per million departures, but they can also be expressed per unit of time, most often one year. There was an average of one major accident for every five million flights in 2012 on Western-built jet (WBJ) aircraft, worldwide. The 380 airlines on the IATA Operational Safety Audit (IOSA) registry experienced no hull loss of WBJ aircraft in the same year. This accident rate was one quarter of the 2012 world experience. One quarter of all accidents are related to runway incursions, with Controlled Flight into Terrain (CFIT) a further important cause, although this appears to be diminishing. An astonishing 60% of fatalities in the five years ending 2012 were due to loss of control in flight (LCIF). *Fly the aeroplane, whatever else is going on.*

Accidents may be expressed by level of operation, category of aircraft, region of occurrence, and whether they are fatal or non-fatal. Up to 30% of fatal accidents may have some survivors and death can be remote from the event. The fatal accident rate for turboprop aircraft is three to four times that for pure jet aircraft. Aircraft with an MTWA <15 tonnes have a fatal accident rate that is three times that of those with an MTWA >27 tonnes. Hull loss rates in WBJ in Africa are twenty times worse than elsewhere. Data indicate that the fatal accident rate, worldwide, for cargo operations is six times that of passenger carriage. There were 29.6 million commercial flights in 2012 with six hull-loss accidents in WBJ flights (IATA) and fifteen fatal accidents out of a total of seventy-five, worldwide. This reflects a hull-loss rate of 0.20 per million flights, or one hull loss for every five million flights. It was the best in aviation history and a nearly 50% improvement over 2011, itself a record year for safety. The year 2013 was better still with a record low total of 265 airliner accident fatalities in twenty-nine fatal airliner accidents worldwide.

But 2014 was different due to various high profile disasters, although it still managed a record low of twenty-one fatal airliner accidents, albeit with 990 fatalities, making it the safest year, ever, but only by number of fatal accidents. The loss of Malaysian flight MH370 Boeing 777-200ER 9M-MRO, which vanished without trace following departure from Kuala Lumpur on 8th March 2014, accounted for the death of 239 passengers. At the time of writing (June

2015) there is still no clue as to what happened, but human intervention at some point in the flight envelope seems very likely – possibly suicide/murder. The accident statistics were further damaged by another Malaysian loss, of Boeing 777-200ER flight MH17 on 17th July 2014, shot down over the Ukraine. This almost certainly involved insurgents backed by Russia; a further 298 passengers and crew perished. These two accidents involving a single airline were associated with twice the loss of life recorded in the whole of 2013. There had been only one previous fatal accident to the Boeing 777 since entering service in 1995 – the Asiana flight 214 Boeing 777-200ER HL7742 which crashed on final approach into San Francisco International airport. Of the 307 people aboard, three died and twelve were critically injured. Over 1,200 of the aircraft have been delivered and it has one of the best safety records of all time.

During the decade ending 2007, 1.1 billion passengers were carried in UK-registered aircraft >5.7 tonnes MTWA for the loss of eight lives in 132 reportable accidents, of which five were fatal. To explain fatal/non-fatal categorisation, the loss of Britannia Airways flight BY226A Boeing 757-204 G-BYAG which crash landed at Girona Airport, Spain, on 14th September 1999 following an approach in bad weather, is an example. There were 236 passengers and nine crew members; two passengers were seriously injured and one died five days later of previously undiagnosed internal injuries. An accident is classified as fatal if there is at least one death as a result.

The reportable accident rate in the decade 1998–2007 in the UK for small-fixed wing aircraft (<5,700 kg MTWA) was twenty-five times higher than in scheduled jet aircraft operations. There were ninety-six fatal accidents involving UK small conventional non-public transport aeroplanes which led to 163 fatal, 105 serious and 241 minor injuries. The reportable accident rate for these (landplanes, seaplanes and self-launching motor gliders <5,700 kg MTWA, but excluding rotary aircraft/helicopters) has been estimated at 179 per million hours and the fatal accident rate at 11.7 per million hours. Eighty-nine per cent of these involved single-engine piston machines. Rotary aircraft have been excluded from these data for the sake of simplicity (*CAP 780:* 2008).

4. *What is the medical (cardiological) contribution to this accident experience, and what is an acceptable component?*

Such data are difficult to come by with certainty, especially in single-crew operations where flight data recorders (FDR) and cockpit voice recorders (CVR) are generally not required. This is related to MTWA and level of operation – scheduled/non-scheduled/private. In the UK, the RAF has the sole responsibility for the post mortem evaluation of the victims of a fatal aircraft accident. Cullen et al (1997) reviewed one thousand such accidents over a forty-year period and found that over all levels of operation, 4.7% of accidents had a medical and 2.2% a cardiological cause. This was in spite of concern that a cardiac abnormality and an unexplained accident does not necessarily imply cause and effect. Some, without good reason, have found these data hard to accept.

In one report, relating to 2004, there were 16,145 UK/JAA professional pilot licence holders. Over the whole year, on and off duty, thirty-six suffered incapacitating events, half of which were cardiac or cerebrovascular. There were four sudden deaths. A male pilot in his sixties had five times the risk of incapacitation of a male pilot in his forties. The annual incapacitation rate was 0.25% in a population which spends 8–10% of its time on duty. In a single-crew operation such events almost always lead to catastrophe.

In an earlier report from the USA in which in-flight impairments and incapacitations in airline pilots were studied over a five-year period, the average age for an incapacitating event was 47 years, and for impairment slightly less. The in-flight medical event rate was 0.58 per million flying hours. The probability that an in-flight medical event would result in an aircraft accident was 0.04. As in the UK study, incapacitating events significantly increased with age and were more serious. The most frequent causes of incapacitation were loss of consciousness, cardiological, neurological and gastrointestinal. Flight safety was seriously impaired in seven of the forty-seven flights and resulted in two non-fatal accidents, reminding us that the medical cause accident risk in the two-crew configuration is not always the square of the individual risk.

The vulnerability of the single-crew operation to medical mishap is illustrated by the crash at Bladon, Oxfordshire on 15th January 2010 of Piper PA-31P Navajo N95RS, shortly after take-off from Oxford Kidlington Airport. It was one of several such accidents over the past thirty years in the UK. The Air Accidents Investigation Branch (AAIB) noted the pathological report on the heart of the pilot in command which demonstrated: *A severe degree of coronary artery disease which would be capable of producing a range of cardiac symptoms including arrhythmias, angina, collapse or sudden death.* The conclusion was that the pilot was dying, or dead, before contact with the ground and the subsequent post-crash fire. The passenger was also a pilot, and owner of the aircraft, but was not trained to fly in the prevailing conditions of poor visibility and low cloud, in which he would have become disorientated. Such single-pilot incapacitation accidents will continue to occur at a rate predicted by age, insofar as it predicts cardiovascular events.

The Piper PA31-350 Navajo G-BMBC, on an ambulance flight from Ronaldsway, Isle of Man, bound for Liverpool, crashed into the Mersey on 14th June 2000. The single-pilot had flown through the Runway 09 centre line at 20–30 kts too high an approach speed, without having lowered the landing flaps, switched on the fuel auxiliary pumps, or the landing lights. This gave the impression of loss of situational awareness by a very experienced pilot. He had also dialled up an incorrect frequency for the airfield NDB. He was demonstrated to have had an enlarged heart and severe coronary heart disease which may have been the cause of distracting symptoms.

5. *What level of routine medical examination is appropriate, what is its sensitivity, and is it beneficial, bearing in mind the parallels with regular airframe/engine review?*

Most passengers prefer that the aircraft in which they fly, and their pilots, are fit for purpose. The medical examination includes a history and physical examination with special attention to the blood pressure, signs in the cardiovascular system, a search for glucose in the urine and a regular resting electrocardiogram – the frequency of which is determined by age and type of licence. Visual and auditory tests are an important part of the examination. The routine chest X-ray has been dropped for lack of justification together with the initial reference electro-encephalogram (EEG).

15. The 'flight deck' of the PA31 Navjo, G-BJLO co-owned with Nigel Reynolds. It illustrates the complexity of a light twin engined aircraft and may be flown by a single pilot. The upper centre of the panel contains two GPS receivers with the radar screen below. The coupled autopilot is below the throttle quadrant. The black square in the centre of the panel above the control yoke, is the PNI (Plan Navigation Indicator). It is not the best venue for a cardiovascular event, even if there is a second pilot in the right-hand seat.

The value of the routine resting ECG is sometimes questioned in terms of its (lack of) predictive value for the detection of asymptomatic disease. It does have some value, however, particularly in older pilots. In a recent paper (2009) almost 30,000 US veterans with a mean age of fifty-six years – older than the mean pilot population by more than a decade – were followed for a mean of 7.5 years. Twelve independent ECG anomalies were identified, all of which were associated with a statistically significantly increased hazard ratio for cardiovascular mortality. Overall, if one anomaly was present the relative risk of cardiovascular death increased by 1.8:1, rising in a linear fashion to 6:1 in the presence of five. This provides a powerful predictor of cardiovascular mortality independent of age, standard risk factors and clinical status.

Twenty-five per cent of those suffering a heart attack in the Framingham study did not experience symptoms that they recognised as important and were picked up at routine bi-annual review. Fifteen per cent of new coronary artery disease presented as sudden death. Such findings support the use of this quick, simple, cheap and non-invasive test in the pilot population. It should be overseen by properly accredited personnel aware that the pilot population differs from the patient population in being generally symptom-free and well.

6. *Is vascular risk factor intervention required in medical fitness assessment?*

The plasma cholesterol is reviewed at initial issue of the licence, and once more at age forty years. The blood pressure is measured on each examination. Increased levels of either are case finding; the AME is not in a treatment relationship with the pilot. Abnormalities do not constitute a reason for denial of fitness, per se, although if present, cardiovascular risk is increased. It can be argued that routine medical review could be carried out in a laboratory with measurements made by a technician, but a good AME is a clinician who should search for potential health problems. Routine clinical review parallels engine and airframe maintenance – it is troubleshooting. However, a Cochrane review (2012) of fourteen studies which included 182,880 subjects in primary care concluded that routine medical follow-up did not have an effect on overall or disease-specific mortality. But the majority of the studies were un-blinded and follow-up was incomplete. Restriction of the analysis to death and hospitalisation may have introduced bias. Routine medical examination of the pilot is an opportunity for preventative medicine, the poor quality of which, on occasion, has led to health disadvantage.

The first communication I presented in aviation medicine was to the International Academy of Aviation and Space Medicine, in London in 1976. It related the fate of five airmen whose high blood pressure had been ignored, or understated, by the AME involved who was 'being helpful'. At that time there was good evidence, now completely secure, that pharmacological lowering of raised blood pressure reduced the occurrence of stroke, heart and kidney failure, and of heart attack. All suffered premature licence loss on account of pathology, which included renal (kidney) failure and the need for renal dialysis, stroke and myocardial infarction (heart attack). Indeed, in the initial study period of thirty months ending in December 1977, a total of fourteen licences were lost overall on account of uncontrolled or inadequately treated high blood pressure. The total number of aircrew/ATCOs at risk would have been of the order of 14,000.

Ignoring treatable, potentially life-threatening, cardiovascular problems is culpable and a failure of clinical responsibility. It also has safety implications but still continues in spite of the latitude and acceptability of modern treatment. The professionalism shown by aircrew with health issues has always been impressive in my experience, no matter how disagreeable the findings and their related certificatory implications.

7. *Is the cost of regular medical review justifiable within the overall safety envelope?*

The cost of an A320 Airbus airliner in 2012 was of the order of £60 million and the Direct Operating Cost (DOC) some £10,000 per hour. This is reflected in a utilisation of perhaps three thousand hours a year, but the figure varies quite widely according to the airline involved. The DOC includes fuel (30% of total), maintenance labour cost, airframe, engine, avionics overhaul, inspections, component and engine overhauls, landing and parking fees, crew costs and catering. The cost of routine medical assessment of the crew (based on two examinations for each of two pilots per year – it is less than this) should not exceed £1,000. This is not a large sum in the context as the aircraft cannot fly without the pilots and they are responsible for its safety. With six crews to an aircraft, the crew routine medical costs approach £6,000 a year or £2 per hour flown by the aircraft. The cost of further investigation, if indicated, will be additional. Human error overlaps with fatigue and 'illness' and is associated with four fifths of all aviation accidents. Yet accountants and the regulator still argue about the cost and desirability of medical review when on the day, the safety of every one of the three billion passengers carried each year is the responsibility of the two aircrew at the front of the aeroplane.

It was towards clarification of cardiovascular risk in the aviation environment that the four Workshops in Aviation Cardiology were commissioned. The search was for strategies in the management of common and not-so-common conditions seen in aircrew. But what is risk?

RISK, THE 1% RULE AND BEYOND

Risk comes from not knowing what you're doing.

Warren Buffett (1930–present)
Essays, 2009

The 1% rule reflects the cut-off point for medical fitness to fly in a multi-crew aircraft. It is predicated in the cardiovascular mortality of a 65 year old European male; rates of death and/or major incapacitating event/year are regarded as similar. It was suggested by Professor Hugh Tunstall-Pedoe at the Second UK Workshop in Aviation Cardiology held at Leeds Castle in the summer of 1988.

The transportation industries, like any human activity, involve risk; good conduct and legislation demands that such risk is understood and properly managed. Risk-taking may be defined as the intentional acceptance of uncertainty – the desire to travel to a distant country outweighs the perceived small risk that the process might end in disaster. Decisions tend to be modulated by perception – subjective judgment about the nature and severity of an unsought outcome versus the benefit of accepting its unavoidable presence. Such attitudes have no place in regulation.

There are different ways of defining risk. Tunstall-Pedoe, in the First UK and subsequent workshops, introduced different aspects of the problem. Measurement of risk demands a numerator, a denominator and a time base.

Statements that a risk is 10% are meaningless without relating it to time or event. Event rates are often expressed in terms of a number over a defined period such as a year, or, in transportation, the number of people carried over a distance – the numerator in aviation is commonly 100 million passenger kilometres.

Absolute risk is the risk of event over a defined period. This may be the chance of a heart attack over the next year, or, the chance of being involved in a fatal aircraft accident on any one trip. It may be expressed in various ways. A one in ten risk over a defined period is also a 10% risk over the period.

Relative risk is used to compare risk of event between different groups. This gives no information on the absolute risk, which may be individually small or large. An example would be the relative safety of turbo-prop versus pure jet aircraft. The former encounter a fatal accident three or four times more often than the latter, but are usually still safe enough. Over a period of forty years Air France has had four times the accident rate of British Airways.

The attributable risk is the difference in the incidence of a condition, for example in a population bearing a certain risk factor such as high blood pressure, and a normal population. In the Framingham community study, the early data showed that the presence of high blood pressure doubled the risk of occlusive vascular disease, tripled the risk of heart attack, multiplied the risk of heart failure four-fold, and of stroke, seven-fold. These data express both attributable risk and relative risk.

The population attributable risk may be described as the increase in risk in the whole population, attributable to the presence or prevalence of a risk factor or risk factors, within it. The cardiovascular event rate in a pilot group will be related to the prevalence of vascular risk factors within it. In aviation the interest is in *absolute* and *population attributable risk*.

Workshop participants were briefed on the prevailing safety standards at the various levels of operation. The key differences between single-pilot operations (in aircraft <5,700 kg MTWA) private and commercial, and multi-crew (increasingly pure jet) operations were emphasised. At the time of the First UK Workshop in 1982, 755 million passengers worldwide flew fourteen million hours for the loss of just over one thousand lives. In these times, when there is an obsessive interest in passenger screening for possible weapons, it is worth recalling that at that time up to one quarter of total annual fatalities were caused by sabotage. The sector time then had a mean of one hour and the best airlines were achieving accident rates of $0.5{:}1\mathrm{x}10^6$ hours whereas overall the rate was of the order of $1.5\mathrm{x}10^6$ hours.

In contrast the single-crew fatal commercial accident rate was of the order of $1\mathrm{x}10^5$ hours. Thirty years later, in 2013–2014, the number of passengers carried in jet aircraft per year has quadrupled, the flying hours trebled and the fatal accident rate and number of lives lost better than halved, in spite of the greatly increased level of activity. The fatal accident rate from single-crew operations, by way of contrast, has changed very little. The risk gradient in relation to MTWA; 2002–2012 (*CAP 1036*), was 1.8, 0.6 and 0.2 accidents per 10^6 hours for aircraft <15 tonnes, >15< 27 tonnes and >27 tonnes respectively. In general terms, the smaller the aeroplane, the greater the risk of fatal accident.

The target for medical cause accident loss of a large jet aircraft was given by John Chaplin (Director of Safety Services, CAA at the time) at the Second UK Workshop in 1988 as spanning $1{:}10^8$ and $1{:}10^9$ hours, whilst the industry target for a catastrophic unpredicted hull loss was $1{:}1{,}000$ million or $1{:}10^9$ hours. The Lauda Air flight NG004 Boeing 767-3Z9ER OE-LAV, from Hong Kong to Vienna on 26th May 1991, exemplifies an unheralded disaster. The aircraft was lost due to an un-commanded thrust reverser deployment on the left engine in flight. This caused an abrupt wing-over followed by a dive, during which the aircraft may have become supersonic. It broke up before it hit the ground. All 223 people on board were killed.

There had been an intermittent warning that the thrust reverser was unlocked on the engine in question; its design had not included a fail-safe mode which should have denied deployment during the climb. Likewise the TWA flight 800 Boeing 747-100 N93119 exploded and crashed into the Atlantic Ocean following take-off from New York in July 1996. All 230 people on board were killed. Following four years of investigation the NTSB concluded that the likely cause was an explosion of fuel vapour in the central fuel tank, probably due to an electrical short circuit. We have not yet achieved the industry target for catastrophic unpredicted hull loss of $1{:}10^9$ m flying hours and are unlikely to do so.

The cardiovascular event rate of the population at any age is not consistent with a $1:10^9$ target fatal accident event rate, if there is only one pilot. Even the target for medical cause accident in single-crew commercial operations – one event in 10^7 hours – is difficult to achieve for an under-forty-five-year-old male in the West. The International Civil Aviation Organisation, by requiring the presence of two pilots trained for the possibility of incapacitation of a colleague (ICAO Annex 1.2.1.5.2a) in all aircraft >5,700 kg MTWA, provides protection of the safety envelope. This is lost if there is a common mode failure, for example suicide of the pilot or food poisoning. Hypoxia (lack of oxygen to the brain) caused the loss of the Helios Airways flight 522 737-300 5B-DBY in August 2005. It occurred following the failure of an engineer to reset a pressurisation switch, compounded by crew failure to complete checks satisfactorily. Or, to respond to several warnings which they believed to be a take-off configuration problem – this can only occur on the ground. All 121 on board died.

Aircraft accidents may be expressed as rates per annum, events per million hours flown, or number of departures made. Death rates and cardiovascular event rates may be expressed per 100,000 or 1,000,000 of the population, or, with the time base of a year, in hours. There are 8,760 hours in a year which may be rounded up to 10,000 for the purposes of mathematical modelling. The aviation fatal accident rate may thus be expressed in the same units as the death or cardiovascular event rate of the pilot(s) flying them. Initially Tunstall-Pedoe referred to the latter as the "cardiovascular crash rate" of pilots which was felt to be too emotive. At the time of the First Workshop the annual cardiovascular mortality of a sixty-five-year-old man was approximately 1% or, one in one million ($1/100 \times 1/10,000$) hours. Since that time male cardiovascular mortality has fallen 40% in the UK.

The 1% rule was predicated on the prevailing cardiovascular mortality of a Western male of 1% per annum at age sixty-five years; this defined the fitness cut-off point, no matter what the somatic age. Insurance actuaries express risk in 'added years' – increased life risk can be expressed in years added to the somatic age. The propositus may bear the risk of one perhaps several years older. The 1% rule is predicated on cardiovascular mortality, not the non-fatal co-morbid event rate: the two tend to be confused. Around every coronary death will be clustered three or four non-fatal co-morbid events, such as new angina pectoris, or myocardial infarction (heart attack). Screening of the pilot population will have removed – by a regulatory 'unfit' assessment – some higher-risk pilots; also there will have been spontaneous events. In regulatory terms, the predicted cardiovascular death rate thus approximates the cardiovascular incapacitation rate. The 1% rule is only one of several means of defining regulatory decision points. It is calculated thus:

There are c. 10,000 hours in a year (1×10^4 – see above). If the death/incapacitation rate of a pilot is 1% (1 in 10^2) during this time, with 10% (1 in 10^1) of the flight envelope being critical (take-off, departure, approach, landing, go-around), and from simulator data we know that training of the second pilot reduces the critical phase accident rate from incapacitation to <1% (1×10^2), then the aggregate risk of a cardiological cause accident should be of the order of 1×10^9 hours (1 in 10^4 x 1 in 10^2 x 1 in 10^1 x 1 in 10^2) – consistent with the industry standard for a very remote event.

There are limitations. The 1% rule works best when applied to coronary artery disease, where there is a massive database. It is not helpful in more capricious conditions such as atrial fibrillation (irregularity of the heart), although the stroke risk in atrial fibrillation may be predicted. It is not helpful, except as a principle, where the database is thin or non-existent. In that case gestalt judgement has to be applied which is based on clinical experience, and knowledge of the conditions under which aircrew undertake their duties. At the time the 1% rule was proposed, the sector time averaged one hour and the critical phase of the flight was of the order of 10% of it. Mean sector time is now between one hundred minutes and two hours and the increased sophistication of aircraft has reduced the critical phase of flight to perhaps 5% of the flight time in larger, but not in smaller aircraft. Dr Stuart Mitchell (now Deputy CMO of the CAA) and Dr Anthony Evans (now Chief of Medicine, ICAO) suggested that as a result there could be relaxation, proposing a 2% rule, although it should be recalled that most hazardous operations (turboprop) have the shortest sector times, the greatest vulnerability and often the least experienced pilots.

One question pitched at specialists by the regulator is "Is the risk of incapacitation in this individual <1% per annum?" The answer frequently comes back in the affirmative but without supporting data. This is speculative. The appropriate question is "What is the annual risk of an event in this condition? What are the consequences and what is the substantiating evidence?" For the 1% (or 2%) rule to operate there has to be adequate outcome data to support it, extending for five years or more. In uncommon conditions such as the ion channelopathies – inherited abnormalities of heart muscle metabolism associated with an increased risk of sudden cardiac death (SCD) – the data are accruing, but still scarce; trends have to be interpreted. In such circumstances the opinion of the bald-headed man at the back of the (Clapham) omnibus has to be consulted. It was he, Walter Bagehot (1826–1877; Master's degree in moral philosophy from UCL in 1846, editor of the *Economist* from 1860 until his death in 1877; author of *The English Constitution*) suggested reflected public opinion. He may also be found on the Bondi tram if you happen to be in contention in Sydney, Australia. The reasonable man should have specialist knowledge of both cardiology and the conditions under which aircrew undertake their duties. A scarce commodity.

The First UK Workshop struck a chord internationally and, as related, several states followed the example. Although never officially adopted, the 1% rule is discussed in the ICAO Manual of Civil Aviation Medicine and became a touchstone, sometimes over-applied, either on account of inadequate data or capriciousness of the conditions under consideration. When Jon Jordan, Federal Air Surgeon in the USA, attended the Second European Workshop in 1998, he expressed surprise at the mathematical modelling of risk used in fitness judgement in the UK. But he was speaking with access to the vastly greater operational base that the USA possessed. At that time more than half of the annual world total of flying hours each year was accrued by the USA and it could justify decisions based on field experience which the individual European nations could not muster.

SPECIFIC ISSUES
IN REGULATORY
CARDIOLOGY

A good head and a good heart are always a formidable combination.

Nelson Mandela (1918–2013)
Long Walk to Freedom, 1995

It is beyond the scope of this book to consider in any detail the multitude of cardiovascular conditions which have been considered by the regulator. Those who are interested could consult the cardiovascular chapter in Ernsting's *Textbook of Aviation Medicine* (fourth edition, CRC Press 2006), *Evidence-based Medicine* (third edition, Wiley-Blackwell 2010) or the cardiovascular chapter in the *ICAO Medical Manual* (www.icao.int/publications/documents/8984cons_en.pdf; 2012), all were written by the author. Nevertheless a glance at three problem areas will help illuminate the differences and difficulties existing in regulatory decision-making. The first and commonest of these is high blood pressure (hypertension), covering aspects of health maintenance, whilst the last two are the commonest cardiological causes of licence loss – coronary artery disease and rhythm and conduction disturbance, with atrial fibrillation being representative.

In the UK overall, the prevalence of hypertension (>140/90 mmHg or on treatment for hypertension) in those aged sixteen years or older is of the order of 30%, with a slight preponderance of men. Blood pressure increases with age, and vascular risk increases with it. A large meta-analysis involving some sixty-one studies and over one million patients was published in the *Lancet* in 2002. It showed that the consequences of hypertension increase with every age decile. At every level of pressure, whether systolic or diastolic, there was no level below which the risk of death from stroke or ischaemic heart disease was not lower. No amount of blarney or wishful thinking removes this ineluctable fact. Risk of a vascular event is also multiplied by co-existing risk factors, when present, such as diabetes, high blood cholesterol and smoking. Such data, per se, do not imply that treating hypertension will diminish or remove the risk but innumerable clinical intervention trials have confirmed this, and demonstrated the benefits of multiple risk factor intervention strategies.

Looking back over the thirty years since the First Workshop, it is striking how cardiological practice and the attitudes to treatment have changed; hypertension is such an example. The view at that time was that high blood pressure was a common age-related phenomenon and higher values were better tolerated as age increased. This was counter-intuitive: age does not protect, it exacerbates. The best treatment outcomes are to be expected in older age groups due to their higher cardiovascular event rates.

Intervention points for the treatment of high blood pressure recommended for aircrew by the First Workshop were 145/90 mmHg age <39 years, 155/95 mmHg age 40–49 years and 160/100 mmHg >50 years. By today's standards the last two levels are excessive, <140 mmHg being the current systolic blood pressure target recommended by the European Society for Cardiology (ESC)/European Society for Hypertension (ESH), unless diabetes is present when the target is lower. Today such levels, without satisfactory treatment, should deny a licence. Treatment was cautiously adopted initially until the CAA had gained further experience; now almost all the different therapeutic groups are permissible as there has been a sea-change in their side-effect profiles. The earlier agents were intolerable to some. Angiotensin converting enzyme inhibitors (ACEI), angiotensin receptor blocking (ARB) agents and slow channel calcium blocking (CCB) agents are accepted. Risk stratification – predicting the probability of a cardiovascular event over a defined period in a symptom-free individual – should *not* deny certification to fly. It may justify restriction of licence privileges to OML status unless there has been further investigation.

★ ★ ★

Coronary artery disease predicts coronary events as Philip Poole-Wilson had stated in the First Workshop; management can be medical, surgical or by percutaneous coronary intervention (PCI) – angioplasty/stenting. Amongst the numerous topics discussed in the workshops, each one devoted time to coronary disease on account of its prevalence, albeit declining in the Western world. It is an area which has seen remarkable investigational, pharmacological and interventional advances. It is also one which illustrates the difficulties the regulator experiences when specialists do not practise the evidence-based medicine they espouse.

There are two main coronary arteries which supply the heart muscle (the myocardium); the branches were described in Chapter 11. The origin of coronary artery disease may be seen in the third decade of life and beyond, and remain occult for many years. It is characterised initially by micro-injury to the endothelial lining of the vessels. This trivial injury slowly progresses to atheroma, a cheesy, often calcified material which increasingly obstructs them. These areas may be localised and are known as plaques. They are metabolically active and can remain stable for long periods. The plaque has a fibrous cap which, if it thins, will fissure and release tissue active substances. These products promote exuberant clotting which may partially, or completely, obstruct the vessel.

If the vessel is obstructed, its territory of supply, being discrete and without overlap, may be associated with death of tissue beyond – myocardial infarction or heart attack. As the blood supply is interrupted to a segment of muscle, it stiffens and loses contractile function. If the segment is sufficiently large, the heart will be unable to function as a pump – heart failure. Or the prejudiced segment of the muscle may support the emergence of potentially lethal rhythm disturbances – ventricular tachycardia/fibrillation, when the rate is so high that the output of the heart falls to zero. In that case the subject is unconscious in ten seconds, and, in the absence of resuscitation, brain dead in three minutes. Something to be avoided on the flight deck, from the point of view of all concerned.

These events can occur with alarming rapidity – 50% of those who die unattended within the first twenty-eight days after the onset of initial symptoms are dead within fifteen minutes, 60% within one hour and 70% within four hours. Nearly two fifths of unattended new myocardial infarctions are fatal and in one sixth there is no recognisable warning – the first presentation is sudden cardiac death (SCD). Sudden death is not the only presentation of coronary artery disease: two fifths each will present with a non-fatal heart attack, or with angina; the remainder with unstable angina. Incomplete obstruction may result in restricted flow of blood to the (exercising) heart muscle – expressed as chest pain – angina pectoris. This may be unstable if there has been recent change due to a non-obstructing clot in the vessel. Maybe this was the case with Captain Key in *Papa India*. Any symptoms related to the heart in a pilot result in loss of flying status.

The regulator is not concerned with the management of the acute disease, but with its outcome following management. The task requires risk stratification of the survivors with, by requirement, asymptomatic disease. This involves reviewing the anatomy and/or function of the coronary circulation. Initially the best evidence was obtained by coronary angiography, a technique which involves the introduction of a radio-opaque dye into the coronary circulation via a small tube (catheter). This demonstrates the coronary artery anatomy. It is not risk-free – there can be damage to the entry vessel, to the coronary vessel (which may provoke a heart attack), and very rarely (<1/3,000) death. The radiation dosage is also significant and of the order of 12–18 mSv (milliSieverts). For comparative purposes the radiation dosage received during a chest X-ray is 0.02 mSv, close to that received in a round trip by air from London to New York. Newer image intensification techniques and digitisation have lowered this burden, but there is increasing concern about lifetime exposure, the objective being to keep it as low as is achievable.

Exercise electrocardiography has some predictive (of outcome) value in the presence of known pre- or post-interventional coronary artery disease. Other techniques, including stress myocardial perfusion imaging (MPI), have greater predictive accuracy. This technique carries a radiation burden similar to angiography, but uses an isotope (often of thallium) to demonstrate perfusion of the myocardium, behaving, as it does, like potassium. Until recently, less popular in the UK, was pharmacological stress echocardiography which uses ultrasonic imaging of the heart before and during provocation with an adrenalin-like drug, dopamine, or an analogue. It has the benefit of being radiation-free. The mass of (symptom-free) outcome data in the coronary syndromes, with and without intervention, enables those with a predicted mortality/major event rate <1% per annum to be considered for certification to fly as or with co-pilot.

At one Joint Aviation Authorities meeting in Neuilly-sur-Seine, Paris in 1999, the prevailing UK attitude to recertification following coronary artery bypass surgery was considered. This was in the light of the Workshop recommendation that follow-up angiography was necessary to prove the absence of graft attrition. The French, led by Médecin-Général Dr Robert Auffret, felt that this further interference was unacceptable. There was deadlock followed by a long lunch, followed by agreement, only for it to be turned over by the French subsequently. With hindsight the French were correct, but in the context of the emergence of outcome evidence from radio-nuclear and exercise electrocardiographic techniques; both anatomical and functional data are predictive of outcome.

If the 'burden' of obstructive coronary disease is sufficient, without defining what that may be, revascularisation may be considered, the choice lying between surgery and balloon angioplasty/stenting. Andreas Gruntzig (1939–1985) was a Swiss cardiologist who carried out the first angioplasty on a live patient in Zürich in 1977, later developing the technique at Emory University in the USA. A true pioneer, he was an instrument-rated pilot who died in poor weather in his Beechcraft Baron – known in the US as the doctor's widow-maker – in October 1985. The technique has evolved from plain old balloon angioplasty (POBA) to the deployment of a small deformable wire basket, or stent, on the balloon; it is left in situ. Newer stents may be impregnated with agents aimed at prolonging the patency of the vessel.

Each new advance seems to have failed to fulfil the hope invested in it. Coronary artery stenting is often the treatment of choice in the management of stable coronary artery disease in spite of several robust randomised trials having failed to show that it is superior to medical therapy in terms of outcome. It is a little better at reducing symptoms. It is inferior to bypass surgery in terms of event-free survival. A high major adverse cardiac event (MACE) rate >50% over the study period was seen in one recent seven-year study following stenting and this has been reproduced elsewhere. It can be argued that additional investigation (e.g. with radio-nuclear studies) can identify the best risk subset to permit certification. Some balance has been restored by measurement of the fractional flow reserve (FFR) – a derivative of the pressure drop across an obstructive lesion – which reflects its severity. This is measured by an intra-coronary pressure transducer. The technique has been shown to reduce the rate of death, or myocardial infarction, when used to guide the use of angioplasty; maybe by deterring its use. Long-term outcome data are still scant. Surgical trials have demonstrated enhanced event-free survival with an annual event rate one third of that following angioplasty – new symptoms, further investigation/intervention, or heart attack. So why is coronary angioplasty/stenting permitted in aircrew?

★ ★ ★

Symptomatic disturbance of the rhythm of the heart is common and potentially licence-threatening; atrial fibrillation is one of the commonest. A former, rather poetic, term was 'delirium cordis', describing a generally fast and chaotic rhythm of the heart. Its prevalence rises sharply with age, being rare (0.4% of the population) below the age of sixty years. It can occur in the normal heart, for example following vomiting, after which sinus (regular) rhythm should restore itself within an hour or two. It may occur without provocation, be paroxysmal (intermittent and self-limiting), persistent (remain until steps are taken to restore regular rhythm) or permanent. The patient may be completely unaware, mildly aware or seriously disturbed by its occurrence. It may be lone – no identifiable cause, although a genetic predisposition has been identified, toxic – e.g. secondary to alcohol abuse or thyroid disease, or secondary to hypertension, heart muscle disease, coronary or valvular heart disease.

In general terms only those with an otherwise normal heart, a single episode with a defined provocation, and lone atrial fibrillation are likely to be considered for recertification. Certification will demand freedom from symptoms, in or out of an attack. Whereas anyone who has experienced the abrupt onset of fast atrial fibrillation will attest how distracting an episode might be during a critical task, there are those who switch rhythm several times a day without being aware of it. One pilot described to me the abrupt onset of symptoms secondary to fast atrial fibrillation late on a difficult instrument approach when he was the Pilot Flying. At the time they were below decision height and committed to landing, which he accomplished without incident. "What else could I do?" he replied, when I questioned him about the event. The situation would have been less favourable if it had occurred in bad weather with adverse terrain, co-pilot inexperience or serviceability issues. James Reason's cheese again.

Assuming normal structure and function of the left side of the heart – a prerequisite for recertification – atrial fibrillation carries a risk of embolic stroke which is up to five times standard, irrespective of whether the disturbance is paroxysmal or established. An embolus is a detached particle, in this case a blood clot, which traverses the circulation until it becomes lodged; when in the brain it is a cause of stroke. The risk is calculated using the CHA_2DS_2-VASc mnemonic which scores risk – relevant to aviation, age, female gender, hypertension and diabetes – the increased risk of stroke. It helps determine when an anticoagulant, rather than aspirin, which is not very effective, should be used to mitigate the increased risk. Only the lowest-risk subjects are permitted, with scores of 0–1.

Remarkably, in its published algorithm the CAA (2015) permits both warfarin and DOAs (direct acting oral anticoagulants) such as rivaroxaban, subject to certain requirements. Had the residual risk of stroke (30% uncovered by treatment) and the additional risk of haemorrhage (bleeding) including haemorrhagic stroke been considered, the generic risk, even in the most favourable circumstances, would have exceeded 2% per annum.

Although an individual pilot with impaired health may benefit if he/she is licenced to fly as/with co-pilot, colleagues may be less certain. A training captain suffered a cardiovascular collapse on a training/positioning leg in a BAC 111 some years ago. He subsequently recovered and landed the aircraft, which he damaged slightly. The captain should not have re-taken control having had it taken from him – a failure of crew performance. Notwithstanding, those on the flight deck pushed notes to each other wondering if he (the captain) should be allowed to proceed. Back at base his crew wrote to the CAA stating that if the Authority was going to license such manifestly unfit people, then it had a duty of care to warn their colleagues before each flight.

Interventional techniques in the management of atrial fibrillation include a surgical approach – the 'Maze' procedure, which wrecks the internal architecture of the left upper chamber (the atrium) and is usually only performed in the context of cardiac surgery. When I reviewed a patient who had undergone the procedure and was back in atrial fibrillation, the worthy cardiac surgeon involved said that it was impossible. You have to believe in what you do. Trans-arterial catheter ablation of triggering foci, often in the pulmonary veins, has some value in younger patients for a limited period, but evidence of prognostic benefit appears to be lacking – an intuitive glance at the architecture of the left atrial muscle would seem to make long-term benefit unlikely.

There is what we called 'polymorphic risk' in the Second European Workshop – the additional unrelated component of overall risk attributable to age alone. This should be considered in addition to the index problem. The 1% rule can be applied to the risk of thrombo-embolic event from the regulatory point of view, but the likelihood of the onset of an episode of atrial fibrillation cannot. Over the years the only pilots who have been declared fit with reasonable confidence are those who are permanently free of symptoms, with an annual combined risk from all-cause stroke is predicted to be <1–2% per annum. If the risk of stroke is such that warfarin is indicated, it is likely to be too high to pilot an aircraft.

The regulator should be prepared to seek specialist advice, draw the line and resist pressure to issue a fitness certificate if the evidence, or lack of it, does not support a demonstrably safe judgement. That is questionable in the case of atrial fibrillation under the EASA requirements.

MAINLY FLYING

Oh, I have slipped the surly bonds of earth,
And danced the skies on laughter-silvered wings;
Sunwards I've climbed and joined the tumbling mirth
Of sun-split clouds – and done a thousand things
You have not dreamed of…

John Maggee (1922–1941)
A US citizen flying with 412 Squadron, RCAF;
killed in a mid-air collision near Digby on
11th December 1941 aged nineteen years

By the time I arrived in Surrey in 1975 I had learnt to fly on a DH Tiger Moth and had accumulated a further 150 hours on various aircraft. The group based on the Piper PA28R/180 Arrow was still functioning but, situated as it was at Elstree, Hertfordshire, the aircraft was not well placed for casual trips. One of the first people I was to meet became a friend; a local general practitioner colleague, Dr Patrick Schofield. Patrick had trained as a pathologist at St Mary's Hospital, Paddington (good at rugby) but decided to move into general practice in Walton-on-Thames. His passion was flying and he later published an article in the *Journal of the Royal Aeronautical Society*, *Why Do I Fly?* His conclusions were diffuse. He introduced me to a group, based on a Tiger Moth, at Fairoaks Airport where I had gained my PPL in the summer of 1958. Its registration was G-BALX and the build year 1939. It was owned by John Burningham, who, for a contribution towards the maintenance costs, allowed one to fly it for the price of the fuel.

The Tiger Moth is not difficult to fly, but not easy to fly well. The modern light aircraft with a tricycle undercarriage is directionally more stable on the ground, but a student has nothing with which to compare. The Gypsy engine has to be started by hand-swinging the propeller. In those days there were still ground crew around who knew how to do this safely. It requires discipline and co-operation, with the use of adequate chocks and magneto switch procedure. On one occasion I saw someone come within a hair's breadth of having their head cut off when he walked back into the propeller arc, just as the engine unexpectedly started on recoil. There are no brakes and no ailerons on the upper wings. The tail and rudder are rather small, with back-pressure on the stick and rudder input needed to counteract adverse yaw – the tendency for yaw in the opposite direction of the turn, in spite of aileron design to minimise this.

Stopping on the ground relies on the tail skid digging into the grass, which airport managers dislike. They dislike most things, apart from hefty landing fees. Pilots trained on modern tricycle undercarriage machinery are often apprehensive of tail-draggers, but in reality, it is simple to keep the aircraft straight with the rudder whilst raising the tail wheel off the ground, slowly, to reduce the angle of attack. The habit of involuntary stick back in the turn to counteract slip used to haunt my instrument flying when the going got tricky – aeronautical atavism.

In the event I did not do much flying on the aircraft – its range is limited to less than three hours at 80 mph and there is the problem of hand-swinging the propeller away from base. We did go to Bembridge, on the Isle of Wight, for a fly-in on one occasion and took part in a spot landing competition. I was useless, not wishing to cause damage. Flour bombing was equally useless and the bags of McDougall's self-raising fell well wide of the target, whilst attempting to emulate a Sopwith Camel at the Battle of Arras. Being older and wiser I did not throw the aircraft around the sky as during flying scholarship days. Then I had thought nothing of pulling a maximum rate turn with full power; then full stick back followed by an abrupt cut of the power. Application of top rudder at this point would cause a stall and flick the aircraft over into a spin. And that was without anti-spin strakes, although these were fitted to John Burningham's aircraft.

G-BALX flew away one day and the next time it came to notice was when it landed on its nose at a private airfield near Battle in Kent. Then on 19th April 1998 it vanished forever, along with the pilot, never to be seen again. Roger Fiennes had flown from Headcorn (Kent) to Dieppe, France, landing at 12.04 hours. He filed a Flight Plan with the Lille Air Traffic Control Centre (ATCC), but this was never activated and the Control Tower at Dieppe was closed. At 14.42 hours Paris North Flight Information Service (FIS) received a call from an aircraft with the correct call sign…

"G-BALX en route from Dieppe to Headcorn, off the French Coast, heading 350, VFR [Visual Flight Rules] estimating mid-channel – the Paris Flight Information Region [FIR] boundary is close to the French coast – at [15].17."

"Paris FIS do not provide traffic information, only general information on request: you can maintain this frequency."

There was no request by the pilot to activate the flight plan and the FIS did not ask if this was required. There was no further visual, radio or radar contact with the aircraft and no wreckage was ever found. The weather was good at the time and well within the limits for such an aircraft, which had only limited instruments. There were no known serviceability issues. The outbound leg had been flown at 1,500 feet over the channel and the aircraft had not been seen on the D&D (distress and diversion) radar at West Drayton as it was too low. There was a presumption that a similar altitude, or lower, was used on the return journey, though apparently not declared.

For an international flight (which crosses the FIR boundary) a flight plan must be filed with the Air Traffic Service Unit (ATSU) at the field of departure. In this case it would have been under VFR (Visual Flight Rules). The departure point ATSU will file a departure message which activates the flight plan. The destination airfield receives the details, including the estimated time of arrival (ETA). On arrival the flight plan is closed; if there is no arrival within thirty minutes of the ETA, overdue action is taken which may activate

SARO (search and rescue operations). But the departure airfield was closed and activation of the return flight plan was never requested of Lille ATCC, or anyone else. There were many conspiracy theories; we shall probably never know what happened. It was odd that there was no wreckage found in what are very busy shipping lanes, and the Tiger Moth is made of light material. Finally, at the time the weather had been good.

But strange things happen. On February 10th 1985, a Cessna F172N G-BFOW was believed to have crashed into the sea 13.3 nautical miles northwest of Alderney. It had been on a flight from Shoreham to Jersey, Channel Islands, with an experienced professional pilot in command. A Mayday call had been declared at 15.54 hours, following an earlier call that there was an unspecified engine problem during the descent. The Mayday call said that the engine had cut out and that ditching was imminent some twelve miles north of Alderney. Jersey ATCC was requested by the pilot to call a Shoreham number. Contact was lost but the aircraft was seen on radar to be tracking west for ten miles followed by a turn to the east, where it vanished. A full air and sea search revealed nothing. Thirteen months later the engine of the aircraft was recovered from the seabed twelve nautical miles south of Swanage. Its main data plate was missing, apparently having been removed, the rivet holes being void. There was possible evidence of a malfunction on one cylinder. It was felt that it was unlikely that the engine had migrated, by way of tidal action, forty miles, the distance involved between the believed point of ditching and the point at which the engine was recovered.

★ ★ ★

The flying group based on the Piper PA28R/180 Arrow stayed together for nearly four years, until the summer of 1978. I gained some 150 P1 hours in it. Built in 1968, it was based at Elstree in Hertfordshire. In the social hierarchy of private aviation, a start is usually made with a simple two- or four-seat aircraft, with subsequent progression to a more complex machine, then a twin, and finally in the ultimate display of tertiary sexual characteristics, to a pressurised twin with round windows. Although a light aircraft, the Piper Arrow has a variable pitch/constant speed (CS) propeller and a retractable undercarriage. These seemingly minor additions to the uninitiated are of limited value. The undercarriage trunnions wear and occasionally the forgetful omit to drop the gear on the down wing leg of the circuit. This results in being surrounded by tall firemen on the runway and derision in the clubhouse.

I once watched a wheels-up landing at Popham airfield, alongside the A303 (itself a reason for owning an aeroplane if you live in the west of England). What was noteworthy was the divergence between the accident report and the events I thought I witnessed. The Piper Aircraft Corporation sought to avoid such events by fitting a second Pitot sensor on the left-hand side of the fuselage. This causes the landing gear to drop if the warning horn fails, or has been ignored. Not a bad idea, but one does not always want the wheels doing their own thing when flying slowly, even if it can be overridden. For all the complexity and expense of the CSU and retractable gear, the gain in cruise speed was only a few knots above the fixed gear PA28R/180.

Mainly details were flown round the south of England, with lunches at the restaurant on the field at Le Touquet at the weekend. It was less than an hour away. Customs regulations were more onerous at the time, clearance having to be sought at a designated aerodrome, which was time-consuming. There was not much in the way of foreign adventure apart from a trip to Holland for the European Society of Cardiology in 1976 – at that time held every fourth year. How different now: an annual event with over 30,000 delegates and many subsidiary working groups and workshops. It was held in Amsterdam, but we landed in Rotterdam because the landing fee was lower. We went on by train.

We stayed at the Grand Hotel Krasnapolsky, again having forgotten to book a cheaper facility. It is on the edge of the famous red light district which, surprisingly, was ignored in favour of Our Lord in the Attic. This implausible name, redolent of some memento from a forgotten visit to the Vatican, belongs to a Catholic church which was concealed in a private house; it is now a museum. It is decorated in the Dutch classical style with marble columns and gilded capitals. There is a painting of the Baptism of Christ (1716) by Jacob de Wit and stucco sculptures of the Trinity over the altar. Perhaps the ladies who sit naked in the shop windows behind end up there when they have put their clothes back on. Catholicism was made illegal in Amsterdam in 1578 when Protestantism was in the ascendant, but Catholic worship was permitted in private; how sensible, and so much more civilised than shooting each other in the back as occurs in other religious constituencies.

Several trips were made to Plymouth, Roborough, near where Mandy's parents lived. The airfield had been opened by the then-Prince of Wales in 1925 (later King Edward VIII), and was closed in December 2011. The prevailing wind is from the southwest and as a result moist, saturated air tends to form cloud as it ascends over the field. Luckily Exeter, where I made more than one weather-related diversion, experiences a Föhn effect and is generally clear and warmer. This is due to dry air adiabatic warming as it descends. An adiabatic process occurs without loss or gain of heat between a system and its surroundings.

A major project intended for the aircraft was my instrument rating (I/R), which ended in initial disappointment as already related. Due to the frailty of the Bendix VOR (VHF omnidirectional range) receivers in the presence of the new Doppler VOR beacons, the aircraft was not really suitable for instrument flying. As a result, and coupled with the difficulties of getting to Elstree, it was decided to go it alone and purchase another aeroplane. This was to be a Grumman Tiger AA5B G-BDYB, aka *Yogi Bear*.

The Grumman American AA1 Yankee was a small sport aircraft with a reputation for being a bit dicey near the stall, with a tricky spinning characteristic. After three turns, recovery was not always possible. This was bad form and the early models had a poor accident record. It was developed into the Grumman Cheetah and Tiger models, the difference being that the former was fitted with the 150 HP Lycoming O-320-E2G engine, whilst the latter had the O-360-A4K 180 HP variant. The fuselage was fabricated from a honeycomb metal sandwich which gave the impression of sitting inside a biscuit box onto which two wings had been stuck. The canopy afforded good all-round visibility. The metal surfaces were glued rather than riveted, which made it 'slippery' and difficult to slow down. Tail strakes had been fitted to discourage adverse spin characteristics; spinning, in any event, was banned. It was quite strong and was cleared for $+4g$ to $-2g$ (G being the accelerative force in multiples of g – the force of gravity), depending on load.

It needed a knack to land it gently and on one occasion my then-fiancée, Susanna, pulled back a bit hard during the round-out on landing at Compton Abbas for lunch. The resulting tail strike collected a decent clod of earth, some grass and a cheesed-off earthworm on the rear tie down ring. The undercarriage resembled a transversally mounted fibreglass ski, which being un-damped, could lead to a bit of a waltz on a grass field if the angle of attack was insufficient and the centre of pressure too far back. The castering nose wheel was held on by a piece of bent tube. If it touched down before the main wheels (strongly discouraged, although I did see it happen to a Fokker F27 at Jersey) the result is a balletic trajectory reminiscent of the owl in the final scene of Act 4 of *Swan Lake*. The aeroplane was kept for about two years and completed some one hundred hours without drama, but being somewhat close-coupled (short in the fuselage) it was not a good instrument platform either.

The Grumman Tiger made way for a Piper Arrow II PA28R/200 G-BDXW, a very similar plane to the group aircraft, but with the much-needed extra power from the 200 HP Lycoming IO-360-C1C engine. There were also five inches of extra legroom in the back, although I do not recall sitting there. In every other respect it was similar to the earlier aircraft and was docile in its handling characteristics. Once again there was a radio upgrade which included a King KNS80, which was able to set up virtual waypoints using the VOR/DME beacons; this was not permitted under IFR rules. It had mechanical flaps and apart from the undercarriage, gave no cause for concern. On one occasion my mother asked for a trip, but not being air-minded was unable to cope with banked turns. We skidded our way round Surrey like Jeremy Clarkson at Dunsfold aerodrome. When I put the gear lever down we had only two green lights instead of the customary three (nose wheel and two main wheels). She did not notice. With furtive recycling there was no change but fortunately a poke at the miscreant lens made it gleam insolently again.

Micro-switches behave like small children in that you never know what is going to happen next. Following a nose wheel warning on the Piper PA31 Navajo years later, my companion pilot expressed surprise when I returned to Fairoaks from Southampton with the gear down (we had obtained three green lights on recycling). The rationale is that if the gear goes safely down, leave it alone; bringing it up may cause it to jam if there is an underlying mechanical problem. On another occasion whilst departing Kennedy on the flight deck of Concorde, the gear-in-transit light refused to go out. Recycling the gear did the trick; just like any other aeroplane.

A number of foreign details were flown in the Arrow including one to a meeting in Nancy, France when there was an aviation strike in the UK. Dr Raphael Balcon, a distinguished cardiological colleague, was anxious to get back to his (private) patients and sat in the back looking apprehensive as we muddled our way back to the UK through the clag, on instruments. Although I flew over two hundred hours in it as pilot in command there were not many epic trips. One day, having taxied in and shut down the engine I was aware of someone prowling around like a host of Midian. He was still prowling after I had had a cup of tea.

"Is this your aircraft?" he asked. "Ever think of selling it?" he wondered. "I might be interested."

I was already looking at the purchase of a Beechcraft Baron, and this was Peter Teichman. So we went for an extended demonstration flight, his only disappointment being that I would not let him fly in the left-hand seat – I was not an instructor and had no idea what sort of a pilot he was. I need not have worried; he is an extremely good one. He had started flying in 1979 and purchased G-BDXW in August 1984. He sold it to buy the Beechcraft Baron G-SUZI from me four years later, when I upgraded to the Cessna 340 IIA G-LIZA. He kept G-SUZI for fifteen years and even considered the purchase of G-LIZA later on, finally selling the Baron in 2004. At the time of writing he has logged some 11,000 flights in eight thousand flying hours, two thousand of them on warbirds.

The Hangar 11 collection is based at the old Battle of Britain RAF station at North Weald; it was put together by Peter. It is remarkable, comprising four aircraft including the only airworthy example of a Supermarine Spitfire Mk XI. This aircraft flew forty sorties over occupied Europe with 16 Squadron, RAF, during 1944 and 1945. It is the subject of a book, *Spitfire in Blue*. Strafed by a Messerschmitt Me 262 'Schwalbe' (the world's first operational fighter jet-powered aircraft), flown by the Luftwaffe in 1945, it has only flown five hundred hours in total. The Hawker Hurricane Mk

IIB flies in the colours of 174 Squadron, RAF. The North American P-51D Mustang served with the US 332nd Fighter Group in Italy during 1945. Finally the Curtiss P-40M Kittyhawk was manufactured in October 1943 and flew with a number of Royal Canadian Air Force (RCAF) squadrons. Peter maintains and demonstrates these formidable aircraft all over Europe, making a significant contribution to our aviation heritage. He demonstrated the Spitfire at my garden party in the summer of 2011 at Brooklands Museum when I was High Sheriff of Surrey. Peter Vacher's Hurricane I, R4418, and the only Battle of Britain Hurricane still flying, gave a splendid display, too. (See photo plates 29 and 30.)

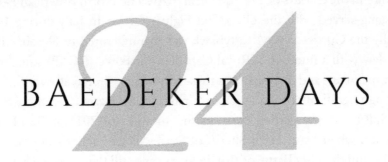

BAEDEKER DAYS

I've topped the windswept heights with easy grace
Where never lark, or even eagle flew –
And, while with silent lifting mind I've trod
The high un-trespassed sanctity of space,
Put out my hand and touched the face of God.

John Maggee (1922–1941), ibid.

The first long trip in the Beechcraft G-SUZI was to Genoa for the Junior Cardiac Society meeting in May 1985; it was held somewhere near Santa Margherita Ligure. The participants included cardiologists in training, mainly in London, and some invited speakers which included myself. The trip out was above cloud and building cumulus clouds became evident as we went further south. These were faithfully marked by the Stormscope, a device for identifying the bearing and approximate range of convective wind shear. This was suggestive of thunderstorm activity, which was avoided. Over the south of France we picked up airframe ice, always to be given a wide berth in a light aircraft, even if, as was the case with the Baron, the aircraft was cleared to fly in known icing conditions.

Due to the high ground to the north it was not possible to descend in the airway and the choice was whether to ask permission to leave it, descending to the south outside controlled airspace, or to continue as planned, when cleared. In the event we continued with diminishing reserves of isopropyl alcohol which de-iced both the propellers and the wind shield, the latter being less important whilst in the cruise. Ice accumulating on the propeller makes itself known by vibration followed by spooky white flashes which bump as a lump is thrown off and hits the airframe. When we were cleared to descend the ice sublimated (evaporated without passing through an aqueous phase) and we landed in Genoa uneventfully.

★ ★ ★

I only got into serious icing conditions on two or three occasions. A light aircraft cleared for flight into known icing such as the Beechcraft Baron should never be flown intentionally in such conditions. Its wing is more prone to contamination in comparison with the swept wing of the big jets and there are a lot of non-de-iced parts of the airframe. The big jets have hot bleed air to the leading edges rather than puncture-prone pneumatic boots, such as are fitted to some light aircraft. They were also fitted to the British Aerospace ATP, aka 'Another Technical Problem'. As a derivative of the successful HS 748, it was not so good and only sixty-four were built, of which two were lost in fatal accidents abroad. They had not been on the UK register at the time. There were two reports of stalls whilst on revenue flights in the UK due to mismanagement of airframe icing, fortunately followed by successful recovery. It can be done (see AF 447; Chapter 16).

On one occasion in March 1988, I was attending a council meeting of the British Cardiac Society in Belfast. It was the day after the IRA murder of two off-duty soldiers who had blundered into a funeral cortege. The tension was palpable. There were two military checkpoints to get into our hotel and a stationary army helicopter above it, hour after hour. One had been glad of the shroud of low cloud hanging over the city, but on the descent we passed through a wet, freezing layer. It is surprising how quickly ice can accumulate, although with pitch-down the effect is less serious. In the climb, the nose-up attitude of the airframe causes unseen accretion of ice on the ventral surfaces, adding to weight and aerodynamic drag. This has been the cause of a number of air taxi hull losses, mainly in North America.

Apart from the trip to Genoa, the other occasion troubled by icing was on a trip to Prestwick to sell the Cessna, which was no keener to go than I was to lose it. On the climb to join the airway out of Fairoaks, the pressurisation door-seal failed and started to squeal. We depressurised and the flight was conducted at Flight Level (FL) 105 (10,500 feet on the standard pressure setting of 1013.25 mb) rather than the planned level of FL 145. We flew through an occluded front, noticed by my son David, who pointed out the large icicles on every non-de-iced surface of the aircraft. Refusal of permission to descend, or turn towards one of the MATZ (Military Air Traffic Zones), resulted in consideration of a PAN (urgency) call as the air speed was declining alarmingly. Advised that descent would be cleared in five minutes I lowered the nose to reduce the angle of attack. At the point at which, had I continued, there would have been an altitude bust, I was given clearance to descend and simultaneously we broke out into bright sunshine between ebullient cumulus clouds. Once again the ice sublimated.

★ ★ ★

The return trip from Genoa was more troublesome. Having obtained start-up and taxi clearance, it was evident that the artificial horizon was taking a long time to erect – it is gyroscopically driven. As a Boeing 727 was stumping about scowling at us we let it play through whilst waiting for the instrument to sort itself. It appeared to be operating satisfactorily. On the climb-out we went into stratus (layer cloud) in which there were forecast embedded thunderstorms. The Stormscope confirmed this and we progressed back to the UK mainly on instruments, refuelling again, as on the outbound, at Clermont Ferrand. We did climb, unpressurised, to 14,000 feet at one point. At that time it was necessary to clear customs at Bournemouth, Hurn, by which time the weather had improved somewhat. As we landed at Fairoaks, the artificial horizon, which seemed to have been functioning quite well, if a bit slowly, toppled and stood on its ear. The engineers pulled it out the next day and sent it back to the facility where it had recently been overhauled. I telephoned and there was laughter at the other end – in reassembly the internal wiring loom had been allowed to drag on the gyroscope rotor, slowing it. If it had occurred whilst on instruments, leaving us on a limited panel with nearby Cbs, it would not have been a laughing matter.

The aircraft was given a new electronics (avionics) fit, re-sprayed blue-on-white using the original Beechcraft colour scheme – always best – and re-registered G-SUZI. As a finishing touch the logo of the European Society of Cardiology (ESC) was painted on the tail. This surprised the president, Professor Paul

Hugenholz, as we taxied in at Santiago de Compostela in northwest Spain to attend a working group meeting of the ESC. On this particular trip three others came for the ride, another of whom was also a pilot.

We flew direct from Fairoaks and the airways distance was towards the limit of our range. All went well until we were over the Bay of Biscay; it is larger than you think. For once the weather was fine although the goldfish bowl effect prevailed, with the sunlight over the shimmering blue water merged with the distant horizon; a cause of spatial disorientation in the untrained. As we and the autopilot slumbered on, the silence, apart from about two hundred or so horses galloping along on each side of us, was interrupted by an R/T (radiotelephony) call.

"Golf Sierra Uniform Zulu India, this is British Airways Speedbird 456: do you read? Over."

"Speedbird 456: Golf Zulu India is reading you fives [strength and readability 5/5]; go ahead."

"Golf Zulu India: Speedbird 456 is relaying a message from Madrid ATCC – you are heading towards an area of intense military activity around Santander. You are advised to alter course."

I'll say – we could do without getting into the sights of some gun-toting conquistador. A bearing was given. VHF communication is line of sight, more or less, and being non-pressurised we were at 10,000 feet, out of range of the Spanish ground relay transmitter. The British Airways aircraft at around 36,000 feet (FL 360) did not have this limitation.

"Golf-Zulu India to Speedbird 456: roger – there was no Notam [Notice to Airmen, an alert to pilots of potential hazards on a flight plan]?"

"Speedbird 456: that seems to have been the case. Listen out on [a frequency was given] and contact them when in range; good day."

"Golf Zulu India to Speedbird 456: thank you sir, good day and out."

This was unhelpful as we now had to take up a more southerly heading which might necessitate a refuelling stop. As we got nearer, we talked to the airways controller who told us that the military were at lunch but that we could proceed, own navigation, to Santiago. The world over, the military has lunch on weekdays and knocks off at 16.00 on Fridays for the weekend. By that time, the fuel was getting low but careful calculation based on power setting, fuel flow, fuel burn and the random thoughts of the fuel gauges allowed us to continue to our destination; provided there was to be no delay on arrival. Radioing ahead we were told that would be the case. We landed with thirty minutes of fuel reserve remaining, not enough for IFR reserve (forty-five minutes) but we were by then VFR.

On our return there again seemed to be ATC problems and another cardiological colleague hoped for a lift back to the UK. This time it was not possible as we had loaded full fuel and although we had two spare seats, we would have been outside our weight and balance envelope. As we neared the French coast there was a geography lesson. There was a south-westerly blowing, with the Bay of Biscay basking in a serene blue glow. This made for a moist westerly airstream over Belle-Île, west abeam St Nazaire and a turban of stratus cloud with associated rain on adiabatic cooling. An occupational hazard for an island in such a position. One wonders at its name, but that is France, as they say.

There were a number of long-distance trips in the Beechcraft including to Stockholm at the invitation of Dr Bengt Andræ, Chief Medical Officer of the Swedish Civil Aviation Authority. The trip was more arduous as there was a need for a refuelling stop at Copenhagen (Roskilde), although this was surprisingly quick and we were soon on our way again. By the time we got to Stockholm (Bromma), the main airport before Arlanda opened in 1983, it was dark and in the hope of expediting our arrival we accepted a visual approach. This was a mistake as the airfield was difficult to identify in the mass of lights, both real and reflected in the water between the many islands. We were the last movement that day and like everywhere else in the world, everyone apart from the customs people had gone home. After shutting down, they came over and insisted on pulling out every single item from the aircraft which was not screwed onto it. Remarkably there was a taxi, and even more remarkably, it took a credit card as we had no kronor. We eventually got to our assigned hotel, exhausted, to find that it was a temperance facility. No wonder the suicide rate there is one of the highest in the Western world.

The stay involved meetings and presentations. Dr Harald Eliasch, a fellow of the European Society of Cardiology, was their advising cardiologist. We visited the palace and the temporary museum (Vasavarvet) of the *Vasa*, but not the ABBA museum which did not open until 2013. The *Vasa* was a warship which sank in less than a mile on her maiden voyage in 1628, which must have disappointed King Gustav II Adolf. She now has a permanent home on Djurgården Island. The tragedy was said to be due to inadequate ballast – such issues are also important in aircraft as anyone who has flown an aircraft outside its weight and balance envelope (and survived) will agree. This is in contrast to the teaching hospitals where, routinely, too much ballast us carried.

She was salvaged in 1961, a decade before the *Mary Rose*, which sank at Portsmouth and was raised with the help of the present Prince of Wales. The *Vasa* is claimed to be the only preserved (95% original) 17th century ship in the world. The *Mary Rose* was been launched in 1522, the century before and capsized in the Solent in front of Henry VIII. She had seen service for thirty-three years and fought against the French and the Scots, both of whom were as difficult then as they have been since. Why she turned turtle in the Solent was never established with confidence, in spite of a public enquiry. Maybe there was an early cover-up; we are good at that in the UK.

The return journey to the United Kingdom was less eventful, apart from leaving my blouson in the restaurant at the refuelling stop in Esbjerg; an obliging *FOLLOW ME* van drove out to the runway and handed it over with the aircraft engines still running.

One of the longest trips made in the Beechcraft was to Vienna in 1988 for the ESC congress that year. We landed at Munich-Riem airport to refuel on the outbound leg. It was 30 degrees Centigrade and the airport is 450 metres above sea level, both conspiring, substantially, to degrade take-off performance at MTWA. The *FOLLOW ME* van led us out to the short eight hundred-metre runway and having copied the flight plan and completed the pre-take off checks, I called:

"Flughafen München Tower, Golf Zulu India is ready for departure."

"Golf Zulu India – would you prefer the main runway, sir?"

With experience one learns the ATC code. "What is your air speed, sir?" means "Buck up, you clown", just as "What is your passing altitude, sir?", when it can be read on the SSR (secondary surveillance radar) output, means "Expedite your descent." An invitation to take the main runway at that density altitude would save them having to call out the fire truck. There were no significant obstacles on the take-off track and I did not wish to be a nuisance. So, being familiar with the eight hundred metres of runway available at Fairoaks (albeit usually close to ISA (International Standard Atmosphere – 15 degrees Centigrade at sea level), I responded: "München Tower, Golf Zulu India, thank you sir, we can take the short runway." Wrong!

There was a pause. "Golf Zulu India, the *FOLLOW ME* van will escort you to the threshold of twenty-five left [the 2,800 metre runway] for departure when cleared."

We complied and took about half the main runway to become airborne. Sometimes the safety angel rides shotgun – this time in the form of the ATCO who knew more about the density altitude at his airfield than I did, in spite of expensive instrument training at Oxford. Never ignore advice from any source however qualified without considering it first.

We flew east along the border, with Czechoslovakia in the north. Ahead lay Hungary and Budapest, where my friend Dr Gábor Hardiscay used to greet me at meetings with a click of the heels, a bow and two very bristly kisses; similar to a collision with an outsize Brillo pad. It was a lovely day, the year before the fall of Communism in Eastern Europe. The iron curtain had been defined in a telegram sent by Winston Churchill to President Truman in May 1945. He later amplified it in March 1946, in his speech at Fulton, Missouri: "From Stettin in the Baltic to Trieste in the Adriatic, an iron curtain has descended across the Continent. Behind that line lie all the capitals of the ancient states of Central and Eastern Europe. Warsaw, Berlin, Prague, Vienna, Budapest, Belgrade, Bucharest and Sofia…"

It was peaceful in the countryside to the north, the violation of which by Germany in 1938 was dismissed by Neville Chamberlain as "a quarrel in a far-away country between people of whom we know nothing". It had fallen under Stalinist hegemony in 1948, part of the calamity of Soviet communism which cost twenty million lives in the 20th century in Eastern Europe and the USSR. About the same number were killed in the name of Communism by Mao Zedong in China, and yet Marxist apologists for two of the most brutal regimes that have afflicted mankind live and have influence amongst us. Usually their defence is on the basis of anti-fascism, fascism itself being a creed no more, or less, criminally repressive.

It was thundery in Vienna when we arrived and there was the usual round of meetings, lectures and dinners. There were evenings at the Schwarzenberg palace and the British Embassy – a magnificent building on der Jauresgasse with some excellent paintings and plentiful champagne. Vienna is worth a visit if you are a spy, or even if you are not, lying as it does as an outpost in the east of Europe. One can listen to zither music and eat *kuchen schokolade* in the cafes, or take a trip on the Wiener Riesenrad, the big wheel built by Walter Bassett (1864–1907), an Englishman. Through half-closed eyes one can picture the meeting between Holly Martins and Harry Lime in *The Third Man* – one of the greatest films ever made. It stands on the Prater, an amusement park.

Likewise, the best Wiener schnitzels in the world are to be found in the shadow of St Stephan's Cathedral, and the jolliest horses in the Spanish Riding School, where the Lipizzaners are trained in classical dressage. Some attend the ESC meeting and worry about cytosolic calcium or ventricular diastolic function. Once whilst in Vienna for a wedding I was asked to the New Year's Eve Opera Ball, but had to return to London that evening for an assignation, which is another story. Luton was the only non-icebound airfield open in the south of England that night and I scrounged a (free) lift on the flight deck of an Austrian charter airline DC9, upon which the passengers sang jolly drinking songs all the way back:

> *Schnaps, das war sein letztes Wort*
> *Dann trugen ihn die Englein fort*
> *Schnaps das war sein letztes Wort*

Dann trugen ihn die Englein fort
Und so kamer in den Himmel
Man hat ihm Milch serviert
Gegen diese arme Handlung
Hat der Lümmel protestiert

There was clapping and a cheer as the captain landed on the skating rink that was Luton that night.

On the day of our departure from Vienna there were thunderstorms to the north and east over the VOR beacon at Wagram, but we were not going that way. Taking up a westerly heading, the sky got darker and more threatening in spite of the invariably favourable weather forecast. Nevertheless the trusty Stormscope was only painting up strikes infrequently, suggesting little thunderstorm activity. No sane pilot goes near a thunderstorm, unless it is unavoidable. The up- and down-drafts experienced can be extremely violent and may destroy the airframe. Eventually we got permission from the airways controller to leave the frequency to interrogate a British Airways aircraft on the same airway high above us about the weather ahead. He had radar, but we did not. "Nothing for 160 miles that we can see," he said, breezily. "Cheerio…"

At that moment we collided with a solid wall of water which continued seemingly for 160 miles. This was the range of the Collins radar he was likely to have been using, and it could only be assumed that the angle of his antenna was set to look at the moon rather than down at our humble level. But all bad weather, like good things, comes to an end and eventually we emerged into brilliant sunshine, although it took some time to clear the frontal activity.

We landed at Liège to refuel only to encounter an almost tropical-size Cb which for reasons best known to itself was not poised over the outer marker radio beacon of the airfield. Notwithstanding, there was a hapless Boeing 727, presumably en route for Brussels, which was searching for a means of avoiding its penetration. It was the picture of a giant sunlit ice cream sundae with an ant crawling over it. Eventually the tower controller asked if we had radar, and could we give a bearing and range of the tempest from the field? Using the Stormscope, the bearing is accurate but the range depends upon a fudge factor applied to the electrical decay characteristics of the lightning strikes. England was bathed in rain-washed golden evening sunshine as we landed back at Fairoaks at 18.45.

One of the last excursions in the Beechcraft G-SUZI, before it was sold to Peter Teichman, was from Perranporth on the north coast of Cornwall. This ex-Royal Naval Air Service field now has a flying club, but at the time (1986) there was not much going on apart from some gliding. The runways were in poor condition and full of loose stone; bad news for the propellers. I had to sit on an appointments committee at St Thomas's Hospital in London and Len Battin flew the aircraft down to pick me up. Len was a quantity surveyor friend and an accomplished pilot. He owned a Piper twin Commanche PA30 which he kept at Fairoaks. We often flew together and once we had a photographic sortie, but the different speeds of the Beechcraft and the Piper Comanche led to a prolonged search for each other somewhere to the south of Farnborough. G-SUZI was eventually turned into an oil painting.

Not having the luxury of a windsock to indicate the wind direction, I took my shirt off and stood like Christopher Robin at the end of the active runway with it flapping in the stiff wind. Len circled twice, landed, taxied over and came to a halt without shutting down the engines. I climbed into the left-hand seat for the flight back and was completing the pre-take off checks when a private car came hurtling up the runway with lights flashing. It stopped in front of our nose. Two men jumped out and one drew his flattened palm across his throat – the signal to cut the engines.

"Shut down this aircraft at once," one of them yelled over the din.

"I will do no such thing," I shouted back through the storm window – the Continental engines were difficult to start when hot. "Anyway, who the hell are you?"

"We are HM Customs, who the hell are you?" they said, pulling themselves up to their full height which was well below the combing.

We explained that we had no narcotics, nor illegals, on board and were allowed to proceed. The disturbance provoked a human factor incident. I only just obtained clearance to cross the Brecon/Berry Head airway before we penetrated it on our VFR return flight to Fairoaks. It was romantically called Amber 25 in those days of wine and roses, perhaps after a glamorous spy. Now it is boringly named N864 – the EU has no style. That gave rise to a reproof by air traffic control: "Golf Zulu India: will you telephone Air Traffic on the following number on arrival…?"

Such events were fortunately rare. The ATCOs in the UK are the best in the world, but they did had a bad habit of dropping one out of Red 1 (no connection with W. E. Johns), when southbound at Daventry to proceed 'own navigation' to Fairoaks, south of the London Control Zone (LCZ). This meant traversing half a dozen MATZ (Military Air Traffic Zones – there was a military in those days) without radar advice, and the inevitable Cbs embedded in layer cloud. One ruse was to file a flight plan for Leavesden (then owned by Rolls-Royce) – it had a STAR (Standard Arrival) chart – and at the last minute cancel it for the alternative, Fairoaks. This used to go down rather badly – definitely not cricket, it was felt by the ATCC in their bunker at West Drayton. On one occasion I was just to the south of the LCZ when the (female) low-level radar operator (London Director on 119.9 mHz) gave a non-standard response to my call for radar advice: "Didn't we meet in a restaurant in Val d' Isère?" She must have known the registration number of the aircraft.

Sometimes a telephone number is more fun than a radar separation: sometimes not. Such conduct is unbecoming in the clipped world of RT (radio-telephony) procedure. One Captain inbound to Heathrow was heard to respond to the answering ATCO, "Is that you, Brian?" Whereupon a whole sequence of Captain Speakings called "Hello Brian, is that you…? "Oh Brian, how nice…" "Hello Brian…"

★ ★ ★

Following the departure of G-SUZI to live at Elstree once more, the Cessna 340 IIA was purchased and re-registered G-LIZA after Eliza-Jane, one of our yellow Labradors. Eliza-Jane was the best but died quite young of an obscure illness with the clinical features of a prion disease. When I related the history to the specialist at the Veterinary Research Laboratory in

Addlestone he volunteered that her clinical features mirrored that condition in cats. This was before the BSE (bovine spongioform encephalopathy) epidemic, and before the condition had gained its notoriety. I had once diagnosed what was then known as (the related) Jacob-Creutzfeld disease in a Lambethian milkman whilst the neurological Senior House Officer (SHO) at St Thomas's Hospital. This was regarded as rather sporting as there was no diagnostic test at the time apart from a brain biopsy.

The attending veterinary surgeon removed Eliza's brain, post mortem, and sent it to the Veterinary Reference Pathology Laboratory in Bristol. The results were inconclusive. She had been fed on pet mince and if the prion syndrome of BSE had crossed the species barrier into dogs it would have had major implications. She never flew, unlike Michael Hessian's dog which enjoyed trips round southern England in his Piper PA 23 Aztec, and was only occasionally ill. When we flew to Basel for an away weekend with Michael and his wife, there were no canine passengers; those were the days before doggie passports.

The Cessna 340 was the best of the aircraft I ever owned (See photo plate 31). Not as responsive in roll as the Beechcraft, nor did it have the load capacity of the subsequent Piper Navajo, but it was the most predictable. It also had a 1,200 mile (total) range from six fuel tanks if you could fly for six hours with your legs crossed. The stall, unlike the Beechcraft which could be a bit entertaining, was a mush with no perceptible buffet and it never, ever dropped a wing (*What, never? Well, hardly ever* – confer W. S. Gilbert – *HMS Pinafore* and Sir Joseph Porter, the captain of the vessel, who was modelled by Gilbert on W. H. Smith, the office boy-cum-bookseller who became the First Lord of the Admiralty in 1878). It seemed to shrug "Well, if you must fly like that…" It was fast and also pressurised (round windows), which enabled one to get above much of the weather. It had six seats and a superficially byzantine fuel system with its six fuel tanks and eight fuel pumps, both the locker tanks, and the inboard tanks venting into the main (tip) tanks. But it was quite logical and there were no mistakes. (See photo plate 19.)

It did have a tendency to yaw in low-level turbulence, and for this reason I decided to fit a yaw damper. This is a small box with a pietzo-electric gel generating an electric current proportional to the yaw moment; an actuator moves the rudder in the opposite direction allowing the passengers to put away their sick bags when the blue light is illuminated. I purchased it in the USA and arranged for delivery to my hotel in Washington. It arrived as a vast box on two legs. Obviously it could not travel in my hand luggage on the Concorde, so rather like the Christmas game, the layers of packing were removed until the rather diminutive gizmo was delivered, which I put my sponge bag.

This was fine until my luggage was X-rayed at Kennedy Airport where a solitary wire was spotted beside my toothbrush; I was instantly surrounded by Secret Service men. Fortunately my explanation was accepted. Fitting it was another story, as the correct polarity could not be predicted. On the first occasion the new blue light gleamed tauntingly as the aircraft went into an increasingly frantic Dutch roll. Out came the floors again. After that, all well though the rudder bar occasionally felt awfully stiff on the ground… It was not a bright light.

There were numerous trips including two to Bordeaux and two to Nice. The first trip to Bordeaux was to attend a meeting of the European Working Party on Cardiovascular Fitness to Drive, in May 1991. We travelled as a family with our sons, David and Toby, and nanny, Penny. It was sponsored by my friend Professor Jean-Paul Broustet, who held the chair in cardiology at the university, as had his father before him. He lived in what seemed to be a château to me but he modestly said that it was really only a *grande maison*. Needless to say that he also had, to use another aviation term, a co-located vineyard. As a cardiologist and vinery owner he was a believer in the medicinal powers of the Bordeaux wines, and even had a letter in *The Times* espousing them. I once found his claret on the menu of a restaurant in Reigate, Surrey, called La Barbe.

Leaving aside the serious business of road safety in Europe, we were given remarkable hospitality by Jean-Paul. For the celebratory dinner we assembled at the *maison* at around 6pm and went on the French equivalent of a pub crawl, involving a visit to the caves of several of his friends. There we were encouraged to purchase as much wine as the wing lockers would hold before sitting down to dinner at 9.45 pm. By this time there was some rotational challenge. There were drinks again before we started – vintage champagne by the magnum, which was followed by eight courses including foie gras and as many further wines; the vintage claret emerged from magnums too. Not being a wine buff is a good excuse for amnesia about what we consumed. I was not flying the following day.

The second trip was at the invitation of Jean-Paul to chair a session of the Fifth World Congress on Cardiac Rehabilitation in July 1992. Two of our rehab sisters, Elizabeth Ringrose and Elizabeth Murphy, came along for the ride to ease pressure on departmental funds. Rehab in cardiology involves return to active life following a heart attack, rather than escaping the bottle. We hit some rough air over the Needles on the outbound which gave some concern but otherwise the trip was uneventful. There was no repeat of that dinner, which was just as well.

Many trips were shorter and in the UK. There was a weekend in Dinard with Len and Liz Battin. On our return there was an adverse weather warning as Hurricane Charlie was expected. Its fury had largely been spent over the Atlantic Ocean as it lost energy over the cooler water. That did not deter the ladies, who were determined to go to the market. By the time we reached the airfield it was pouring with rain. Having strapped the passengers in, I had to undertake the ground checks and became saturated in the process. By the time I got in, steaming like a wet Labrador, the whole craft was fogged up and I was unable to see the instruments, let alone interpret them. We departed into the bumps and even found a gap between the cloud layers, which was relatively clear. During our descent on the approach to Hurn we went back into turbulence, cloud and heavy rain. Whilst being radar vectored to the ILS, the Air Traffic Controller's voice was becoming staccato, even staccatissimo:

"Golf Zulu India, we have lost you on the radar, sir. How do you wish to proceed?" (Funny question.)

"Hurn Tower, may I make a procedural join to the [single at that time] ILS?"

"Golf Zulu India, that is approved; call beacon outbound and when localiser established. There is no conflicting traffic – do you wish a circle to land when visual?" There was a tailwind on the runway.

"Golf Zulu India – negative, sir." (Are you crazy?)

So we landed at high speed, but it was not quite over. The ladies took four hours to get back to Fairoaks by train, at their insistence, whilst Len and I took twenty-five minutes. Later Liz sent me a picture of 'the pilot who flew bravely on when his passengers had deserted him', taken from the rear seat. It was a bit blurred, but then the Beechcraft is a strong aeroplane.

During one special detail we studied the effect of incapacitation in flight on the part of the handling pilot in a light aircraft. For this we used G-LIZA in the non-controlled airspace to the south of the London TMA. It is noteworthy that in spite of the regulation surrounding the OSL (operational safety pilot), and its proposed further liberalisation under EASA, so far as I can ascertain no-one, apart from myself in the UK, has explored incapacitation in flight in a light aircraft. And this is in spite of fatal accidents having been caused by illness of the pilot in such circumstances. Following briefing, Len was asked to relax completely on the controls at a moment of his choice, assuming whatever position into which he slumped or fell.

Nothing much happened on the first occasion, but he managed to get his foot wedged in the rudder bar which impaired directional control. On another occasion he fell over the control yoke and the aircraft went into an abrupt, powered, spiral dive which was difficult to manage as gravity maintained the stick forward and to port, which served to accelerate the dive. After cutting the power, levelling the wings was difficult; almost impossible. The philosophy of licensing medically substandard private pilots to permit them to log the hours they fly, with another pilot untrained in incapacitation drills, needs to be re-evaluated and probably scrapped.

Then one day it happened for real. I was undertaking some 'limited panel' flying practice with Len when it became clear that there was an intermittent problem on the KCS55a PNI (Plan Navigation Indicator), or its associated gyroscope. This was evidenced by a warning flag. We were outside controlled airspace but mostly in IMC (broken cloud in this case). Flying on limited panel is defined by failure of one or more of the basic six flight instruments of which loss of the AI (attitude indicator), also called the AH (artificial horizon), is the most serious. As a result it is the most commonly practised exercise and the AH had been obscured by a card for the purposes of the exercise; then the PNI failed.

At that point Len let out a cry and said that he had a great pain in his back and would have to lie down in the back of the aircraft, which he did. So we had a failed instrument and a medical incapacitation. Technically the latter was not relevant from the safety point of view as the Cessna 340 is a single-crew aeroplane and I was in the left-hand seat. We abandoned the exercise and landed back at Fairoaks without further mishap. Sadly Len was subsequently diagnosed as having suffered a pathological fracture of a lumbar vertebra. In an airliner, accidents due to an unforeseen single event leading to catastrophe should be exceptionally rare. In a single-crew/single-engine aircraft the mission is vulnerable to the loss of a single major system, the pilot representing one such system. Although medical incapacitation is rare, it may be catastrophic to safety. Len was incapacitated by his pain and would have been unable to control the aircraft had he been in command; especially on limited panel.

My final aircraft, a Piper PA31-310 G-BJLO, a Turbo Navajo B (two Lycoming TIO-540-A2Cs), was shared with Nigel Reynolds, a four-times Emmy Award winning cameraman who had his own production company, Red Apple. We ran it as RJ Aviation Ltd. This was grown-up stuff, built in the USA for air taxi operations; it had been converted to six from eight seats. It was non-pressurised. The additional space was used for the toilet which was little more than a potty (of the *pim-wim* type), with a lid which could do circuits of its own in turbulence; so one had to be pretty desperate. (See photo plate 32.)

It was a strong, well-mannered aeroplane provided the weight and balance was correct. Rivets stuck out into the boundary layer and whistled our importance as we sped along with a fuel consumption of thirty-two gallons, imperial, an hour. Unlike its smaller brother, the Piper Aztec PA 23, it had a hydraulic pump on each engine, rather than just one on the critical engine. It was often used for navigational training to the airfield restaurant at Le Touquet. Twice we went to Le Bourget where they roll out a red carpet to keep your Gucci loafers off the tarmac. When the account for Eurocontrol en route navigation, approach, landing and parking charges had been met, there should have been enough red carpet left over to cover the entire main runway (07/25 – 9,843 feet).

The last time I flew into Hurn in April 2001 in the Navajo, the conditions were rather the same as on the Hurricane Charlie trip. There was only one other aircraft on the rain-lashed apron and that was G-LIZA.

SPREADING
THE MESSAGE

America has never quite forgiven Europe for having been discovered somewhat earlier in history than itself.

Oscar Wilde (1854–1900)

Our work in progress on a rational and scientific approach to medical fitness determination in the aviation industry became known through meetings of the Aerospace Medical Association (AsMA) and the International Academy of Aviation and Space Medicine (IAASM). The former is based in the USA; the latter has a secretariat which has been based at different times in New Zealand and Canada. Forty years ago the former was dominated by the military, mainly US, and preceded by the presentation of the flags of the attending nations. The meetings were held in major conference centres including Chicago, Miami, Nashville, San Diego, San Antonio, Seattle, New Orleans – even Anchorage and others including Reno, Nevada and Las Vegas (ugh). The Academy meetings were everywhere else in the world and included Sydney and Brisbane, Australia, which I visited several times. It was beside a swimming pool, discussing cardiological issues with Jon Jordan, the US Deputy Federal Air Surgeon, at an Aerospace Medical Association meeting in San Diego that I learned that our elder son, David, decided to arrive three weeks earlier than planned, back in Surrey.

A band, sometimes military, sometimes from a high school local to the conference centre, played *Liberty Bell* and other Sousa marches at the opening ceremony. A colour guard would march up wearing gleaming chromium-plated helmets – real Action Man stuff, with stamping of patent leather boots, shouting and slapping of rifles. Many of the delegates were smart reservists in uniform and when their signature tune (marches of the different services) was played, they would leap to their feet and salute. The Louis Bauer lecture was usually good value, but the accent of the meeting, unsurprisingly, was military aviation medicine with much on casualty evacuation and the special senses; there was little on cardiology. As time went by there was a lessening of the military input with concomitant burgeoning of the civilian side with contributions by the FAA (the US Federal Aviation Administration), ICAO and JAA/EASA, Canada, Australia, China, South America and ASEAN-Pacific.

The International Academy is a more nebulous affair, but where its meetings miss out academically, they are accessible to representatives from many nations and win on collegiality. The standard of papers submitted for the London meeting of 1995, when I was on the scientific committee, was embarrassingly low, with acceptance for reasons of expediency otherwise the delegates would not obtain the necessary funding to come. The standard has risen in recent years. It meets in venues across the world, memorable conferences having been held in Budapest, Bucharest, Nice, Vienna, Zagreb, Cairo, Delhi, Bangalore, Singapore, Sydney, Brisbane and many others. The contributors included aviation medical specialists, including some AMEs (Authorised Medical Examiners), airline medical officers and regulatory doctors from organisations such as the CAA, JAA/EASA and ICAO.

I presented at these, lecturing on behalf of ICAO, and contributed to ICAO regional meetings at venues including Zeist (the Netherlands) in 1985, Nairobi (Kenya) in 1985, Dakar (Senegal) in 1986, Kos (Greece) in 1988, Paris in 1989, Jakarta (Indonesia) in 1990, Budapest in 1993 and Bangkok (Thailand) in 1991 and 2005. Kos was memorable as Susanna, David, Toby and Nanny Penny all came too. We travelled on an Olympic Airways A300 Airbus to Athens, then on a Boeing 707 to Kos. Our family group, and Geoffrey Bennett, CMO of the CAA, were the only other passengers on the vast aeroplane. I sat under the same (now very geriatric) plane tree beneath which the tourist board claim Hippocrates taught. The Hippocratic method remains unsurpassed for the learning of medicine. Observe and study the patient, rather than the disease, at the bedside under the guidance of an experienced teacher. Use the classroom sparingly. As Sir William Osler said, *the good physician treats the disease; the great physician treats the patient who has the disease.*

Not all the networking was at the aviation medical conferences, and some invitations were received from ICAO contracting states who were seeking an exchange of ideas in specialist areas. These included Dublin, Paris, Oslo, Stockholm, Lisbon, Cologne and Geneva in Europe, with others further afield such as Dubai and Singapore. Memorable invitations included a government-sponsored visit to the regulatory authorities in Pakistan who were, in line with the ICAO lead, removing the responsibility for civil aircrew certification from the military. This process the UK had undergone a decade beforehand. It took place in 1981 and three of us flew out – Dr James Alexander, Deputy CMO of the UK CAA; Air Commodore, later Air Vice-Marshal, Paddy O'Connor, neuro-psychiatrist to the Royal Air Force; and myself.

We travelled in a rather tired-looking Pakistan International Airways (PIA) Boeing 747-100 with smoky Pratt and Witney JT9D engines. The Iran/Iraq war was in full swing so we avoided Tehran and flew direct to Rawalpindi. There we accomplished a landing following a descent through the deep umbra of the tropical night without seemingly any visual references apart from what looked like a sixty-watt bulb somewhere on the approach. We were met by our hosts, Colonel Ayoob of the Pakistan regulatory authority and Dr Shakut Verji of Pakistan International Airways. A Dr Malik was also hanging about; he later tried to persuade me to fly out on a regular basis and do private clinics.

Having completed the landing formalities we were driven to the Intercontinental Hotel. It resembled its brethren anywhere else in the world apart from the Islamic window design and the persistent smell of curry. On the unlit roadway ghostly figures in traditional dress, the *shalwar kameez* which resembles an operating theatre fatigue worn with a waistcoat, loomed up and vanished silently again. Sometimes they wrapped themselves with an additional tonneau cover. Soon our hosts pointed to the left and said, "That is the jail where they hanged poor old Bhutto."

Zulfikar Ali Bhutto (1928–1979) was the ninth Prime Minister of Pakistan (1973–1977) and its fourth President (1971–1973). He was a barrister called to the bar at Lincoln's Inn having gained his LLB at Oxford following an earlier degree at Berkeley, California. He was the founder of the Pakistan People's Party and served as its chairman until 1979. Following a military coup by General Zia ul Haq, he was arraigned on a probably false charge of procuring the murder of a political rival: it had been his opponent's father who died in the attack. He has the dubious accolade of being the father of his nation's nuclear programme. It was a time of considerable political turbulence and in 1977, when he was deposed by the General, he underwent what was regarded as a sham trial. There were several appeals before his eventual execution in 1979.

Benazir Bhutto, his daughter (1953–2007), who was twice Prime Minister, was later assassinated following her return from exile whilst she was campaigning for office in opposition in 2007. Zia ul Haq (1924–1988) was the military dictator and President until his death in an aircraft crash along with the American ambassador. He had turned the secular internationalism of Bhutto back to create an Islamic state based on sharia law. Conspiracy theories abounded, including the suggestion of a bomb in a crate of watermelons. The rumpuses of Westminster seem tame, by comparison, although even Westminster has seen the gunpowder, treason and plot of 1605. Only one British Prime Minister has been murdered – Spencer Perceval (Harrow and Trinity College, Cambridge), in 1812 by a merchant with a grievance: he had been a lawyer.

The hotel was dominated by an Islamic wedding lasting three days. We were invited. The very good-looking bride and groom, decked out in brightly coloured silks and satins, sat on a dais and received us coolly. The male guests wore brightly coloured clothes and each carried a green canary, or some such, in a cage. Our first presentation was to the new Military Medical School. The morning started with a reading from the Koran, lasting half an hour, by an overweight Mullah in a turban. The arrangements had overlooked the fact that my slides would not fit into the projector carrier but fortunately one was located on the other side of town. We had lunch in the Officers' Mess where we sipped Coca-Cola; Pakistan is a dry state. British army webbing belts with polished brasses were *de rigeur*.

We were shown, with pride, the new cardiac catheterisation laboratory in the military hospital, paid for by foreign aid. The equipment was sparkling, but the paint was shabby and there were soiled surgical gloves on the floor. Poor attention to detail. We also were shown round the coronary care unit and saw a twenty-nine-year-old bank worker in heart failure following his second myocardial infarction (heart attack). The layout of the unit we subsequently adopted at St Peter's Hospital. During the ward round, we visited a private patient in his own room recovering from the same problem. He was smoking a cigarette. "You are not to do that," said my colleague, swiping it from his mouth and throwing it out of the window.

At the time we were there, now over thirty years ago, the attrition rate of PIA pilots from cardiovascular disease was seven times that of the UK. They all smoked, but this was only part of the answer – epidemiological evidence, since, has indicated that natives of the Indian subcontinent have four times the prevalence of the 'metabolic syndrome' of Northern Europeans as they Westernise. This tetralogy of trunkal obesity, high blood pressure, high plasma cholesterol and type 2 diabetes is associated with a substantially increased risk of cardiovascular disease. This preponderance, when compared with the West, has been attributed to a metabolism that is better adapted to physical work on a relatively impoverished diet.

In the afternoon we visited some lecture theatres where everyone stood up as we appeared. I met a doctor who had studied at St Thomas's Hospital whilst I was there, and he showed us round. There was no electric light in the classrooms – when it got dark, everyone went home. There was a session on pharmacy taking place in one which was particularly aromatic. The students were making up Pulv. Picis. Carb. Co., or some such concoction, with a mortar and pestle. Later the powders were placed in a glass-stoppered bottle and sealed with sealing wax. The label was handwritten in ink with beautiful copperplate writing. A year or two later I received a letter from the General Medical Council (GMC) asking for a report of the visit and whether I felt the school was fit for reciprocal recognition of pass degrees in medicine. I responded that that had not been the purpose of the visit and I could not comment. I did say that the students were unlike their colleagues in the United Kingdom on account of their general deportment, good dress, politeness and nice manners. The school was subsequently recognised by the council.

There was little separation of the airline from the government, the regulator and the armed forces, which facilitated our travel about by PIA. Airline ticket availability seemed limitless. We flew to Lahore in an A300 Airbus during which I sat in the jump seat. At altitude, an impressive network of canals was pointed out: "You, the British, built those," the Captain told me, pointing out of the window. I reminded him that it was unlikely that we did the digging, and that the hard work would have been down to them. As we were on finals to land there appeared to be two Bofors anti-aircraft guns on either side of the runway which were trained on us, and which swung menacingly as we grew closer. "They like to practise," said the Captain; excellent – one wondered if they had any ammo in the breach.

Lahore has a number of interesting artefacts; the first of which we saw was Kim's gun. This weapon, which was cast in 1762, is also known as the Zamzama gun. It took part in numerous battles and sieges in Northern India and was eventually damaged beyond economic repair, coming to rest outside the Lahore museum. It was later moved to Tollington Market in time for a visit by the Duke of Edinburgh in 1970.

Humpty Dumpty suffered the same fate. A large cannon used by the Royalists in the siege of Colchester during the English Civil War in 1648 was called Humpty Dumpty. It was brought to the ground from its redoubt in St Mary at the Wall by parliamentary gunfire. All the King's horses and all the King's men were unable to effect a repair. Being an aficionado of Kim and having read the Mowgli stories by Rudyard Kipling many times in boyhood, it was good to see the gun on which he sat astride at the opening of the eponymous tale. *Zamzama*, or 'mighty fire-dispensing dragon', is a term of sexual prowess in Afghanistan.

The Shalimar gardens were started in the 17th century by Khalilullah Khan. They remained in the ownership of the Arain Mian family for the next three and a half centuries before the family displeased General Ayub Khan and the gardens were nationalised in 1962. Although our host said they had originally been on seven levels, there are now three served by pools which contain 410 fountains. They are beautiful in their architecture and layout and were created a World Heritage site in 1986, shortly after we were there. They are a place where the local people relax in the relatively cool environment.

16. *Kim's Gun outside the University Hall in Lahore, Pakistan. It was cast there in 1762 in copper and brass from local pots and pans. It was damaged at the siege of Multan and, like Humpty Dumpty before it during the siege of Colchester in 1648, was beyond repair. It is also known as the Zamzama, an Afghan term for sexual prowess.*

We paid a brief visit to Islamabad where the King Faisal (bin Abdul-Aziz of Saudi Arabia) mosque was under construction, along with much of the city. Then we flew on to Peshawar, this time in a geriatric Fokker F27. Peshawar is surrounded by mountains. After cruising at about 20,000 feet for a while, for no obvious reason, the captain started the descent into the invisible airport below under a massive duvet of layer cloud.

"Are you doing a NDB [non-directional beacon] let-down?" I asked, wondering as to the whereabouts of the field, especially as the ADF (automatic direction finder) needle seemed to be aimless, and the VOR indicator was clearly asleep.

"You see that peak over there?" There were dozens. "If we descend here on this heading, it works out, *insh'Allah*," replied the good Captain. And with his help it did.

We met two British council workers who were stationed out there and looked after the British Library. They lamented the spending cuts which had followed a period of profligacy. The consequence was that promised scholarships were not deliverable to the hopeful. It was later burnt down. Quite how much their modest effort impacted on the greater canvas of British influence was difficult to judge. If government, rather than the pursuit of power, was the objective of the political class, we would be likely to be in a better position in the world. Some of our effort is rewarded, however. I asked Shakut Verji whether he listened to the BBC World Service – it is to be recalled that its funding was transferred to the BBC itself from the Foreign and Commonwealth Office on 1st April 2014. "Yes, yes, we all do, especially when things go wrong. You are sometimes wrong, but you are always right."

17. One of the ubiquitous guards on the Khyber Pass. There are frequent notices in English and Urdu warning travellers to be back in Peshawar before nightfall. There are also severe but unspecified penalties for photographing the local women.

On the same evening we were invited to the house of a fellow doctor for drinks, which in a dry state means neat whisky in lieu of the ubiquitous Coca-Cola. After a loading dose, a patient unexpectedly turned up seeking advice and my colleague asked if I would like to offer an opinion. As soon as I entered the room, to my embarrassment, the patient ignored my colleague and waited for my view. He was anxious and hyperventilating. Finding nothing amiss after taking a history and performing an examination, I reassured him and suggested he picked up his bed. As I was leaving the room my colleague overturned my confident reassurance – "Maybe, maybe not" – and gave him an appointment for the next morning. Private practice is the same the world over. I wondered if he charged the patient for my input.

★ ★ ★

Our hosts found reasons not to accompany us to Peshawar, and none would accompany us up the Khyber Pass.

"It is OK for you, my friend, but not for us."

We hired a man to take us. In common with all cab drivers from that part of the world, he had rescued his Commanding Officer under fire during the Second World War and earned the Military Medal. The pass runs through the Spin Ghar Mountains connecting Central with Southern Asia, and was part of the old Silk Road. It was of importance from the military point of view. Had we come eight centuries earlier we might have met Genghis Khan coming in the opposite direction on his way to create the largest contiguous empire in history. Like his 20th century successors, Stalin and Mao Zedong, and lately Islamic State, murder of civilians was his speciality. Two and a half millennia earlier it would have been Darius the Great, or a bit later Alexander the Great. The region is a Federally Administered Tribal Area and is beyond the jurisdiction of the Pakistani police and military.

As we left Peshawar on the GT Road, which later became the N5, there were notices warning travellers not to be out after dark. Nor could one photograph the native women without incurring some unspecified, but definitely unpleasant, penalty. We did see them in the distance and took careful photographs with help from the Nikon F2 Photomic and its long lens. They had beautiful carriage and collected bundles of firewood on their heads, rather as girls at English finishing schools used to, with the *Encyclopaedia Britannica,* before it went digital. Initially the ground was flat and there were square forts where the local families lived. They co-habited with granny in one corner, mother-in-law in another and the wife, or wives, in another. To brighten up a dull day they would take pot shots at their neighbours and occasionally at passers-by. Soon we were ascending the narrow road alongside the single track railway, also built by the British after the Great War; it was in disrepair. The Khyber Pass Railway from Jamrud, Peshawar to Landi Kotal in the pass above the Afghan border was opened in 1925.

The scenery was extraordinary and must rank amongst the most beautiful on earth. The terrain and colours reflect the highlands of Scotland until it is appreciated that it is arid and the ground stony. There was almost no traffic. On stopping to answer the call of nature, take a photograph or admire the view, often a small stone bounced past on its way down the mountain. On looking round there would be a tall and imposing Pashtun warrior with rifle and bandolier of bullets, seemingly also admiring the view, or perhaps passing water, whilst studiously ignoring us. On one corner we came across a vast lorry highly decorated with tassels, mirrors and chromium bric-a-brac lying on its side. Its cargo of a zillion oranges was bouncing down the pass together with a considerable amount of freshly squeezed orange juice; the brown dust was clinging to the descending rivulets. *Insh'Allah*, they intoned – the cop-out for all religions when something unexpected or unpleasant occurs: blame the Almighty One, not exuberant cornering, poor axle loading or a broken spring.

Ten miles up the Khyber, as they say, we passed Fort Jamrud, now occupied by the Pakistani military, but in the past held by the British. It seemed closed for business. On the rock outside, the British regiments had carved their regimental badges in the stone in the date order that they were there. After 1947 the Pakistani units continued the tradition. The frontier with Afghanistan is on the far side of the pass marked by a line, shortly before, of what our driver called "Churchill's teeth". These are concrete tank traps built to deter the anticipated German invasion of India during World War

Two. They did not look as though they would have held up a perambulator. The frontier was manned on both sides but the local Pathans (Pashtuns) seemed to wander across without the need for paperwork; helpful if you are illiterate. A posse of about thirty tall Afghan soldiers headed for our observation platform at one point, causing some consternation but stopped short, eyeball to eyeball, with their opposite numbers.

On the way back we passed a refugee camp full of Afghans. The young men were gone, fighting with the mujahideen, but as we stopped to take photographs a ten-year-old ran over and quickly established with our driver that we were Americans (to my dismay). "Give me four F16 fighters", he said, "and I will get the Russians out of our country." It is *their* country. And that was well before we had been trounced there for the third time in our history. I hope he is safe – if some Afghans had landed in Guildford to get rid of Tony Blair, we might have reached for our twelve bores too.

Time was getting on as we turned back towards Peshawar. There was still time for a detour and we headed for the illegal guns factories near Darra Adam Khel. There it is possible to buy a genuine Mk III or IV SMLE rifle, or copy, complete with all the appropriate War Department markings. A Kalashnikov AK47, or ArmaLite AR15, costing $150 (then), would turn you into a real terrorist. Any gun could be copied overnight and tried out by firing it up the street. The streets were alive with the sound of gunfire (confer Richard Rogers and Oscar Hammerstein II and Julie Andrews' opening song – *The hills are alive…*). We must have looked pretty odd, an Englishman, an Irishman and a Scotsman amongst all the mayhem; suddenly there was a tap on my shoulder and two huge Pashtuns stared, expressionless. After a near-cardiac arrest it transpired that they would like their photograph taken. On the way back we came across some children playing cricket in the dust as the sun set. Again they ran over but this time in the hope that we were talent scouts.

Our driver dropped us off at our hotel, refusing payment as he said he would be back to take us to the airport for the trip to Rawalpindi. Such was the level of trust. It was dark by the time we checked in and time for devotions, all departing passengers, apart from us, were on the floor orientated towards Mecca. A non-ICAO local contribution to aviation safety, maybe.

18. *Cricket up the Khyber. We attracted attention as our driver did not deny that we might be talent scouts. For once he could not pass us off as Americans.*

Eventually we were strapped in, just forward of the chemical toilet, the contents of which seemed to be everywhere but in the toilet itself. After the engines had started there was a furious banging on the door, which was opened to a blind, diplegic boy who groped his way onto the aircraft and sat down. It was like a biblical omen. Fortunately for all, it did not seem to portend anything sinister, and the F27 bumped its way back to Rawalpindi without incident, flying, as they say, on a wing and a prayer. The ADF needle swung moodily as it waved goodbye to Peshawar.

We took an evening flight from Rawalpindi to Karachi. I sat next to the Foreign Minister who attempted to explain the intricacies of sharia marriage. It is both a social and legal contract which can be terminated by either side. It does not have to be a written agreement. Permission from *Wali* (custodian – e.g. father or grandfather) is strongly recommended. Marriage is encouraged as an act of *Sunnah* – the way of the Prophet. There should be two adult Moslem males or one male and two adult

Moslem female witnesses. Polygyny is permitted in Islam but polyandry is forbidden. Not an equal opportunities religion (but nor is Roman Catholicism). After we had been airborne in the Boeing 747 for over three hours, Colonel Ayoob went up to the flight deck to find out what was going on. It turned out that we had been holding off a violent electrical storm over Karachi and were returning to the alternative, which was Rawalpindi. Back we came, by which time it was 2am and the only liquid refreshment looked as though it had been drawn from a local pond. That had been a courageous operational decision.

One evening after we finally reached Karachi, on 2nd February 1981, the PIA DC10-30 AP-AXE was destroyed in a hangar fire. The engineers involved used the opportunity to scarper, leaving others put out the fire in the stricken craft. It broke its back after it had been partially dragged out of the hangar. We went to look and photograph it the next day.

Our final meeting was with the airline, including its doctors and pilots. After I had spoken, the pilot who was Head of Safety said nice things

19. 'A bit late on the round out, Hoskins' (confer Flight International). The DC10-30 AP-AXE which caught fire in the hangar and burnt out; Karachi, February 1981. No-one was injured.

then sternly demanded what my qualification was to talk about aviation in the context of the circulation. I responded that I held twin engine and instrument ratings. "That's fine," he said.

Karachi is an interesting place, if hot and rather smelly. Large crowds and aggressive begging – we were grateful for chaperoning by our hosts, especially in the markets. The Shitehawks (*Milvus migrans* – Black Kite) constantly wheel above the city in a failed attempt to keep the place clean. Sadly a stork, the Great Adjutant (*Leptoptilos dubius*), so called because of its marching gait, is now endangered. It used to be widespread and was so good at its job, as a scavenger in Calcutta, that its image formed part of the municipal coat of arms. On the seashore we met some friendly goats with smiling faces and a tendency to butt in the stomach those they encountered, in the hope of the delivery of the local equivalent of a cheese sandwich. They had very soft fur and long ears. Disappointed, they got on with the business of the day, which in their case was recycling cardboard boxes.

Further along a ship was being scrapped by the technique of driving it on shore and tearing it to bits. No health and safety or environmental concerns there. On our last night we went for a drink (of Coca-Cola) at the Sind Club (founded in 1871) and built in the Southern Italianate mode. "Just as it was when you were here," we were told; "except one thing – we [they] would not have been allowed in." Two, actually: I doubt if we would have been drinking Coca-Cola. There had been a notice, only removed at partition in 1947, which stated *natives and dogs not allowed*. It was 1952 before local people were permitted to join. Women are still not permitted to do so.

The flight home was tedious. Originating in Rawalpindi, the aircraft 'went tech' in Karachi and we were marooned on the tarmac with a faltering air conditioning unit for many hours. Eventually a high pressure pipe with a large tear in it was produced in triumph by the elaborately moustachioed engineer who had disappeared inside the wing. We watched donkeys pulling the baggage trolley across the airfield with altogether better humour than their Western counterparts. Ten hours late, after nearly twenty-four hours on the aircraft and long after the soft drinks had run out (even in First) we alighted at Heathrow only to be challenged by a customs official.

"Where are you from?"

"Rawalpindi."

"You are not – there has been no flight. Show me your ticket." It could not be found. "What is in your case?"

"A lot of dirty washing and two large brass elephants."

"Are you still this?" he asked, noting that I was pompously described as a consultant cardiologist in my passport. I felt like replying that I had taken holy orders and was now selling sandals. "Have you any drugs?" he asked, eying the elephants' legs and trying to see inside their feet.

"Drugs! I am loaded with drugs!" I said, and produced a large number of bottles. "Anti-malarials, anti-diarrhoeals, anti-spasmodics, antibiotics, anti-pyretics and anti-customs," I said, incautiously, of the only unlabelled one. "You had better go," he said.

SPREADING THE MESSAGE FURTHER

The only thing to do with good advice is to pass it on. It is never of any use to oneself.

Oscar Wilde (1854–1900)

There were two visits to India to present papers at different meetings of the International Academy. The first was to Delhi and the second to Bangalore, 'the Silicon Valley of India'. Notwithstanding its title, to me it looked like much of the rest of the country – a gigantic car boot sale, at least in the cities. The most surprising thing was the amount of elephant traffic on the roads and the toleration of (sacred) cows slumbering at the traffic lights at road intersections. After the meeting in Delhi we went on tour – not easy at that time. We asked about travel to the Taj Mahal, in Agra, Uttar Pradesh, and were assured that flying or a taxi was the answer. The Indian aviation accident statistics did not altogether favour travel by air and we were almost persuaded to go by the "very fast, very comfortable cab, *sahib*, with very, very air conditioning". We were promised it would take "a very small two hours". In the end we went in a remarkably tough bus and it took six hours, negotiating the potholes without demur. At that time motorways were a novelty and their use was not entirely understood – one carriageway was usually reserved for accidents whilst the other was used for two-way traffic. On the way back we stopped for tea at a place obscured by a fog which consisted entirely of insects.

The Taj Mahal is breathtaking. It was built in the first part of the 17th century in the Mughal style. It was the memorial and tomb for the third wife of the emperor Shah Jahan, Mumtaz, who died during the birth of her fourteenth child. The cenotaphs of Mumtaz and Jahan lie in the crypt beneath the tomb in an atmosphere so foetid that it is impossible to breathe. Her cenotaph lies in the exact centre of the tomb with that of her husband, a larger one, by her side. The inscription on the cenotaph of Jahan reads: *He travelled from this world to the banquet-hall of Eternity on the night of the twenty-sixth of the month of Rajab, in the year 1076 Hijri.* Something to look forward to; hopefully it is air conditioned.

We were asked what was "different" between the four minarets. They look identical. The answer is that they all lean out slightly so that in the event of an earthquake, or collapse for other reason, they do not fall on the marble dome of the mausoleum. Clever chap, Shah Jahan. We looked at the famous bench where HRH Diana, Princess of Wales had had her photograph taken in February 1992. Ken Edgington and I had our photograph taken, too, sitting upon it which raised some eyebrows back in the Department in Gatwick, where it was posted up.

After our return to Delhi we caught the 'Pink City Flier', complete with wood-burning locomotive, called an express because it only stopped between the stations. There was the usual involvement: the ticket wallah, the platform wallah, the seat wallah and so on. The bag wallah was a tiny man who lost half of his height when our considerable luggage was dumped on his head. The train stopped in at Jaipur, Rajasthan station, fortunately so because when I went to admire the engine it was evident that someone had taken up the rails a few feet ahead.

Jaipur is called the Pink City because everything was painted in this colour by Maharaja Ram Singh to welcome the Prince of Wales in 1876. So it has remained. We stayed at the Ramburgh Palace hotel, which had once belonged to the Maharajah. It had a wonderful indoor swimming pool in the old tradition. Outside a fakir endlessly played a pipe to amuse his rather fed-up looking cobra whose home was a tatty reed basket. Sometimes there was a violinist to provide the local equivalent of Musak (elevator music), too. Luckily for the snake, it is deaf to the fluty notes, having a closed inner ear which interprets vibration, rather like a deaf aid. So does its stomach. It also has a Jacobson's organ, called thus because it was first described by Frederik Ruysch (1638–1731). This is a chemo-detector which seeks out pheromones, whilst the rattlesnake, viper and python have the back-up facility of thermo-sensitive pit organs. Best avoided. We were lucky enough to be there during a plague epidemic which scared off most travellers, especially Americans, leaving the place to ourselves and (now) 1.3 billion Indians. One and a half million people migrated as a result from Surat, Gujarat; there were fifty two recorded deaths. Probably more people were killed in Delhi on bicycles than ever lost their lives to Yersinia pestis that year – Stay Calm and Carry On, as they used to say. All we saw was the gravely carried-out medical examination by a pretty young doctor at check-in. This consisted of our heart rate being recorded at the wrist. Osler would have approved.

We visited the Hawa Mahal or The Palace of the Winds, our guide pointing out the interesting "fadace" (sic). It is two hundred years old and is barely one room thick. It has a thousand crevice-like windows through which the women of the royal household could watch the goings-on in the street below without being seen. Perhaps they passed notes and emblems of desire, too. The Jantar Mantar observatory in the city is nearly three hundred years old and has a sundial which is one of the biggest in the world; and one of the largest stray dogs' homes. We took an elephant up to the Amber Fort, the home of the Rajput Maharajahs. It was shimmering in the heat, and we visited both it and the adjacent Jaigarh Fort which guards it (and was the site of a famous gun foundry at one time). Both were built, or improved upon, three hundred years ago. They overlook Jaipur.

The elephant commuted daily from digs in Jaipur 11 km away and plodded up the hill to the Sun gate, through which we progressed to the Jaleb Chowk and the Lord Ganesh gate. Lord Ganesh, one of the Hindu gods, is a chap worth knowing because he removes the obstacles in your life. An elephant is piloted by a mahout, who rides on its shoulders and hooks his *thotti* around the base of the creature's offside ear. This serves both as a joystick and throttle, a bit like a helicopter collective control, although, like Fordson tractors, elephants have their own internal governors. The motion is a lumbering Dutch roll, rather as though a yaw damper has been disabled, not unlike flying a Chinook helicopter at low level. The whole palace needed a good scrub but was impressive in its majesty. The famous

Man Sagar Lake and the Jal Mahal palace within it, we saw, but the stench of pollution was indescribable; the two are now undergoing restoration.

Finally we visited a mysterious hill palace where there were no other guests (plague) and we had the place to ourselves. It had an atmosphere of vague threat, not helped by the repeated failure of the electricity supply, which pitched everything into inky blackness through which some stringed instrument was scratched continuously. Faces appeared, watched, said nothing and disappeared, reminiscent of the film *Don't Look Now*, starring Julie Christie and Donald Sutherland. But that was set in Venice, which can also be as smelly in the summer. A family of musicians with pretty, unveiled daughters allowed me to photograph them. The vast air conditioning box in the room contained nothing but straw and an insomniac mouse.

Bangalore, by way of contrast, was mainly work apart from a *tuk tuk* (tricycle motor scooter) race back from a reception to our hotel with Tony Evans, now Chief of Medicine at ICAO. I lost. Having overslept, the following day I missed the coach for the official visit to the local Indian Air Force base. Eventually, on arrival, I was greeted by a charming Wing Commander with a vast airman's moustache (how do they get them inside the oxygen mask?), who airily waved aside security and invited me in for a cup of tea. The military the world over, when it is not fighting, shouting or stamping, drinks tea. The air display, which included formation flying by HAL Cheetahs and BAE Systems Hawks, was accomplished. The country is hard work by Western touring standards, but a magical place.

★ ★ ★

Following the devaluation of the pound by Harold Wilson's government in 1968, it was announced that the UK would be withdrawing (as of January 1971) from 'East of Suez'; Singapore was included. The term had originally been coined by Rudyard Kipling in his poem *Mandalay*, written in 1890 following a visit. It was there that he fell in love with a *Burma girl* (not difficult) he saw on the steps of the old Moulmein Pagoda, *lookin' lazy at the sea*. He remembered her in his lines in *The Road to Mandalay, where the flying fishes play…* It is not a road, but the Irrawaddy River. Kipling received the Nobel Prize for Literature in 1907, the first English-language writer to receive it and its youngest Laureate. This was before Malala Yousafzai, the Pakistani schoolgirl activist for female education, who was shot at the age of fifteen years in October 2012 by the Taliban.

The sudden departure of the UK forces from Singapore during the withdrawal from 'East of Suez' was recalled by my friends, Doctors Jarnail Singh, now Chairman of the Singapore Civil Aviation Board, having replaced Lim Meng Kin, his predecessor, during a visit with Claus Curdt-Christiansen, then Chief of Medicine at ICAO. At one point Meng Kin remarked that he had no idea that there were hills in the state before the British left. They had occupied them for the minimal benefit the altitude gave to the prevailing temperature and humidity. Similarly in Penang. He also said that he was a banana – white on the inside but yellow on the outside. Dear Meng Kin (now, sadly, no longer with us), why did you feel this way? We all are brothers, friends and colleagues – what awful legacy have we left that made you feel like that?

Of the ICAO regional meetings in which I participated, those in East and West Africa and Indonesia, organised by Silvio Finkelstein, were particularly memorable. The trip to Kenya to the East Africa office of ICAO was brief and lasted less than forty-eight hours. I was met unexpectedly by an English physician colleague who worked at the main hospital, which was familiar, equipped as it was with British hardware. Our first official engagement was to view the new Air Traffic Control tower. As if to prove that Kenya is a mature bureaucracy, there was no-one to meet us as the senior guy had not been told about our visit. That was not a good start, though things improved from his point of view when he found out that I, as about the only European present, was English. He pointed out that whereas Kenya had always used Plessey radar, now the upgrade was with Thomson-CSF, a French product. Somebody murmured about backhanders. The meeting went well but English was not the first language for some. Take-off from Nairobi was delayed by a broken headlamp glass on the inbound aircraft due to debris on the runway, and a dog doing its business on the apron before start-up. It took off across the airfield with several push-back tenders in hot pursuit. But that is Africa, as they say.

Senegal lies on the west coast of Africa, the capital, Dakar, being situated on the Cape Verde peninsula. The Portuguese were probably the first

Europeans to visit, in the 15th century, followed by the Dutch, the British and the French. The inshore island of Gorée, three kilometres off the coast, served as a trading post for slaves from the 17th century until slavery was abolished in 1818 by the French. This was against the wishes of the local chieftains who lost the income therefrom. The British had passed the Abolition of the Slave Trade Act in 1807. Slavery and exploitation still exist worldwide, including in the United Kingdom, two hundred years later.

Senegal became independent in 1960 and remained within the francophone sphere of influence. Tall and elegant, the Wolof is the largest ethnic group and account for about half the population. The predominant religion is Islam. During the space shuttle programme, Dakar airport was identified as a possible diversionary airfield in the event of a TAL (transoceanic abort landing), and the runway was extended with aid from the United States. Later it was abandoned for this role due to a potentially hazardous dip in the runway surface. It was never used for the space programme, though none of the Senegalese taxi drivers I have met around the world seem to know this fact. Dakar also contains the West African regional office of ICAO.

I had been invited out by Silvio Finkelstein together with Dr Geoffrey Bennett, CMO of the UK CAA, for an ICAO regional meeting. The language of the meeting was French and the ICAO chair was Dr Jean-Pierre Chambion, Silvio's deputy at ICAO. There was no direct flight from the UK and for some reason we initially proceeded independently, meeting in Geneva to catch the Swiss Air connection. It was uneventful whereas our arrival was not. After clearing customs we passed to ground side. Whilst making to leave the airport we were quite unprepared for the spectacle ahead. In front of the facility there appeared to be a necropolis of battered old cars with yellow roofs, mostly, but not all, on the move. This was an image of motorised Bedlam unequalled by anything seen in Delhi, Bangkok and Jakarta, or even the Hangar Lane gyratory on a wet Friday evening in winter. They were missing windows, windscreens, sometimes bonnets, and generally were in an advanced state of dilapidation. Each had a screaming driver anxious to get the fare into town.

We selected one which was more complete than some, to the chagrin of everyone else, including the man who tried to insert himself, gondolier-like, into the deal. After about four kilometres we asked for confirmation of the price. The door was flung open and we were invited to leave, or be summarily ejected together with our luggage into the dust and heat. The price was the universal airport fare at the time: $50 – like it or you can walk. Le Méridien was a haven of Gallic calm after the hurly-burly outside, even down to the faint aroma of French plumbing. Courteous staff glided about and we could have been anywhere in the world, especially as we were mugged after tea.

The meeting was an opportunity to learn about the local cardiovascular problems and experiences of their specialists in the context of their emerging civil aviation activity. We also explained the mechanisms we had evolved to assist regulatory decision-making. We met a number of people including a Scottish engineer who seemed to be holding the place together. Such engineers are a premium Scottish export, which, along with porridge and whisky, are often to be met in what they quaintly call the armpits of the world. I was invited to visit the teaching hospital as the guest of the locally born professor of cardiology who had trained in Paris. For a clinical specialist it was a dream world, with much teaching-standard clinical material (aka patients).

Austin Flint (1812–1860), a US physician who described the mid-diastolic murmur of aortic regurgitation due to turbulent mixing of antegrade mitral and retrograde aortic flow, and Carey Coombs (1879–1932), an RAMC major in the Great War who served in the UK, France, Egypt and Mesopotamia, and who described the mid-diastolic murmur of (active) rheumatic mitral valvulitis (common then in army recruits) were there too, as wraiths. Woe betided the classical physician who diagnosed acute rheumatic fever in the presence of aortic regurgitation, without performing the Wasserman reaction to rule out (quaternary) syphilis. This was an alternative explanation for the mid-diastolic murmur. Now the echocardiogram rules and the old skills are largely lost.

Rheumatic heart disease is much commoner in Africa and the Middle East than in the West, with the problem of infection on the abnormal valves (endocarditis) also commoner. The first (and almost the last) case of acute rheumatic fever I saw was in a ten-year-old boy during my final medical examination at Guy's hospital. He refused to let me listen to his heart in spite of the 2/6d I gave him, which was not returned. I passed. Without high dose intravenous antibiotic treatment for several weeks, endocarditis is fatal, sometimes in days. But it may endure for months, depending on the organism involved. Due to poverty, and habit, the first visit is usually to the witch doctor where the standard treatment includes the shaking of bones. Although no trial seems to have been conducted, the outcomes are poor and the next visit is to a qualified doctor who prescribes what can be afforded, usually about five days of oral antibiotic therapy. As a result, the cases in the hospital had signs of severe, incompletely treated disease often in need of valve surgery. But at that time only two patients a year could be sent for treatment in Paris paid, for by the French government.

I was asked to see a teenage girl who was emaciated and in severe right-sided congestion of the circulation. She had the clinical signs of tricuspid valve stenosis which appeared to be isolated and likely to have been congenital. I looked at the echocardiogram and wondered aloud about the diagnosis. This was a mistake. My locally born French colleague had come to a different conclusion – constrictive pericarditis – and was not impressed by my suggestion, which in England would have passed as an innocent straw dog yapping on the diagnostic trail. In France the professor is king and beyond question whereas in the UK getting one up on the professor is regarded as a sport akin to hare coursing, or maybe bear baiting in the case of a surgical chair. The sadness in the girl's eyes, knowing that there was no hope in the circumstances, remains in my memory.

Before leaving I visited the 'slave' island of Gorée, now recognised by UNESCO as a world heritage site. It has been visited since, inter alia, by Nelson Mandela and Barack and Michelle Obama. The House of Slaves was built in the late 18th century and reconstructed fifty years ago. There is controversy about its original purpose. Some claim it was the private residence of a wealthy (female) Senegalese trader, and that the house and the infamous *Door of No Return* were relatively unimportant in the tragedy of the twelve million slaves taken from Africa. Others have stated that up to one million souls may have passed through the portal en route for the New World. What is sometimes overlooked is that the dreadful business could not have taken place without the active participation of local tribal chiefs who rounded up the captives of inland squabbles and sold them to the traders.

After the brief visit it was time to return to the unwell of Surrey. The final evening was a reception from which I had to leave early; Geoffrey Bennett remained behind. This time I was given a vast official Mercedes car and a massive driver, an Oddjob-like figure with no obvious Auric Goldfinger in evidence. Unlike Harold Sakata he had teeth like a Bechstein piano keyboard. When we got to the airport the near-riot conditions still prevailing were subdued by him and I was led through the crowd which parted like the Red Sea, to mix metaphors. Immigration and customs were ignored and I was delivered to airside where the welcoming colours of KLM on the tail-plane of the aircraft were lit up like a harbour beacon in a storm. No sooner had I sat down than a crowd of enthusiastic peddlers of every conceivable bit of bling descended like blowflies, ignoring the IATA *Airport Development Reference Manual* (ADRM) guidelines. The night ride back across the Sahara desert was smooth.

★ ★ ★

The meeting in Jakarta was longer and more action-packed. We stayed at the Hotel Borobudur in central Jakarta. It is located in acres of tropical garden. We had meetings and gave lectures to delegates from the countries in the Far Eastern region of ICAO. We were taken shopping to vast malls where we were met and escorted to the point of interest. Each purchase involved a half a dozen people. We paid an official visit to Bandung in Western Java. It had been developed in the 17th and 18th centuries by the Dutch East India Company in an area where tea was grown. Our interest was focused upon the Industri Pesawat Terbang Nurtanio factory (now Indonesia Aerospace), which was manufacturing the Spanish-designed CASA 212, a non-pressurised twin turboprop transport aircraft under licence. To get there we were up with the dawn and climbed aboard the train at Gambir station, heading for Bandung. It was quite rickety and at times, and as with the line from Bangkok to Kanchanaburi in Thailand, ran over skeletal wooden viaducts. The effect was breathtaking. At one moment we would be looking out over paddies or jungle, the next we would be in cloud with no visible means of support, over a gorge, as we wobbled and shook our way across. Breakfast was delivered by a young man with a huge grin as he arrived with a stack of some dozen plates of egg, bacon, tomato and sausage for the benefit of the Europeans. The inevitable happened, the train lurched and the whole lot landed on the floor along with the poor fellow's grin.

We were shown round the aircraft factory where there were two vast flatbed milling machines shaping the spars which had been cut with high velocity water jets. Some aircraft were being test-flown in the background but there did not seem to be the scope for a trip. Next we were taken to exercise our wallets at a jean production facility. On a later occasion we visited the Headquarters of the Indonesian Air Force (Tentara Nasional Indonesia Angkatan Udara) and learned about their plans to re-equip their medical department. In crude terms (number of personnel and of aircraft) it exceeds the current strength of the Royal Air Force although its capability, sophistication and combat readiness is much less. It flies a variety of aircraft including the BAE Hawk trainer, best known in the UK as being the equipment of the Red Arrows aerobatic team.

But then there was something completely different.

CONCORDE

Sans doute, Concorde décédé hier à l'âge de 31 ans tout ce qu'il restera le mythe d'un bel oiseau blanc.

Le Figaro, following the loss of AF 4590
on take-off from Charles de Gaulle aerodrome, 25th July 2000

One day in May 1984 Geoffrey Ratcliffe, at the time engineering director at British Airways, telephoned. It was one of those modal occasions when the questioner expects the answer to be in the affirmative. Would I like to go to lunch in New York, travelling there and back on Concorde on the flight deck?

When I was first in Surrey I had been to the British Aircraft Corporation (BAC), Weybridge, Concorde production line. The nose and fuselage as far back as the forward entrance were engineered there, as were the fin and tail section. They were also machining a double curved profile on the engine nacelles for the McDonnell Douglas DC10. There was concern about the future. Concorde was an aircraft like none other. People waved to it whilst it taxied. On take-off the noise and the shock diamonds of the after-burners were shattering. As it growled overhead our house outbound to the west it was impossible not to look up. On its last flight over us to New York from Heathrow, flying into the setting sun, it had the colour of burnished gold. On landing everyone stopped to watch. (See photo plate 33.)

The technology was breathtaking and yet well dated by the time it left service. I had watched at Farnborough in September 1956 as the prototype Olympus engine flew in a modified English Electric Canberra bomber. The Canberra had captured the world altitude record (>60,000 feet) in 1953. Also present at that meeting was the technology demonstrator Fairey Delta FD2, flown by Peter Twiss, who had captured the world airspeed record in March of the same year, raising it to 1,132 mph (1,811 km/h) or Mach 1.73. As the BAC221, it was used for research into the ogee wing, later the pattern for the Concorde.

In March 1959, Sir Morien Morgan and his Supersonic Transport Advisory Committee (STAC) – set up in 1956 but pre-empted by a project group, two years before – reported to the then-Ministry of Aviation that a Supersonic Transport (SST) aircraft was feasible. Various proposals were considered and the Bristol 223 was adopted over a shorter, slower, medium range craft. Ten years later, on 2nd March 1969, the Anglo-French prototype flew for the first time. The later specification had required that it flew at near-conventional speeds on approach and landing, whilst being able to achieve Mach 2 – twice the speed of sound – during the cruise. And it had to maintain it for more than three hours. The range was to be four thousand miles, the service ceiling 60,000 feet and the payload at least one hundred passengers, cargo and fuel.

The contract was awarded to the BAC with the requirement to identify a risk-sharing partner. In the event this was the French company Sud-Aviation. After the Anglo-French SST consortium was set up, for a time two projects were pursued. The French medium range SST (Super Caravelle) was dropped in 1965 in favour of the Bristol 223 concept. This, in essence, became the original Bristol 198 proposal, much modified. The new maximum all up weight (MAUW – later MTWA or maximum take-off weight authorised) was to be 400,000 pounds, the length twenty feet greater, and the four Rolls-Royce Bristol Olympus/Snecma 593 Mk 610 engines would produce a total of more than 152,000 lbs of static thrust on take-off. Astonishing, the concept of kerosene being converted at that rate into so much controllable energy.

The Concorde treaty, when it was signed, had no break clause. This was insisted upon by the UK Government to prevent the French from reneging on the deal – the investment was being made by the UK taxpayer. The British Aircraft Corporation had refused to commit its own resources. In the event it was the Labour government that was prevented from reneging in 1964. The spelling of the name, Concorde, with an 'e', was adopted by mutual consent by Sir George Edwards of BAC and General André Puget of Sud-Aviation, contrary to the story that got around of an English capitulation to French chauvinism. Julian Amery, the Minister involved, was reportedly livid that he had not been involved. It was not until 1967 that there was concordance between government literature about the aircraft, which was always spelled *Concord*, and the agreement between Sir George Edwards and André Puget, which spelled it *Concorde*.

Not many people seem to know that air is quite heavy and that the weight of the air in a squash court is about one tonne. This is obvious when you watch a four hundred tonne, fully-loaded Boeing 747 taking off – the lift has to come from the atmosphere. Drag (resistance to forward motion through the air) is a limiting factor in (supersonic) flight and this is related to the wing span. Short wings give little lift at low speed and demand high speeds for take-off and landing. Thus was born the slender delta concept, or, in the case of Concorde, the complex ogee (double) delta planform which generated lift for take-off, in part by thrust which pushed the aircraft up on a wedge of under-wing air, and in part by slow vortex generation compressed by the incident airflow over the upper wing surfaces. This sometimes gave an impression of a bumping at low speeds (and at a low frequency) to the passenger, or it did on one occasion when I was leaving New York.

The prototype aircraft were 001, built by Aérospatiale at Toulouse, and 002, by BAC at Filton, Bristol. Concorde 001 made its first flight on 2nd March 1969 and first went supersonic six months later. Concorde 002 flew from Filton on 9th April 1969, piloted by Brian Trubshaw whom I met later and encouraged to talk at St Thomas's Hospital. The two prototypes met for the first time on 7th June of the same year at the Paris Air Show. They were nineteen feet shorter than the production aircraft. They were followed by two pre-production models – 01 and 02.

There were to be six prototypes, one of which, No. 202 or G-BBDG, is on display at Brooklands Museum. It was involved in development work and route-proving but never carried fare-paying passengers. It was cannibalised for spares before the wings were cut off for transportation to Brooklands. I reminded British Airways of my ICAO obligations in the hope of a trip, but "with the pressures of training" this did not come about. Concorde finally entered service in 1976. One who did make it was Patrick Forman, then with the *Sunday Times*. I asked him for his impression. After some general comments, he added that it was noisy – "This is your Captain shouting"; a line pinched by one of his tabloid colleagues. He added that the windows were hot, which they are in the cruise, for the following reason:

The troposphere is that part of the atmosphere above the frictional boundary layer of the surface of the earth – itself up to five thousand feet in depth. The troposphere is the lowest part of the atmosphere and contains four fifths of its mass and almost all of its water vapour. The temperature decreases with altitude (the lapse rate) until the tropopause when it becomes constant for a time at about –56 degrees Centigrade. Above the tropopause is the stratosphere. The depth of the troposphere is approximately 30,000 feet at the poles and up to 55,000 feet at the equator. It contains the weather. Above that, the supersonic ride is calm if a bit noisy. In spite of an outside air temperature (OAT) of –56 degrees Centigrade, the temperature on the nose of a Concorde at altitude and Mach 2 was +127 degrees Centigrade. As a result the length of the aeroplane increases several inches in supersonic flight as judged by the position of the combing adjacent to the engineer's panel.

Concorde did not achieve the success it deserved, in spite of it special status, for a number of reasons. Notwithstanding, it has been claimed that the aircraft made a profit of over £500 million for British Airways over the twenty-seven years of its service. There was initial protectionism expressed by way of noise limitation objections on the part of the United States, which had cancelled its Mach 3 project – the Boeing 2707 – in

1971. This had been due to a downturn in the industry at the time of the launch, concerns about the sonic boom, impact on the ozone layer, a quadrupling of the oil price, competition with the Boeing 747 and denial of overland supersonic flight for environmental reasons. And there was the subsequent loss of the Tupolev Tu 144 'Concordski' at the Paris Air Show in 1973.

It did, however provide a daily transatlantic service for twenty-seven years. It was eventually retired for economic reasons, three years following the Paris crash of AF4590, bound for New York on 25th July 2000. That incident itself was another example of the 'Swiss cheese' model of accident causation. Specifically, the aircraft was loaded nearly one tonne above its design weight and took off with an eight-knot tail wind. There had been an axle spacer left out during reassembly of the left main wheel bogey following a routine service which caused the aircraft to veer to the left on take-off, with related 'shimmy'. This was dismissed as not contributory by the French official enquiry. A previously departed aircraft, a Continental Airlines DC10, had shed a non-standard strip of metal onto the runway which was not, but should have been, checked for debris before the Concorde took off. This was picked up by a tyre at a speed close to 190 kts, the lump hitting the 100% full No. 5 tank, causing a shockwave within it. The resulting hydraulic rebound split the tank.

In 1995, Aerospatiale, following a request from the AAIB, recommended modification of the water deflector on the undercarriage in a Service Bulletin (SB) which was not given Airworthiness Directive (AD) status by either the UK or France. This followed several tyre burst incidents, four of which had occurred in the USA and been described as *potentially catastrophic* by the NTSB. British Airways, but not Air France, carried out the modification.

How the fire started is uncertain – it was forward of the after-burners, and associated with a compressor surge in both of the port-side engines, and loss of power. The flight engineer shut down engine No. 2, but not in response to the Captain's command. Electrical damage rendered retraction of the undercarriage to increase speed impossible. The aircraft did not fully leave ground effect. It was reported that the Captain,

Christian Marty, had been uneasy about the aircraft beforehand and requested that an afterburner be rechecked; this was not subsequently felt to have been involved in the accident causation...

Shortly before Concorde was returned to service in 2001, the so-called 9/11 attacks took place in New York, Washington and Philadelphia, bringing about a significant reduction in supersonic traffic. At the same time the manufacturers announced that foreseeable support costs were to rise from £60 million to £100 million and, as a result, the aircraft was withdrawn from service in October 2003.

★ ★ ★

On the appointed day Geoffrey Ratcliffe duly presented himself at our house at 09.30 to take me to the Concorde departure lounge. From there one could admire the aircraft, drink champagne and eat caviar canapés, if that was your habit at that time of the day. The excitement of the occasion was only slightly marred by muted concern about the whereabouts of a lost interline bag which had originated in Libya. As a premium target, security on the aircraft was always tight, as I was to learn on a departure from New York.

Once aboard I was invited onto the flight deck for the start-up, taxi and take-off. Not a lot of room. Indeed the cabin, which held a hundred passengers, was the diameter of a 1950s aircraft and it was only just possible to stand up. The seating was comfortable but not up to the club class standard of today. I sat behind the Captain, on the left, and adjacent to the flight engineer (F/E). The F/E station in the Concorde was not a soft option. He was responsible for the aircraft systems and fuel management, the latter being involved with the trim of the aircraft by shifting fuel forward and aft as well as from side to side.

Before starting and during the pre-start checks, the various speeds appropriate to the weight of the aircraft (MTWA 185 tonnes), the runway, its condition, the outside air temperature (OAT) and atmospheric pressure were factored into the 'speed bugs'. These are movable flags on the air speed indicator (ASI). V1 is the take-off decision speed – if an engine failure occurs below this speed, take-off is aborted; above it there is an irrevocable commitment to take off. Vr is the rotation speed – the nose is raised to a pre-determined angle following which the aircraft accelerates to V2. V2 is the take-off safety speed – this minimum speed must be reached at low level if an engine is inoperative.

Start-up involved the use of a ground trolley, which was associated with a noise like a giant cheese grater as each engine was turned and allowed to warm up. This was due to the slight bowing of the shaft as it cooled from the dull red heat at which the 'hot end' worked. Ask anyone in the know the cleverest part of the engine, and he/she will answer that it is the lubrication. Without lubricants nothing will move, or at least keep moving. The nose was lowered five degrees. There was a strongish whiff of burnt kerosene – "Not to worry," someone said. Taxiing was unique to the aircraft. The pilot sat thirty-eight feet ahead of the nose wheel and ninety-seven feet ahead of the main undercarriage, making for a significant overlap of the grass areas. There was a pronounced bounce due to a whipping motion of the extended nose and the sensation, if you were on the flight deck, was akin to sitting in a tractor seat. This was so severe on taking off on Runway 13L at Kennedy Airport, New York, that sitting in the same position I was unable to do more than hang on. The oscillation was such that focusing was impossible due to vertical nystagmus (up-and-down movement of the eyeballs); no doubt the Captain had some trick up his four-ringed sleeve. The motion was of sufficient concern to the engineers that it was monitored by strain gauges to detect potential fatigue in the front part of the fuselage.

Once on the move on the taxiway Air Traffic passed our flight clearance, which included cruise climbing towards Bristol. There clearance would be given to operate between 50,000 and 60,000 feet over the Atlantic Ocean. The final operating altitude depended on OAT and fuel burn, the aircraft rising with its declining weight. As we moved along everyone nearby stopped and some waved. We waved back. We lined up, two tons of fuel lighter than when we had started.

"Speedbird Concorde 191 authorised for take-off as cleared."

"Speedbird Concorde 191 rolling."

"Three-two-one now!" called the Pilot Flying. The reheat switches had been selected – on – before take-off, and ignited at approximately 75% of power during throttle advance. The throttles were slammed fully forward, to be held by the flight engineer. Failure of ignition of one afterburner was allowable only if the all-up weight permitted it. Failure of two was a no-go situation as the aircraft was unable to achieve supersonic flight without them.

The acceleration was breathtaking. V1 was reached at about 170 kts and Vr at about 195 kts. After about seventy seconds (previously calculated), the Pilot Non-Flying called:

"Three-two-one – noise" (abatement).

And the flight engineer retarded the throttles a predetermined amount whilst switching off the afterburners. It was like hitting a wall, so abrupt was the deceleration. The afterburners increased thrust by about 25% and in this initial stage of the flight about one further tonne of fuel will have been burnt. The climb continued at reduced power and with the airspeed just below the sound barrier – Mach 0.95. This continued until the point in the Bristol Channel at which, following clearance, the throttles were pushed fully forward, the afterburners relit and the aircraft climbed towards its operating altitude. On the way it would pass through the sound barrier at Mach 1. The afterburners were switched off again at Mach 1.7 with continuing acceleration towards Mach 2. The Russian Tuplovev 144 ('Concordski'), believed to have been built, in part, with stolen technology, had to keep the afterburners switched on to maintain supersonic flight. It never entered commercial service.

There was no impression of a barrier apart from the behaviour of the pressure instruments – the Vertical Speed Indicator (VSI) and the Air Speed Indicator (ASI) – which went bananas as the shockwaves moved backwards over their static air vents. Eventually the aircraft reached Mach 2 or 1,350 mph, which was held by the Mach 'Max Cruise' mode of the autopilot and auto-throttle. In the aircraft it was peaceful above the weather, although there was engine and slip-steam noise; ahead was the deep indigo of space with the curvature of the earth visible on the horizon. For the next three hours or so the aircraft would be at full throttle and Mach 2, continuously – faster than a rifle bullet.

Then something unexpected happened. The Captain, John Hutchinson, turned round.

"Would you like to come and sit in my seat?"

John Hutchinson started his career with BOAC. He was an acting flight officer (in training) on Speedbird 712 on 8th April 1968 when the Boeing 707-465 suffered a serious engine fire, with separation before the emergency landing. Due to confusion over the checklists and in spite of a successful landing, five of the 127 people on board lost their lives. Sadly this included Stewardess Barbara Harrison who was awarded a posthumous George Cross for her efforts to save the passengers. John went on to be a senior Captain on the Concorde and Master of the Guild of Air Pilots and Navigators (now the Honourable Company of Air Pilots). He was also in demand as a commentator at air shows.

I moved in, having memorised the layout of the instruments. This was not much different from any other large aircraft. At the top in the middle was the attitude indicator (the artificial horizon); below it the plan navigation indicator (PNI) with its gyro compass readout, VOR radio navigation indicator, ADF and distance measuring equipment (DME) indicators. To the upper left was the air speed indicator (ASI), below it the Mach meter and below that another VOR indicator. The pressure and radio altimeters were on the right, with the VSI as a strip in between. We were comfortable at Mach 2.

"If you press that button [on the control yoke], you will disengage out the flight director."

"And if you press it a second time the autopilot will disengage too."

So I did, and for half an hour hand-flew this unique aeroplane. When I pressed the button for the second time it seemed that there was the smallest bump on the yoke, just like other aircraft when the clutches which hold the control yoke disengage. Was this the explanation? Concorde was tremendously sensitive in pitch. The least finger pressure was all that was needed to climb and descend. Attention was riveted upon the centre dot of the attitude indicator. The slightest pitch up and the aircraft gained five hundred feet, and the Mach speed decayed – perhaps to Mach 1.96, and vice versa.

"Is someone hand-flying this aeroplane?" asked a pilot who was dead-legging the trip and had come onto the flight deck; maybe he was concerned that the autopilot was hunting.

"Try a Rate 1 turn," said the Captain.

"With all this high-value cargo?"

So I did, but there is no chance of getting lost with such a manoeuvre. Even with fifteen degrees of bank, the heading only changed very slowly. After a while there was the need for preparation for the descent and I moved out. What an experience, and one for which I will always to be grateful to the Captain, co-pilot and flight engineer. At least I was in compliance with ICAO Annex 1, 1.2.4.5.2., if not with 1.1.2.8.2.

We landed at Kennedy an hour before we had taken off from Heathrow. I took the limousine to mid-town Manhattan and walked around Tiffany's in the footsteps of Audrey Hepburn and George Peppard, twenty years beforehand, when I was still a medical student. There is, or used to be, a toy shop next door where I bought a teddy bear for our son, David, who had been born three days earlier. There was time for a lunch of buffalo mozzarella salad before returning to Kennedy for the journey back to London at 13.30. I flew the aircraft again on the way back, too, and arrived to be picked up by Geoffrey at 22.00 or thereabouts. Not a tiring day – a normal one time-wise in my speciality. David was asleep in his cot on my return. What an astonishing achievement the whole Concorde project was; conceived, designed and made in England, too, with a bit of help from the French.

I did fly in the Concorde on one more trip. On that occasion we completed the journey in three hours and six minutes, west to east with the blessing of a hefty tailwind – close to the record. We had troubling buffeting immediately after take-off, perhaps related to those low speed vortices, during the noise abatement procedure. The passenger next to me looked alarmed in spite of flying on the aircraft thrice weekly. The crew looked blank when I asked them what it was.

As we passed southeast abeam Nova Scotia, the Captain pointed out Sable Island, a narrow strip of land, less than a mile wide and about twenty-six miles long, with surf breaking upon it. It is administered by Canada. It is inhabited by wild horses which, legend has it, swum ashore at the time of the Pilgrim Fathers when a ship was wrecked upon the reef and the crew lost. The truth is probably more prosaic. There was an attempt at colonisation by the French in the 16th century. There are 350 recorded wrecks off what has been suggested is a terminal moraine from the Pleistocene age which ended about 12,000 years ago with the commencement of the present interglacial Holocene period. There has been a succession of inhabitants over the centuries, recently in an attempt to conserve its ecology. There are four or five permanent residents now.

Geoffrey did arrange another visit. This time it was to the Hong Kong Aircraft Engineering Company Limited, known as HAECO. Now it is a leading aeronautical engineering group providing a range of services including airframe maintenance, engine overhaul, freighter conversion, line maintenance and fleet technical management. I was passing through to give a lecture to the International Academy of Aviation and Space Medicine meeting held in Brisbane that year. HAECO was based at Kai Tak which at that time was the international airport of Hong Kong. It had opened in 1925 and was closed in 1998 when the new Hong Kong International Airport at Chek Lap Kok opened. Anyone who has flown the approach for real, or in the flight simulator, to Runway 13 at Kai Tak will remember it. It involved flying the ILS in a north-easterly direction until a giant orange and white checkerboard was identified, at which point a forty-seven degree visual right turn lined the aircraft up with the runway; all this at low altitude over Kowloon.

At the HAECO facility I was taken round by the chief engineer. There were ten or so early Boeing 707 aircraft from Communist China which were returning to the USA for refurbishment and/or scrapping. They were in poor condition and simply furnished. All showed dilapidation and significant corrosion. The pressure hulls on some had blown outwards and there were holes with small tears. Some appeared to have been repaired by a shipwright with large aluminium plates and vast rivets. Some had been left unrepaired. Two were to fly back to the USA at 10,000 feet as they could not be pressurised. Others had to be scrapped. But they had flown on in spite of this – what a credit to the strength and redundancy of those aircraft that they were still flying.

DÉNOUEMENT

...time Rhamnusidis iram! (confer: fear the wrath of Nemesis)

Ovid (43 BC–17 AD); *Metamorphoses 14, 693*

At the beginning of our working lives we look up at the heads of our professions with respect, even awe. Some ape the mannerisms, echo the opinions and tumble about at the anecdotes of those with the soubriquet of 'the good and the great'. Later we find these emperors are quite often not so much scantily clad as pretty much in the buff. Strategy, initiatives, decisions – believed to be the product of careful thought and robust review – are scratchings on the back of an envelope. Conformity and toadyism are the roadmap (or is it the toolkit?) to reward and honour; knowledge, experience, originality and leadership are in eclipse.

Management occupies the best suites, the costliest furniture and the best-shod PAs. The MBA (master of business administration) rules, OK, and like the cuckoo in the nest, has kicked out the science degree. Soft-shoed conmen – management consultants – are hired at prodigious cost to give verisimilitude to dodgy preconceptions. That this is the ascendancy of the apparatchik and the neophyte is less important than the demise of good faith, and the atrophy of leadership. Mendacity is king, and honesty a vice if it patinates the escutcheon of the brand, focuses on responsibility, obstructs management whim or impedes profit or personal advancement. These maxims appear to span public life, the statutory bodies and politics.

★ ★ ★

A recession is when you have to tighten your belt; depression is when you have no belt to tighten. When you've lost your trousers, you're in the airline business, said Sir Adam Thomson (1927–2000), founder and chairman of British Caledonian, once voted the best airline in the world before it was taken over by British Airways. Aviation is full of aphorisms. *The only way to make a small fortune in aviation is to start with a large one* is based on the irony that risk in the air is broader than the avoidance of accident on the ground. Accountants travel as dark riders – spoilers on the aerofoil of progress.

It was a coincidence that within a few days of the foundation of the CAA in 1972, Marshal of the Royal Air Force Sir Dermot Boyle unveiled a plaque in the RAF Officers' Mess at Farnborough. It commemorated the 60th anniversary of the formation of the Royal Flying Corps (RFC). This morphed into the Royal Air Force on 1st April 1918. The plaque also recalled the arrival of the Royal Engineers balloon factory from Aldershot in 1905, which became the Royal Aircraft Factory with the establishment of the RFC in 1912. Later it was renamed the Royal Aircraft Establishment (RAE) in 1918, to avoid confusion with the newly formed Royal Air Force. Number 1 Squadron, RAF, now flying Typhoons, can date its origins back to No. 1 Balloon Company at the Royal Arsenal at Woolwich in 1878. It became the Air Battalion of the Royal Engineers in 1911, and No. 1 Squadron, RFC, a year later. It finally became No. 1 Squadron, RAF, in 1918. It is now only one of seven front line squadrons remaining (in 2015); there were still 37.5 squadrons in 1991 – the time of the First Gulf War.

The need for strong defence is one of the lawns of ignorance of the political class, which as a rule has little experience, and no understanding, of the military. It prefers to throw vast sums of funding borrowed on behalf of the taxpayer to pay for advisors and lush up corrupt regimes in the hope of buying certain sectors of the electorate. By 2030, according to a recent House of Commons Library report (March 2015), overseas aid will have overtaken the defence budget. Soon we will have no armed services, just the gleaming citadel of the MOD, fashioning arcane memos, promoting flag officers to the Serpentine pond, rewarding itself vastly and collecting knighthoods. And like King Cnut the Great (990 – 1035), will be inundated.

★ ★ ★

The Royal Aircraft Establishments, Farnborough and Bedford (which opened in 1946), at the time of this anniversary (1972) were at their post-war peak, employing six thousand people in what was a government-funded research and development effort. This was about to dwindle along with our relative influence. RAE Bedford was to close in 1994, and RAE Farnborough had become the Defence Research Agency (DRA) in 1991. The DRA and other MOD organisations finally merged to form the Defence Evaluation and Research Agency (DERA) in 1995.

From their separate foundations, RAE Farnborough and RAE Bedford were centres of excellence, and of innovation. Farnborough had designed and manufactured thirty types of aircraft before such activity was discontinued in 1916. This included the Farman Experimental (FE 2), The Bleriot Experimental (BE) and the Scout Experimental SE5a, one of the outstanding fighters of the Great War of which over 5,200 were subsequently built elsewhere. These institutions were responsible for an extraordinary diversity of original ideas and research, including the development and trial of numerous experimental aircraft. The second of two wind tunnels, opened at Farnborough in 1935, together with the advanced (supersonic) wind tunnels at Bedford, were used to study the aerodynamics of the Concorde. The unique pressure and thermal stresses on its airframe during supersonic flight were evaluated on the Farnborough site. This sought to determine its fatigue life in a programme which continued after the aircraft had entered service.

The cause of the DH 106 Comet 1 disasters was investigated by the Accident Investigation Section, based there. It was shown to be due to fatigue failure of the pressure hull and led to redesign of the aircraft. As a schoolboy I watched as the sealed fuselage of a Comet aircraft, taken from the fleet, was rhythmically pressurised and depressurised in a water tank until it ruptured after some three thousand cycles. Following considerable modification it flew again as the Comet 2 with the RAF, and in civilian form as the Comet 4, powered by the Rolls-Royce Avon AJ 65 engines which had replaced the original DH Ghost 50 engines. But we had lost the lead in passenger jet transport.

The in-flight break-up of the de Havilland DH110 at the 1952 Farnborough air show, in which the test pilot, John Derry, and twenty-nine spectators lost their lives, was also investigated there. The disaster was attributed to aerolastic flutter (high speed aerodynamic buffet overcoming structural damping of the innate periodicity of the wing), which caused failure of the wing root in a high g (gravitational effect) left turn following a supersonic fly past. The RAE boffins (a term they were said to dislike) supported the flourishing aircraft industry, both civil and military. On one occasion, Brian Trubshaw, later Concorde chief test pilot, flew a prototype atomic bomb out of the field in a Vickers Valiant. The (dummy) bomb came loose and was dropped in the Thames estuary, without mishap, although a diversion had to be made to RAF Manston on account of damage to the airframe. Dummy bombs, but no dumb bunnies from the Health and Safety Executive, flew on that mission.

★ ★ ★

The RAF Institute of Aviation Medicine (IAM) was a separate entity on the site. In 1945 it succeeded the wartime RAF Physiological Laboratory, which had been set up eleven days before the outbreak of the Second World War in 1939. It carried out basic research into the effects of altitude, acceleration and deceleration, g effect mitigation in high performance aircraft, and weightlessness; there was much interest in the special senses. Some of this work was dangerous, even heroic, with rocket-propelled sledges and ejection ramps. Real *Boy's Own Paper* stuff. I recall seeing a patient from Farnborough at St Thomas's Hospital following an incident with a mercury seal – he had contrived to prevent the arterial blood he was sampling from himself coming in contact with air. In doing so, he had tipped a significant volume of elemental mercury into his circulation. The X-ray images of his hand were extraordinary – like a leaf coral.

The IAM had been staffed, in part, by service medical officers. With the contraction of the armed services and the abandonment of the service hospitals by Secretary of State for Health, the Right Honourable (later Baroness) Virginia Bottomley (1992–1995), it was unsustainable. Some of the research staff and facilities were moved to the DERA Centre for Human Sciences. Most of the old IAM buildings have been demolished and replaced by housing. It was closed in 1994 as part of the defence cuts associated with the so-called peace dividend, an infantile and subsequently undelivered financial bonus supposedly marking the end of the Cold War. It was another case of political myopia and indifference, leading to assets and expertise built up over generations being squandered.

Now Farnborough is an airport, a business park, a housing estate, a museum, the home to the Air Accidents Investigation Branch (AAIB) and the headquarters of QinetiQ, a British defence technology company and part of the former UK government Defence Evaluation and Research Agency (DERA), privatised in June 2001. Samuel Franklin Cody will have turned in his grave. The asinine 'private sector knows best' mindset was in evidence when the coalition administration (sunk May 2015) announced the appointment of two American companies, Bechtel and CH2M Hill, to run defence procurement at the MOD – the former reportedly with a reputation, itself, for going over budget on (US) contracts. Clearly the UK is incompetent and is out of its depth on the world stage; and our politicians have no sense of national pride. Watch as the contracts go overseas as our defence-related industries atrophy. It is time we left the UN Security Council to those with greater ability and sense of responsibility.

It could be concluded from the obsession with the private sector that our public servants are inferior, in terms of quality and leadership, when compared with their private sector equivalents. Historically this was not the case and it is the political class which is more clueless. Leadership with accountability is needed to cut the over-manning and waste in Whitehall procurement. The saving could be usefully employed by the Armed Services for the protection of the UK homeland and the nurturing of our science and technology. As we are now too feeble to manage defence procurement, our defence-related industries will be dismantled. The French and the Germans evidently have no such difficulties. They, not us, are the new Europe. *Goodbye to all that*, as Robert Graves wrote in 1929, after the Great War.

★ ★ ★

From its foundation in 1972 onwards, the nascent CAA inherited a formidable reputation for all-round excellence. Its component parts included the old Air Registration Board (ARB) and other, related, agencies. It was charged with the regulation of aircraft certification (including test flying), licensing and medical certification of pilots, aircraft engineers, air traffic controllers, commercial air operators including airlines, aerodromes, organisations involved in the design, production and maintenance of aircraft, ATOL (Air Travel Organisers' Licensing) holders and the registration of aircraft – 19,000 in the UK at present. On the operational side at that time the chief test pilot was D. P. Davies. He had flown in combat during the Second World War and joined the ARB in 1949. He wrote what is still one of the best books on the subject – *Handling the Big Jets*, published by the ARB – in spite of the third and last edition having been published over forty years ago.

Davies was responsible for the certificatory flight trials of the world's first passenger jet aircraft, up to and including the big jets and Concorde. The ARB would refuse to issue a certificate of airworthiness (C of A) to foreign-built aircraft without full evaluation. When Sir Giles Guthrie wrecked the export potential of the Vickers VC10 for BOAC by preferring the US Boeing 707 on the grounds of economy, the ARB insisted that Boeing fitted a rear ventral fin to the aircraft to improve its longitudinal stability. This modification was subsequently made generally available by the company. The small economic disadvantage of the VC10 initially was due to the extra 'hot and high' performance demanded by BOAC in its original specification. However the rear-mounted engines did impose a weight penalty from the resulting requirement for a stronger wing.

On the Atlantic run, the passengers preferred the VC10 to the Boeing 707. Due to the ill-judgement of Guthrie, only fifty-four were built, fourteen for the RAF. I only flew the VC10 on one trip – to see a paediatric cardiologist patient in Ghana at the request of the University Hospital in Accra. We took off in bad weather from Heathrow, the 1102 'combi' of Ghana Airways becoming airborne in twenty-five seconds, courtesy of its big wing and Rolls-Royce Conway engines. On arrival at Kotoka airport I was arrested for taking a photograph of it. The VC10 held the record for the fastest Atlantic crossing before Concorde arrived. We have a gene in the UK, not expressed by our European cousins, for behaving like numbskulls and shooting ourselves in the brain on the grounds of financial expediency and short-term political gain.

The CAA, Davies told me, had also criticised McDonnell Douglas for the lack of a lock to prevent the asymmetric deployment of the leading edge lift device (slats) on the DC10. There was also lack of redundancy in, and communication between, the stall warning systems on both sides. It demanded a modification for UK certification. When the port engine of the American Airlines DC10-10 N110AA, flight 191, separated on take-off from Chicago O'Hare in May 1979 due to improper maintenance procedures, the leading edge slats were damaged causing loss of lift on that side. This was unknown to the pilot as there was no indication of their relative position. In trading speed for height, the port wing stalled and two hundred and seventy-one lives were lost. The passengers were able to watch the trajectory of the doomed flight on the newly installed television.

Sometimes the CAA was not so quick on the draw. The Lufthansa Boeing 747-100 D-ABYB flight LH540, which crashed on take-off from Nairobi in 1974, was a classical demonstration of accident causation. Fifty-nine of the 157 people on board were killed. Lufthansa used a non-standard start-up procedure which involved closure of the bleed air valves deploying the Krueger leading edge (LE) slats; the trailing edge (TE) flaps are hydraulically activated on this aircraft. These are lift devices. On the occasion of the crash, the flight engineer had not reopened the valves following start-up. There was no take-off configuration warning (TOCW), indicating that the Krueger flaps were still stowed. This had been deactivated by the correct position of the master flap lever which deployed both the LE and TE devices.

The problem had occurred on eight previous occasions but had been ignored by the FAA as the TOCW was not mandatory. There had been an incident involving a British Airways Boeing 747 two years beforehand when half of the LE flaps failed to extend due to a maintenance error. This was duly reported to the CAA. Approval from Boeing was sought for a simple rewire to bring an LE flap-stowed warning up on take-off, if appropriate. The FAA ruled that the modification was superfluous. Five months before this accident, John Boulding, safety officer at British Airways, learnt that the safety problem British Airways had reported had not been disseminated. He was said to have written three letters to the CAA, three months before the accident, saying: *...the industry has already* *had two close shaves and the next operator **and the passengers** [my emphasis] might not be so lucky…*

There was no response, even though the last letter had been written to the relevant official's home. The CAA denied having received any communication and in response to admonishment by BALPA, which had accused the CAA, the FAA and Boeing of complacency, responded by reminding the airlines of their responsibility to ensure that their correspondence was received by the CAA.

★ ★ ★

Plus ça change. Forty years later, as the CAA dumbs down with the rest of the UK and abandons its pre-eminent regulatory position in Europe, there are not only problems with communication, but in the wider world, with vision. In 2014, the Boeing Pilot and Technical Market Outlook for 2014–2033 forecast the need for half a million *new* commercial airline pilots to fly the 21,000 additional aircraft entering the world fleet over the next twenty years. To help solve the problem, one solution suggested is that there could be only one pilot flying, interacting with a ground control. Ever squawked the loss of communication code 7600 on your transponder, Brian? Or flown with clenched buttocks on account of gastro-enteritis?

Now, as EASA has recently examined, there is the widely canvassed promotion of the Cruise Relief Pilot (CRP) and co-pilot (CRCP). Rather than train all pilots to the same standard, there are to be cruise pilots, accredited to fly above 20,000 feet and unqualified for the approach or landing phases. Just who will board this asylum of the air? These people will never have been baptised by solo flight. They will be computer jockeys only, where there is already evidence that go-faster toy management training is inadequate at times. Only 10% of fatal accidents originate in the cruise, although the recent accidents, to flights AF447 (2009) and QZ8501 (2014), were due to loss of control by fully qualified pilots in this phase of flight. Both were weather-related. How can it be true in this day and age, that for whatever reason, the man-machine interface is such that LCIF (loss of control in flight) is the most important cause of fatal accidents?

Aviation presently absorbs 3.5% of world GDP and its activity overall is expected to increase by at least one third over the next decade. The constructors enjoy building, the airlines are keen to hire, the self-loading cargo is anxious to board and the regulators are aching to increase bureaucracy, but there appears to be no cohesive policy on training the required number of pilots. And while you are there, Brian, ground engineers, too. Why are we brainwashed about cost when pilot training is such a small but vital part of the overall financial, and safety, envelope? The culture needs to be re-examined – not bowing to minority group pressure (by accountants) is one aspect of leadership.

★ ★ ★

Alice fell victim to LCIF as she dropped into the rabbit hole. Mindful of thrust-attitude coupling, she applied her 4-5-4 rule: Power: 4/5ths of N1; attitude: + 4°, wings level with the rudder. She made a safe landing. Her aviation knowledge she had to obtain, retrospectively, from the flamingo with whom she was to play croquet. On her return from the Looking Glass world, she brought with her some random jottings from the Red Queen who, likewise, had no knowledge of, or affiliation with, aviation. Humpty Dumpty, who paid words extra for over-working them, also contributed. He used to reward them on Saturdays.

Between them the following emerged:

- All public transport aircraft exceeding 5,700 kg MTWA should carry at least two, or more, classically trained pilots – dependant on the length of the flight.

- There should be an international initiative to identify solutions to the acute pilot shortage, involving the industry at all levels. The investors are out there. We need engineers, too. Training also needs to be beefed up by some operators.

- Zero hour contracts mirror 'the Lump' in the building industry in the UK fifty years ago. This practice was abolished in 1972 after an acrimonious strike. Two men were jailed. Pilots, like anyone else, need regular employment. They also need recency to retain their licence. If this is not adequate, it is unsafe. If they speak up they are vulnerable. This practice needs regulation as it has the potential to threaten safety.

- There is scope for a better forensic understanding of CFIT (controlled flight into terrain) and LCIF (loss of control in flight) in the search for common threads of causation. These will include inadequate training and inappropriate/inadequate flight-deck discipline which may have societal, or cultural, origin. Aircraft have to come down sometime, somewhere, so perhaps CFIT is more understandable than LCIF

- It is not excusable for a pilot to be so far behind a serviceable aircraft that control is lost. There are human performance limitations, but airline pilot capability has to be demonstrably robust in the face of adversity. Yet 1,773 lives were lost in eighteen accidents in the years 2002–2011 due to LCIF accidents. This is the most important cause of accidents in terms of loss of life.

- As the pilot ruins his/her trousers sliding down the wrong side of the Yerkes-Dodson stress/performance curve, the operational environment could be simplified. The throttle position could be analogue, and the stick positions locked together and indicative of both pitch and roll input, on both sides of the aircraft. But the Airbus family is very safe indeed.

- When the autopilot develops acopia – as we say in medicine – reversion to a standard flight mode should be clear-cut and neutral. Protection will be enhanced by better hands-on training at the edge of the flight envelope in real aircraft rather than in synthetic flight. This costs, but should help reduce the number of occasions when the mission, and all on board, are lost.

- An RQ (Red Queen) button, available in extremis, which sheds the digital claptrap and reverts the aircraft to a standard configuration, bears consideration. The pilot should be trained to fly away from this point in any unusual attitude, or configuration, in any aeroplane, anywhere and in his/her sleep.

- Weather briefing needs to be improved. Significant weather is not always very predictable, but its extent and eventuality should be fully assessed for each flight, and avoidance pre-planned well ahead – so far as it is possible. Air Traffic Control needs to be fully integrated and responsive to the need for possible severe weather avoidance, *propter hoc.*

- Aviation medicine, with its speciality add-ons, is seen as a tedious necessity. This is wrong. Personnel medical fitness standards are inexpensive to apply in the context of the total aviation scene and are an important safety component. There should be *PROPER* oversight and speciality input in the resolution of problems, and in the development of Standards. Regulation should be a hands-on affair and not distanced by contract.

- In the UK, splitting the AMS off from the co-located AeMC will weaken both. The proposal found no support during the consultation process (*CAP 1276*). This in itself was an expression of confidence by its clientele in the status quo. Loss of the specialist clinic will mean loss of daily AMS access to specialist advice, with concomitant degradation of EASA Standard generation. This has already been weakened by non-specialist drafting. The one-stop regulatory culture will be lost with privatisation by contract.

- There should be NO qualification of the Class 1 standard, apart from an operational limitation (to fly as/with a co-pilot), if this is indicated. ***Fitness to fly should have visible boundaries.***

- Regulation in aviation should be led by people who know what they are talking about – engineers, test pilots, airline operations people and medical specialists. This applies at national, regional and international level.

Said Alice.

NEMESIS ET EXIT

Nothing is more dangerous than an idea, when it's the only one we have.

Émile-Auguste Chartier (1868–1951); philosopher, poet and pacifist.

"You do not go into regulation if you wish to be liked," said Dame Deidre Hutton, DBE, at a Guild of Air Pilots (now the Honourable Company) Livery dinner in 2013. Fasten your seat belts. She was appointed to the chair of the CAA, her qualification being the *Queen of the QUANGOs (Daily Telegraph,* 15th November 2009). She had come from the Food Standards Agency. According to the *Telegraph* she confessed, on appointment, that she knew "nothing about aeroplanes". Of course not. Aviation, although highly technical, has always tended to be the arena of the instant expert. Likewise the CEO, Andrew Haines, had come from the railways.

At least the heart is a pump. My great grandfather designed the first mass produced steam locomotive, a 2-2-2 called the *Jenny Lind*, for the London, Brighton and South Coast Railway. Lind (1820 – 1887) was an opera singer known as the *Swedish Nightingale*. She was admired by Schumann, Berlioz, and particularly, Mendelssohn, who often wrote entreating her to….. Having settled in London, she became a professor of singing at the Royal College of Music. Meanwhile, back at the Barrow Shipbuilding Company, my forebear's steam valve-gear was eponymously named and extensively used, especially in Russia where 4,500 were installed on their O Class locomotive – half of a total production run of 9,129 both before and after the Russian revolution. The 5 ft gauge predominated.

Ah, steam!

Now Alice for the flight deck, and the White Rabbit as a dispatcher, I suppose?

Regulatores, quo vadis?

★ ★ ★

As of April 2015, the CAA Medical Department was heading for the ITCZ with its Pitot heaters switched off. After forty years, during which it achieved an international reputation, senior management had gone into the détente of the mind set by setting out to privatise some of its services. Like British Airways before it with its ethnic tail-planes, in an act of self-mutilation it was about to hobble its identity. In the case of British Airways, it is claimed that PhD theses were written in the USA on: *How to destroy a brand.*

No doubt encouraged by the Government 'Red Tape Initiative', a paper had emerged – *CAP 1214* (November 2014); *Consultation on the Future Structure of the CAA's Medical Department:*

'The purpose of this consultation is to seek the views of all interested parties on the options available to the CAA for carrying out aeromedical regulation and oversight and enabling the provision of aeromedical services'.

Reasons given for the consultation (which was to be ignored) included:

1. Cost
2. The problem of the regulator overseeing its own service (governance)
3. Fitness of the Medical Department for the future – a metaphor for "Let's privatise and get rid of these turbulent doctors."

These bland and seemingly innocuous statements bore the presumption, subsequently proved correct, that in common with other organisations such as the NHS, policy had been petrified before consultation took place. *CAP 1276* was not far behind (February 2015) and suggested, with some circumlocution, that the fence was still under load as the implications had, unsurprisingly, not been thought through. It intoned: *By reducing the total cost and by ceasing activities that are not essential, the CAA believes it will be possible to lower the total burden to industry…*

This was sophistry, or worse, dissembly. These 'non-essential' activities, such as the initial medical examination and specialist back-up, have to be performed somewhere, and be paid for by someone. It is also a highly specialised area. I made two PIDA protected (whistle blower) statements in a decade, to senior management of the CAA over concerns about governance. Partly, they related to this issue, but an exit-block was present, as we say in cardiology. I pointed out, inter alia, that it was lamentable at that time to return to the AMEs the fee for reading the computer generated ECG reports, involving five seconds of professional time. It cost the department one tenth of its annual income. I was told that it was a 'bribe' (sic) to encourage the AMEs to go online. This sum alone had covered the cost of the specialist clinic and required a further charge to be passed onto the industry. People do not like to be confused with the facts once their minds have been made up.

It is disingenuous of the CAA to emphasise the discrepancy between the income derived from clients attending the Centre and the cost of providing this service, said one of the (identity redacted) respondents to *CAP 1214*, minuted in *CAP 1276*. Others commented on the 'pathetic' level of financial data. The Medical Department specialist consultation charges are half, and the investigational charges one third, of the prevailing market rate. The CAA should be charged with failure of due diligence in terms of its policy of cost recovery. Buttressed by process and detached from reality, the combination of these deficits was to be the Sidewinder missile primed to disable the Medical Department. Had the CAA charged the market rate, the department could have made a profit.

The publication *CAP 1276* claimed that outsourcing the AeMC clinic would reduce cost to the industry. Where was the evidence? And without the evidence, where is the governance? It cannot do so – a private, even a non-profitmaking, clinic will charge market rates, or more. It could reduce cost to the CAA, but that is a different issue. What else can be stripped out and scrapped? The total annual departmental budget was put at £4.3 million a year, in *CAP 1214*. The cost of medical oversight of aircrew is an unbelievably small percentage of the overall cost of the operation. It approximates to 0.01% per hour flown based on a Direct Operating Cost (DOC) of the aircraft of £10,000/hour, medical certification of the two pilots costing < £1,000/year - <£1/hour flown or a penny or two per ticket. On the day the priceless lives (unless you are a lawyer) of each and every one of the 3.1 billion passengers who travel by air each year ultimately depend on the performance of the two aircrew up at the front. One pound sterling an hour, give or take, is not much – truly a widow's mite (Mark 12:41–44).

The Aeromedical Section (AMS), whose functions with the nuts and bolts of certification are largely mandatory – legally required – and the Aeromedical Centre (AeMC), which performs medical examinations – a non-mandatory function – occupy the same space in Aviation House, Gatwick. They are complementary, but the former has oversight of the latter. Initially EASA frowned upon the lack of separation. Later it accepted co-location, provided the Head of the AeMC was not the CMO. Concern about the CAA overseeing its own clinic may be an issue of governance, but it is not enshrined in the European law relating to EASA. It appears to be an idée fixe on the part of the Authority. There has been no demonstrable search for an alternative solution to improve the status quo, itself an issue of governance. But this cannot be confirmed as the authority sought exemption from response to my enquiry under the Freedom of Information Act, 2000 (FOI).

Advice was sought from 'an external consultant' and other persons unknown. When their identity and contribution were requested by the author under the FOI, it was refused on the basis that it might inhibit the free and frank provision of advice [Section 36 (2) (b) (i)], and free and frank exchange of views [Section 36 (2) (b) (ii)]. Finally Section 36 (2) (c) was applied as transparency in this case was deemed to be prejudicial to the conduct of public affairs; like private affairs, some might feel. The 'qualified person' who refereed this adverse decision was the CAA Finance and Corporate Services Director. Maybe not an impartial opinion – unlike the Independent Person under section 28(8)(a) of the Localism Act, 2011, who cannot be an employee. This relates to County Councillors. Further protection was sought under Section 40 – details of staffing and their remuneration had been given to third parties (with their permission?), and Section 41 – there were some non-disclosure agreements in force for unstated reasons. When one is off-side, one hopes no-one is looking.

There are few aspects of public life where secrecy enhances judgement or public confidence and this manoeuvring is counter-current to accepted best practice; and the governance so widely espoused by the CAA. There is also an irony. The CAA board has stated that the AMS should not have oversight of the AMS but the Secretary of State for Transport, under the FOIA section 36 paragraph (5)(o) appoints the 'qualified person' (an employee) to be the arbitrator on information provision.

★ ★ ★

The value of the specialist clinic needs amplification. The CAA clinic doctors who carry out the routine medical examinations, as AMEs, are specialists in occupational health and aviation medicine. They do not have clinical responsibility beyond that. The different niveaux of the medical hierarchy may seem esoteric, but there is divergence in knowledge, practice, experience and attitude. The cardiologist (or other attending clinical specialist) will have undergone years of additional clinical training and research after qualification, and have concomitant direct patient care responsibility, elsewhere. The occupational health physician will not. This does not diminish the importance of the latter – it should be a team effort and the relationship symbiotic for the benefit of the airman under review.

The CAA clinic specialist has no treatment relationship with the applicant (pilot) and in common with the regulator, must not interfere with the management of the usual medical attendant (i.e. the general practitioner or hospital specialist). The phenomenon of a doctor in a functionally non-patient-care role is not limited to the CAA. It may be seen in academic appointments in the university hospitals where clinical 'respectability' is limited to a weekly outpatient clinic, and a cup of tea with a ward sister. It is also seen in Public Health and the pharmaceutical industry.

Once the specialist clinics (including psychiatry, neurology, respirology and ophthalmology, in addition to cardiology and general internal medicine - GIM) were underway, the benefit was evident in terms of quality assurance. By the time the CAA Board was planning to close down and outsource the in-house specialist service in 2014-5, there were between 400 and 500 cardiological consultations and nearly 600 cardiovascular investigations being carried out at the Gatwick AeMC each year. The number of resting electrocardiograms was evidently not recorded but is believed to be of the order of 18,000 per year. Starkly, in the light of the Germanwings pilot suicide with the murder of 149 passengers in March 2015, there were also some 200 psychiatric consultations annually (data obtained under the FOI from the CAA, May, 2015). Is it sound to distance regulation of these problems in the interest of saving a few bucks?

★ ★ ★

One unexpected educational side effect of the availability of specialist advice to the AMS was evident. On occasion, occupational health medical staff gave the impression of acting *ultra vires* in specialities in which they were not accredited. This is unsafe, especially when consultant opinion is overruled without further discussion. Likewise, it is unsafe for a specialist physician, without aviation knowledge and experience, to pronounce on fitness to fly; this is the property of the occupational specialist, acting on specialist advice. In future, just how well, or badly, specialist advice to EASA will be presented, second or third hand, remains to be seen.

Difficult licensing decisions used to be reviewed by the Medical Advisory Panel (MAP), chaired by the CMO, whose decision was final under the ANO. Now the MAP has been replaced by the Cardiovascular Review Panel (CVRP) and is chaired by another, and a further (adversarial) appeal process has also been introduced. This is another retrograde step. We spent forty years developing confidence and rapport with the industry, particularly with the pilots, through a collaborative approach. Now it has been overridden by management theory.

★ ★ ★

There is a case for a national medical specialist training provision in aviation. A lot rides on the first medical examination for the individual. This was one reason why the newly formed Civil Aviation Authority, back in 1976, set up the clinic in its Medical Department when it assumed this responsibility from the RAF. The cost of obtaining a professional pilot's licence – CPL/IR, ab initio, is some £80,000 at current prices and its validity also has to be maintained both in terms of experience and medical fitness. Without a current medical certificate, a licence is not valid. If an anomaly is found during the initial medical fitness assessment, the applicant needs review with a rapid and authoritative opinion, otherwise training should not be undertaken. There may also be a requirement for ongoing supervision. As the RAF specialist medical advisory service was run down, the CAA assumed this responsibility. It is now resiling from what many see as a non-statutory duty of the regulator.

To give a clinical example, a cardiological review would be triggered by the discovery of Marfan's syndrome in an applicant. This an inherited abnormality of a gene encoding *fibrillin 1,* responsible for connective tissue structures such as cartilage and bone. Affected individuals may develop valvular heart disease, or enlargement of the great vessel, the aorta. Survival, unrecognised and untreated, is usually into the fifth decade; with good management it should be longer. The regulator needs advice, both on fitness for the certificatory interval – maybe one year – and guidance for the future. There should be a 'gipsy's warning' attempting to foresee later certificatory implications for the benefit of the applicant. Older pilots, in contrast, are more commonly evaluated on account of acquired conditions such as coronary artery disease, or a disturbance of the heart rhythm.

★ ★ ★

For four decades the CAA clinic and its specialists, together with the MAP, have helped to determine the fitness of aircrew when it has been in doubt. It is a unique national resource providing a fast, professional service for the resolution of specialist medical problems.. It was strongly supported by respondents to *CAP 1214* in *CAP 1276*. Audit reveals a fifteen-fold reduction in professional licence loss from cardiovascular cause over a generation, at least part of which is attributable to this service. The specialists have also contributed to the corps of knowledge in the department and thereby to the evolution of the Implementing Rules (IR), and the Acceptable Means of Compliance (AMC), for EASA.

It is hard to imagine a more specious excuse for winding up a proven service, supported by a large majority, than the need for a Chinese wall between the regulator and its own clinical executive arm. Running a medical clinic to the highest ethical standard is not rocket science, not even paper dart science. Governance could be addressed by external audit involving EASA, or the Royal College of Physicians / Faculty of Occupational Medicine. The planned alternative – to outsource, where AMS control will be remote – will ensure that a similar service is unachievable. Good regulation should be a partnership between the regulator and the regulated – the pilot with a medical issue or the airline with an operational one. Good conduct demands that the former be efficient, fair, prompt and proportionate. It should also be honest, direct and forthright and not indulge in deceit or casuistry.

Regulation is a service industry and should behave like one; in some ways the CAA does not – the delayed response to correspondence, at times, has been grotesque. It should exercise professional judgement and involve experts in a transparent and expeditious manner. It should be served by a board properly qualified in aviation, and intelligent, informed corporate governance. One of the pilots who responded to *CAP 1214*, in *CAP 1276*, stated:

In my experience the term best practice is a misnomer and is often used to prejudice any alternative views. In other words if it's not best practice it must be inferior…

The CAA, as predicted, pre-decided the outsourcing of the AeMC and associated specialist clinic services presumably on the basis of its secret advice. It claimed that the (unachievable) intention was to reduce the financial burden on industry. It struck out for the high ground of corporate governance, even at the expense of closure of a service which thirty-one of the thirty-nine responses to CAP 1276 fully supported, many of them, strongly so. Only two spoke against it. Governance in action?

★ ★ ★

On March 24th 2015, the Germanwings flight A320 4U 9525 from Barcelona to Düsseldorf crashed as a result of suicide of the pilot, Andreas Lubitz, with the murder of the remaining 149 passengers and crew on board. The aircraft was destroyed. Such events are fortunately very rare, but not unknown. In the twenty-one years up to 2003 there were thirty-six suicides and one attempted suicide in general aviation in the USA. Internationally the figures are more difficult. National regulators tend to dispute such causation, but one event every two years over the last two decades, worldwide, is likely to be somewhere near the mark. The Malaysian MH370 disappearance may also be an example, but the Germanwings loss was in the European operational area. The pilot had concealed his treatment for depression although the treatment he had been receiving could have suggested a psychotic illness. He had been flying against medical advice; on the day of the crash he was on sick leave. Such outcomes are impossible to prevent completely and there are confidentiality issues, but a competent airline medical department and efficient regulatory oversight should diminish, so far as is possible, the risk of an adverse event - psychiatric or otherwise.

There is commercial pressure on the AMEs to maintain the flying status of their clients. This they have to ignore. Some may not. EASA had already reportedly expressed concern at non-conformity of regulatory oversight by the German LBA (Luftfahrt-Bundesamt), due to staffing shortage. In late 2014, accountability was being called for by EASA, upon the LBA. It may be another example where, as with the UK CAA, cost is more important than performance and quality. The CAA Medical Departmental audit by EASA was also deemed deficient at its MEST (Medical Standardisation Team) visit to Gatwick in 2013, on the grounds of inadequate supervision of the AMEs. This problem had been evident for a long time. Unlike Potiphar's wife who had eye on Joseph, an AeMC has to be beyond approach. It will not be easy to keep a tight ship when it is fragmented, outsourced and regulated from a distance.

In its haste to please Cerberus, the three-headed dog of governance, the CAA could be open to the suggestion of neglect of duty as it plans to divest itself of its (non-mandatory) responsibilities to licence holders, against their wishes. Whether mandatory, or not, there has to be a well-qualified, rapid and secure pathway to the resolution of difficult licensing decisions. And this by doctors properly schooled in the specialities needed, including aviation medicine.

They should also be adequately overseen and regulated, and have access to a suitable training environment similar to the Gatwick AeMC. If training adds a fraction of a percentage point to cost, so what? It will have to be borne rather than accepting the delusion that 'contracting out' will magically produce an alternative led by anything more than the profit motive. Power without responsibility - the prerogative of the harlot through the ages, as Stanley Baldwin remarked of the press barons in 1931, at the suggestion of Rudyard Kipling. There was little barking about governance during the thirty-eight years I was at the CAA and no medical governance meeting before 2010. Now it is being used as a hound of war – the brooding gerund, prowling in non-finite verb form to slay the innocent and the unwary.

★ ★ ★

There are other policy developments which have also given concern. The CAA decided to examine protocols whereby insulin requiring diabetic subjects could be considered for professional licences. This had been a contentious issue world-wide for some years. Previously such applicants had been deemed unfit both under both ICAO Annex 1.6.3.2.16 and EASA - MED.B.025c (i). A joint meeting on the subject was held with specialist diabetologists and EASA representatives at Aviation House, London - Gatwick, in February 2014. None of the recently retired physicians advising the CAA Medical Department, all accredited in GIM and very experienced in aviation medicine, were invited to contribute. The outcome was by no means unanimous.

Under ICAO Article 37 each Contracting State undertakes: *to collaborate in securing the highest practicable degree of uniformity in regulations, standards, procedures…* while ICAO Article 38 states: *that if a State deems it necessary to adopt regulations or practices differing in any particular respect from those established by an international standard, it shall give immediate notification to the International Civil Aviation Organization of the differences between its own practice and that established by the international standard…*

What the CAA did next was in apparent violation of both Articles 37 and 38 by the use of ICAO Annex 1.1.2.4.9 (the flexibility clause) and EASA AMC1 MED.B.001, which is similarly empowering. Each individual applicant was treated as a one-off. But neither of these clauses is intended to facilitate new rule creation; routine approval under 1.1.2.4.9 of a particualar type of case reflects abuse of their primary purpose of flexibility: to allow single 'exceptional cases' ('special issuances' in the United States). I was informed – again with the help of the FOI: ...*that as we are certificating people following individual assessment, a difference does not need to be filed (with ICAO).* Someone needs to reread ICAO Articles 37 and 38, it seems.

To a jobbing cardiologist on an Airbus passing Clapham at 60 decibels, this suggests casuistry. Nevertheless, the CAA did, with the backing of Ireland obtain, under a new regulation promulgated in March 2015 (updating EC 216/2008 and EC 1178/2011 with EC 2015/445 which included EASA PART ARA.MED.330), the ability to issue fitness certificates to insulin-requiring diabetic applicants. This was provided the process was part of a research project and subject to certain requirements and forward review. As of May 2015 only the UK and Ireland, together with Canada, issue professional medical certificates to type 1 diabetic subjects. That was until the USA unexpectedly followed suit. There was a precedent for such action, back in the 1970s following the adoption by the UK of beta-blocking agents in the treatment of hypertension. One thinks of those whales, killed and eaten by the Norwegians and the Japanese in the name of research.

There are a number of problems in diabetes. These include the possibility of clinically occult falls in the blood sugar with associated impaired intellectual performance. This may pass un-noticed. And the level of the blood glucose is re-assuring only up to a point if it is within the normal range - there is a lag between the brain and blood glucose concentrations when one is on the move. Even the most stable diabetic can be upset by infection, fatigue, irregular meals or circadian challenge against which no amount of monitoring can guard. Professor Perrier (France), who contributed to the CAA/EASA meeting, in a letter to the journal *Lancet Diabetes and Endocrinology* in March 2014 in reply to an earlier communication on the subject, stated that: *The changes proposed by the authors are not medically justified, not ethically and practically admissible, and could jeopardise flight safety.*

Finally, who would undertake a bad weather approach to Innsbruck where the holding altitude on the easterly runway is 13,000 feet, no descent is permitted below 10,500 feet until established on the localiser at 20.4 nm

DME distant (there is no glideslope) and the minimum descent height (MDH) is 1807 feet – when the in-flight glucose check of the Pilot Flying was on the margin, or low? Or perhaps he/she would prefer to go by train? I would, even if he/she had used his/her GlucoCheck in good time before the KUHTAI NDB. If Innsbruck is excluded to such pilots, where else as well? It bears consideration that there should be *NO* qualification to the Class 1 standard, apart from an operational limitation (to fly as/with co-pilot), if this is indicated. ***Fitness to fly must have visible boundaries.***

As Professor Perrier concluded: *In the future, will pilots with any disorder with the potential to jeopardise flight safety be able to fly because there is a specific protocol to manage in-flight complications?*

Remain calm and wait for the first accident… Murmured one Euro-regulator. Wherefore art thou, EASA?

★ ★ ★

Recently, EASA promulgated an Acceptable Means of Compliance (AMC) allowing consideration of pilots who have undergone aortic valve replacement with a mechanical prosthesis. The aortic valve is the exit conduit for blood leaving the left side of the heart. It normally has three leaflets (cusps). About 1.1% of the European male population are born with a bicuspid variant form. This was first described by Leonardo da Vinci five hundred years ago, at about the time he designed his 'ornithopter'. As a rule, it functions well until middle years when the valve may narrow. About half of such subjects have an additional abnormality of the gene encoding fibrillin 1 (confer Marfan's syndrome); they are at risk from dilatation of the aorta and leakage of the valve. Late outcomes include heart failure and rupture of the vessel.

The valve may also become infected – endocarditis, which potentially has a high mortality. If the stenosis (narrowing) passes unnoticed (unlikely in a pilot, although it is on record), fainting (syncope), heart failure and sudden cardiac death are late complications. It may be replaced with either a tissue valve (often from a pig), or a mechanical valve, such as the St Jude prosthesis. This significantly improves the outlook, but does not render it normal. Preceding hypertrophy (thickening) of the heart muscle, or dilatation will worsen it, as will irregularity of the heart (atrial fibrillation) which precludes certification in this context. The enduring risk in the aviation context is one of embolus (blood clot) originating from the prosthetic valve, and a cause of stroke.

A recent study of 4,253 such patients aged 50 to 69 years, reviewed fifteen-year actuarial mortality rates; two fifths were dead at fifteen years. But only the best risk subjects are potentially acceptable in aviation. Cumulative fifteen-year stroke rates were broadly similar at 7.7% and 8.6% respectively. The re-operation rate was 12.1% in the bioprosthetic valve group and 6.9% in the mechanical valve group. Major haemorrhage (attributable in part to anti-coagulation) was seen in 6.6% of those with a bioprosthesis, and 13.0% of those with a mechanical valve. Even with careful selection, the cumulative annual event rate of a mechanical valve is outside the 1% (or 2%) guideline each year. Strange advice? The construction of the IRs and AMCs is not debated, or modified, by experts.

Hark, yet again, that fearful sound, Of tempest all around. Chorus in Act III: *Oedipus at Colonus* by Sophocles (died 406 BC)

★ ★ ★

Probably the most fulfilling part of my time in regulation was functioning as a clinical cardiologist and helping those professional, or other aspiring, pilots to achieve fitness to fly when this was in doubt. Sometimes, inevitably, there was disappointment, but hopefully, those involved understood and accepted the basis for denial. A professional pilot does not willingly take a sick aircraft into the air, and so it is with personal lack of fitness.

"You have accounted for a greater loss of pilots than the Luftwaffe,"

David, 2nd Baron Trefgarne, PC, sometime Minister of State for Defence Procurement, was wont to say before strapping himself into his DH Dove and romping off into the bundu south of Fairoaks with an emphatic roar from the Gipsy Queen engines. Sometimes the landing gear was not too keen on retracting, and the mechanism would bite your finger…

The figures for licence loss suggested otherwise. I was always impressed by the courtesy and consideration shown by the professional pilots I saw. They were in double jeopardy from both impaired health and future employability. I cared about their outcome. This did not always extend to the PPLs, who did not seem to appreciate the need for regulation and regarded the CAA as an over-rewarded trip wire in the pathway to their aspiration to fly. "I see no need for all this – you are only here to give yourself a job," I was told more than once. *Come fly, come fly with me.*

★ ★ ★

The turn of the century was perhaps the best period. It coincided with the completion of the four workshops with active commitment and involvement of the CAA, and input from many talented colleagues. Apart from any other consideration, as a professional update they were second to none. There was also advisory work for ICAO and JAA, with demand for guidance from diverse quarters. And my precious instrument rating was still current. It had been a privilege to have been involved in such an exciting world, and one in which the UK had held such a commanding lead. Now it is on the wane, some might say on account of lack of vision and of leadership. The appointment of the OBE for services to the aviation industry had also come along. When I collected the Buchanan Barbour award at the Royal Aeronautical Society in 1987 from the then-President, John Fozard, the next recipient was given an award for: 'helping his company (possibly Rolls-Royce) through a difficult time'.

"It has always been a difficult time," said a venerable Air Vice-Marshal in a loud stage whisper after the citation had been read. And in many ways it has.

★ ★ ★

But things were on the move and back in Marathon, Nemesis had fled her redoubt near Rhamnousia (after which she is sometimes called) and crash-landed in Gatwick South Area. I was informed that I had too much 'power' (sic) and there was no room for specialist advisors in the European consultative machinery. The guidance material would also be written by non-specialists, with clinical recommendations being overruled if they did not accord with the views of the non-clinical AMS; sometimes without consultation. This was as undesirable professionally as it was unsafe. Next, I was disarmed by the misleading statement that I was the highest-paid employee in the authority. Too bad. Phthonos, God of envy and a buddy of Nemesis, was somewhere in the London TMA that afternoon.

The EASA Implementing Rules would in future be promulgated as bureaucratic breeze blocks and the Acceptable Means of Compliance would be debated by medical non-specialists in Cologne, sometimes being brought back to the CVRP for comment. Amendments would also have to be passed by the Jinns in the legal department for costly nit-picking in a far-off subject about which they knew nothing (medicine that is). During the drafting of Standards for ICAO, JAA, CAA, DVLA (Driver and Vehicle Licensing Agency), European Driving Agency and Royal Automobile Club Motor Sports Association (RAC - MSA), we found it best if someone produced an initial draft for knocking into shape by experts.

No grand idea was ever born in a conference, but a lot of foolish ideas have died there, remarked F. Scott Fitzgerald in *The Crack-Up* (1945), a collection of essays published after his death in 1940. We were to confirm this all those years ago in Neuilly, notwithstanding Robert Auffret's splendid lunch. Committees, after all, are best at generating heat, not light. We had more success, perhaps, in the meetings before Jean-Paul Broustet's banquet in Bordeaux in honour of European road transport safety. But that involved speciality experts. Likewise in Miami for the JAA. Now we are back on instruments again, heading towards the high ground in instrument meteorological conditions with the circuit breaker of the ground proximity warning system pulled. Hopefully it will be reset, but controlled flight into terrain remains one of the single most important causes of aviation accidents. Apart from loss of control in flight, that is. Which seems to be where we are now.

★ ★ ★

On 17th December 2012 I pocketed my stethoscope, took a photograph of the consulting room on my phone (how things had changed) and left Aviation House, Gatwick South Area for the last time. It had been more than forty years since the Papa India disaster, and thirty-eight since I first attended Shell Mex House to report upon ECGs after a day at the London Hospital. Later we drove to the Athenaeum for a dinner with the medical consultants.

That is the story. It had been a good time: don't forget to fly the aeroplane.

EPILOGUE

I know but one freedom, and that is the freedom of the mind.

Antoine, comte de Saint-Exupéry (1900 – 31 July 1944 when he was lost in a P38 Lockheed Lightning over the Mediterranean sea); pioneer aviator, writer and poet.

TLAs

Mainly TLAs (Three Letter Acronyms)
TLAs have become an art form in themselves. The following are used in the text and/or are commonly used in aviation and in the Armed Services. Non-recurring medical TLAs and post-nominal, honour, acronyms are not listed. The reader will notice at times the use of the capital in the word Standard. In this manner it reflects the regulatory requirement; elsewhere, with lower case, it is used as the noun.

AAIB Air Accident Investigation Branch
AIB Accident Investigation Branch
AD Airworthiness Directive
A(D)I Attitude (Direction)Indicator
ADF Automatic Direction Finder
ACI Army Council Instruction (ACI)
AeMC Aeromedical Section (EASA)
AltMOC Alternative Means of Compliance (EASA)
AMC Acceptable Means of Compliance (EASA)
AME Authorised Medical Examiner
AMSO Air Member for Supply and Organisation
ADRM Airport Development Reference Manual (IATA)
AOC Air Officer Commanding
ARIDU Air Data Inertial Reference Unit
ASI Air Speed Indicator
AsMA Aerospace Medical Association
ATA Air Transport Auxiliary
ATCO Air Traffic Control Officer
ATPL Air Transport Pilot's Licence
ATOL Air Travel Organisers' Licensing
ATSU Air Traffic Service Unit

BA British Airways
BAC British Aircraft Corporation
BAE British Aerospace Electronic (Systems)
BALPA British Airline Pilots Association
BAOR British Army of the Rhine
BARC British Automobile Racing Club
BEA British European Airways
BMW Bayerische Motoren Werke AG
BO Body Odour
BOAC British Overseas Airways Corporation
CAA Civil Aviation Authority
CAP Civil Aviation Publication
CASA Civil Aviation Safety Authority (Australia)
Cb Cumulo-nimbus (thunder cloud); also colloquially known as a 'Charlie
    Banger'
CCF Combined Cadet Force
CIMP Commission Internationale Medico-Physiological
CMO Chief Medical Officer
CPL Commercial Pilot's Licence
CO Commanding Officer
CVRP Cardiovascular Review Panel
CVR Cockpit Voice Recorder
CRM Crew (cockpit) Resource Management
CSE Channon Svejdar Erlanger (CSE Oxford, 1962)
DH de Havilland
DHC de Havilland Canada
D&D Distress and Diversion
DERA Defence Evaluation and Research Agency
DF Direction Finder
DME Distance Measuring Equipment
DOC Direct Operating Cost
DRA Defence Research Agency
EASA European Aviation Safety Agency
ECG Electrocardiogram
EFTS Elementary Flying Training School
ERFTS Elementary and Reserve Flying Training School
EU European Union

FAA Federal Aviation Administration
FAI Fédération Aéronautique Internationale
FCO Foreign and Commonwealth Office
FDR Flight Data Recorder
F/E Flight Engineer
F/N Flight Navigator
F/O First Officer
FIR Flight Information Region
FIS Flight Information Service
GDP Gross Domestic Product
GPWS Ground Proximity Warning System
GWR Great Western Railway
HAECO Hong Kong Aircraft Engineering Company
HAL Hindustan Aeronautics Limited
HP Horse Power (also Handley Page)
IAE International Aero Engines consortium
IAASM International Academy of Aviation and Space Medicine
IAM Institute of Aviation Medicine
IATA International Air Transport Association
ICAO International Civil Aviation Organisation
IOSA IATA Operational Safety Audit
IFR Instrument Flight Rules
ILS Instrument Landing System
IMC Instrument Meteorological Conditions
IFALPA International Federation of Air Line Pilots Associations
IR Implementing Rules (EASA)
I/R Instrument Rating
ISARPs International Standards and Recommended Practices (ICAO)
ITCZ Inter Tropical Convergence Zone
JAA Joint Aviation Authorities
JCR Junior Common Room
KGB Комитéт госудáрственной безопáсности
kHz kiloHertz
LAPL Light Aircraft Pilots Licence
LMF Lack of Moral Fibre (also Lima Mike Foxtrot)
LNER London North Eastern Railway
MAUW Maximum All Up Weight – see MTWA

MAYDAY *M'aidez* – life-threatening urgency
mb millibar
mHz megaHertz
MOD Ministry of Defence
MTWA Maximum Take-off Weight Authorized
NDB Non-Directional Beacon
NF (11/14) Night Fighter (Meteor 11/14)
NTSB National Transportation Safety Board (US)
OAT Outside Air Temperature
OM (beacon) Outer Marker (beacon)
ORL Operating-pilot Restriction Limitation
OSL Operational Safety-pilot Limitation
OTC Officers Training Corps
OTU Operational Training Unit
P 1/2/3 Pilot (in command/second officer/third officer – student)
PAN (call) Urgency. *En panne* = broken, in French; (Pay Attention Now/
    Possible Assistance Needed)
PNI Plan Navigation Indicator
PPRuNe Professional Pilots Rumour Network
QFE Altimeter pressure setting to read zero feet on ground
QNH Altimeter pressure setting to read altitude above sea level
QRA Quick Reaction Alert
QRS Vector representation of ventricular depolarisation
RAE Royal Aircraft Establishment
RAF Royal Air Force
RCP Royal College of Physicians
RFC Royal Flying Corps
RSM Royal Society of Medicine
RFTS Reserve Flying Training School
RN Royal Navy
SB Service Bulletin
SES Single European Sky
SID Standard Instrument Departure
Snecma Société nationale d'études et de construction de moteurs d'aviation
SOP Standard Operating Procedure
SSR Secondary Surveillance Radar
STAR Standard Arrival (pattern)

TCAS Traffic Collision Avoidance System
TAF Terminal Aerodrome Forecast
TAF (2) Tactical Air Force (Second)
TAL Transoceanic Abort Landing
TMA Terminal Manoeuvring Area
T/SI Turn and Slip Indicator
UK United Kingdom
UMT Units of Medical Time
UNESCO United Nations Educational, Scientific and Cultural Organization
US(A) United States (of America)
USSR Union of Soviet Socialist Republics
V1 Take-off decision speed (commitment to take off)
Vr Rotation speed
V2 Take-off safety speed (with one engine inoperative)
VAD Voluntary Aid Detachment
Vna (also V4) Initial climb speed
Vne Velocity never exceed
VDF VHF Direction Finding
VHF Very High Frequency
VMC Visual Meteorological Conditions
VFR Visual Flight Rules
VOR VHF Omnidirectional Range (navigation)
VRFTS Volunteer Reserve Flying Training School
WBJ Western Built Jet
WOSB War Office Selection Board
WO Walter Owen (Bentley)
WS Wireless Set
Y (service) Wireless (service)

REFERENCES

The following are some of the reference sources used in the preparation of the manuscript. It is noteworthy that not all texts are in agreement. They are in publication date order. It is not a comprehensive list – the scientific literature may be sought from the cardiological texts cited: it moves rapidly and needs interpretation.

Dodgson C. L. (Lewis Carroll). *Alice's Adventures in Wonderland*. 1865; London: Macmillan and Co. *Alice would have understood aviation regulation.*

Dodgson C. L. (Lewis Carroll). *Through the Looking Glass*. 1871; London: Macmillan and Co.

Bagehot W. *The English Constitution*. 1877. New York: Appleton. *Bagehot was a journalist and the editor of the Economist. He was born in Langport, Somerset.*

Santos-Dumont A. *My Airships: the Story of my Life*. 1904. London: Grant Richards. *The author was the first man to make a powered flight in Europe – after he wrote the book.*

Montagu Lord, Baden-Powell B. *A Short History of Balloons and Flying Machines*. 1907. London: *The Car Illustrated*. *Published at about the time of S. F. Cody's first flight on Laffan's Plain, Farnborough.*

Yerkes R M, Dodson J D. *The relation of strength of stimulus to rapidity of habit-formation*. Journal of Comparative Neurology and Psychology 1908; 18: 459–482. doi:10.1002/cne. 920180503: downloaded March 2015

Bryan G H. *Stability in Aviation: An Introduction to Dynamical Stability as Applied to the Motion of Aeroplanes*. 1911. London: Macmillan and Co. *Flight with formulae.*

Greenhill G. *The Dynamics of Mechanical Flight*. 1912. London: Constable and Company. *Tricky unless you are a mathematician.*

Hamel G, Turner C C. *Flying: Some Practical Experiences*. 1915. London: Longmans, Green and Co. *First lessons: accident prevention, cross-country flying – everything one needed to know then (and now)*.

Claxton W J. *The Mastery of the Air*. 1915: 2nd Edn. London: Blackie and Sons. *A brief introduction to the history of flight; it ran into many editions and is available on Kindle*.

Kean E J. *Aeronautical Engines*. 1916. London: E. and F. N. Spon. *As it says on the cover*.

Judge A W. *The Design of Aeroplanes*. 1917. London: Whittaker and Co. *Flight with fewer formulae*.

Anderson H G. *Medical and Surgical Aspects of Aviation*. 1919. Oxford: Oxford University Press. *A distillation of wartime experience of medical fitness to fly*.

Camm S. *Aeroplane Construction*. 1919. London: Crosby Lockwood and Son. *An early publication by the designer of the Hawker Hurricane, Typhoon, Tempest, Hunter and Harrier*.

Sykes F H. *Civil Aviation*. Flight 1919; xi: 1506–1508. *The early years of regulation*.

Thomas G H. *Aerial Transport*. 1920. London: Hodder & Stoughton. *Early civil aviation*.

The Air Council. *Manual of Air Pilotage*. 1930. London: HMSO. *A practical manual of meteorology, navigation and general airmanship for the RAF pilot*.

Yancey L A. *Aerial Navigation and Meteorology*. 1929. New York: Norman W. Henley Publishing. *Historical treatment of an art dressed up as a science*.

Glauert H. *The Elements of Aerofoil and Airscrew Theory*. 1930. Cambridge: Cambridge University Press. *Tricky; unless you are a mathematician*.

Handbook of Aeronautics. 1931. The Royal Aeronautical Society; London: Gale and Polden. *A compendium of the formulae needed for aeroplanes to fly*.

Airman's World: A Book about Flying. 1933. London: George Routledge and Sons. *A general text with some fine early aerial photographs*.

Liddell Hart B H. *A History of the World War 1914–1918*. 1934. 2nd Edn; London: Faber and Faber. *A standard text on the subject*.

Jordanoff A. *Through the Overcast*. 1938. New York and London: Funk and Wagnalls Company. *A useful, if verbose, North American excursion into the impenetrable fog that is meteorology*.

Harben N R. *The Complete Flying Course; a Manual of Flying Tuition*. 1938. London: C. Arthur Pearson. *All you need to know – given to me by a lady patient who learnt to fly before the Second World War*.

Manning W O. *Aeroplanes and Engines (Airsense)*. 1941. London: Pitman. *A wartime primer for those involved with aviation.*

Williamson G W. *A Primer of Flying. An Introductory Course into the Art of Flying*. 1941. London: Isaac Pitman. *As it says.*

Caaudwell O. *Aero Engines: for Pilots and Ground Engineers*. 1941. London: Isaac Pitman. *Aimed at those involved in the maintenance of wartime aircraft.*

Dimbleby R. *The Frontiers are Green*. 1943. London: Hodder & Stoughton. *Richard Dimbleby's journeys in the Middle East during the campaign in Africa.*

What Britain has Done – 1939–1945: A Selection of Outstanding Facts and Figures. 1945. London: Ministry of Information. *War production statistical source.*

Scott Fitzgerald F. *The Crack-Up*: Ed. Wilson E. 1945. New York: New Directions. *A collection of essays published after his death in 1940. Includes other work.*

Sheppard J T. *The Oedipus at Colonus of Sophocles*. 1949. Cambridge: Bowes and Bowes. *Patricide, incest, self-blinding and predetermined responsibility for destiny and death. Strong stuff.*

Churchill W S. *The Second World War; Volume VI, Triumph and Tragedy*. 1954. London. Cassell.

Brickhill P. *Reach for the Sky*. 1954. London: William Collins. *The story of Douglas Bader.*

Wolff L. *In Flanders Fields: The 1917 Campaign*. 1958. New York: Viking. *A readable account.*

Taylor A J P. *The First World War: an Illustrated History*. 1963. London: Hamish Hamilton. *A brief and easily readable history of the subject.*

Scott J D. *Vickers: a History*. 1963. London: Weidenfeld and Nicolson. *The history of this great British aircraft and ship-building company.*

Bramson A, Birch N. *The Tiger Moth Story*. 1964. Letchworth: Air Review Ltd. *The history of a great aeroplane.*

Taylor A J P. *English History 1914–1945*. 1965. London: Oxford University Press. *A standard text on the subject.*

Lee A G. *The Flying Cathedral*. 1965. London: Methuen and Co. *Biography of S. F. Cody.*

Fairlie G, Cayley E. *The Life of a Genius*. 1965. London: Hodder & Stoughton. *The Life of Sir George Cayley. The first author was the model for Bulldog Drummond by Sapper, later continuing the tales after Sapper's death.*

Bonham-Carter V. *Winston Churchill As I Knew Him*. 1965. London: Eyre and Spottiswoode. *A fascinating account of Winston Churchill as a young man by the daughter of Herbert Asquith.*

Moorhead A. *The Desert War: the North African Campaign 1940–1943*. 1965. London: Hamish Hamilton. *Celebrating the 25th anniversary of the Battle of Alamein; a good text on the subject.*

CAP 311. *Report on Accident to Trident G-ARPY near Felthorne on June 3rd 1966*. 1968. London: HMSO. *This forgotten accident relates the still not understood (then) deep stall characteristic of the aircraft. Training issues were raised in the subsequent Papa India report.*

Ramsden J M, editor. *Flight 1968*; pp 909–911. London: Iliffe Transport Publications Ltd. *An analysis of the stable stall.*

Curtis L. *The Forgotten Pilots: Story of the Air Transport Auxiliary, 1939–45*. 1971. Henley-on-Thames: G. T. Foulis. *A lament, in part, for the under-acknowledged contribution made by the Air Transport Auxilliary (ATA) in the Second World War.*

Davies D P. *Handling the Big Jets*. 1971. 3rd edn. Redhill: ARB. *After forty years still one of the definitive texts on the subject.*

Robinson D H. *The Dangerous Sky: A History of Aviation Medicine*. 1973. Henley-on-Thames: G. T. Foulis. *A text on the earlier history of aviation medicine.*

Trident 1 G-ARPI. Report of the Public Inquiry into the cause and circumstances of the accident near Staines on 18 June 1972. Civil Aircraft Accident Report 4/73. 1973. London: HMSO. *A seminal accident which led to changes in flying personnel medical licensing, and aircrew training.*

Bader D. *Fight for the Sky: the Story of the Spitfire and the Hurricane*. 1973; Ipswich: W. S. Cowell Ltd. *In some ways a retelling of the earlier story by Paul Brickhill – Reach for the Sky.*

Gibbs-Smith C H. *The Rebirth of European Aviation*. 1974. London: HMSO. *A standard text on the early history of aviation.*

CAP 371. *CAA Safety Regulation Group. Avoidance of Fatigue in Aircrew: Guide to Requirements*. 1975: 1982; 1989; 1990; 1992; 2004. Norwich: TSO. *This originated as the (Douglas) Bader committee.*

CAP386 CAA Annual Statistics 1974 and 1975. London: CAA. *Useful numbers for comparison.*

Tolkien J R R. *The Silmarillion*. 1977. London: George Allen & Unwin.

Combs H, Caidin N. *Kill Devil Hill: The Epic of the Wright Brothers, 1899–1909*. 1979. London: Secker & Warburg.

Smallpeice B. *Of Comets and Queens*. 1981, Shrewsbury: Airlife Publishing Ltd. *Support for the British Aviation Industry cost him his job as chairman of BOAC, at the hand of Julian Amery.*

Johnson H. *Wings over Brooklands*. 1981. London: Pitman. *The story of the birthplace of British aviation, and of motor sport.*

Gardner C. *British Aircraft Corporation: a History*. 1981. London: Batsford. *A story of political incompetence in aviation as good as any since. Are there any of political competence?*

Terraine J. *The Right of the Line: the Royal Air Force in the European War 1939–1945*. 1985. London: Hodder & Stoughton. *A definitive treatment of the subject.*

AAIB Report 1/87. Reims Cessna F172N G-BFOW. Ditched 13.3 nm Northwest of Alderney, CI on 10th February 1985. 1987. Farnborough: AAIB

Reason J. *Human Error*. 1990. Cambridge: Cambridge University Press. *Cheesy.*

Forman P. *Flying into Danger: the Hidden Facts about Air Safety*. 1990. London: William Heinemann. *Written in Patrick's inimitable style: his take on aviation safety.*

Sturtivant R. *British Research and Development Aircraft: Seventy Years at the Leading Edge*. 1990. Yeovil: Haynes Publishing Group. *Well-researched early epitaph for a once great industry in the UK.*

Joy M, Bennett G. *Rehabilitation of Aviators with Potentially Disqualifying Cardiovascular Problems*; in Broustet J-P. *Proceedings of the Vth World Congress on Cardiac Rehabilitation*. 1993. Andover: Intercept. *Proceedings of the symposium in Bordeaux; excluding the banquet. Dit ne plus.*

Barnato-Walker D. *Spreading My Wings*. 1994. London: Patrick Stevens. *A personal story, told by the daughter of Woolf Barnato – one of the 'Bentley Boys' – of her time with the ATA.*

Moses H. *The Faithfull Sixth: a History of the Sixth Battalion: the Durham Light Infantry (DLI)*. 1995. Durham: Durham County Books. *About the 6th DLI in two World Wars.*

Bresco R O, Sangal S P, Nesthus T E, Veronneaux S J H. *Study suggests longer life expectation for retired pilots than their counterparts in the general population*. 1996. Alexandria VA: Flight Safety Foundation: *Human Factors and Aviation Medicine*; 41: 1–6

Joy M. and Broustet J-P. *Cardiovascular Fitness to Fly and to Drive; the Interface between Cardiology and Statutory Fitness Requirements in Diseases of the Heart* 2nd edn.1996; eds Julian D G et al. London: W B Saunders. *Now somewhat out of date, this chapter positions the cardiologist in the role of guiding the regulator.*

Epstein A E, Miles W M, Benditt D G et al. *Personal and Public Safety Issues Related to Arrhythmias that may Affect Consciousness: Implications for Regulation and Physician Recommendations.* Circulation 1996; 94:1147–1166. *The Washington, DC meeting.*

Gero D. *Aviation Disasters; the world's major civil airliner crashes since 1960.* 1996. Yeovil: Patrick Stephens.

AAIB Bulletin 9/98 EW/C98/4/5. DH82A Tiger Moth, G-BALX: disappeared 19 April 1998 on a flight Dieppe to Headcorn, Kent. 1998. Farnborough: AAIB.

Ministre de l'Equipmnt des Transports et du Logement – Bureau d' Emquetesment – Bureau d' Enquetes et d' Analyses pour la Securite de l' Aviation Civile – France. 2000. Accident on 25 July 2000 at La Patte d'Oie in Gonesse (95) to the Concorde registered F-BTSC operated by Air France. Paris: BEA. REPORT translation f-sc000725a. AAIB Bulletin No: 1/2001

AAIB Report EW/C2000/6/5. Accident Report on the crash of Piper PA 31-350 G-BMBC into the Mersey River on 14th June 2000. 2001. Farnborough: AAIB

Jackson R. *The Encyclopaedia of Military Aircraft.* 2002. London: Paragon. *Thumbnails of over 650 of the world's combat aircraft from 1910 to 2000.*

PS Collaboration. *Age-specific relevance of usual blood pressure to vascular mortality: a meta-analysis of individual data for one million adults in 61 prospective studies.* The Lancet 2002; 360: 1903–1913. *Meta-analyses do not come bigger than this, nor show more convincingly the cardiovascular risk of high blood pressure.*

Orlebar C. *The Concorde Story,* 6th ed. 2004. Oxford: Osprey. *A standard text on the subject.*

Curtis L. *Lettice Curtis: her Autobiography.* 2004. Walton on Thames: Red Kite. *A personal history; and of the ATA.*

Mitchell S J, Evans A D. *Flight safety and medical incapacitation risk of airline pilots.* Aviation Space and Environmental Medicine 2004; 75: 260–268. *An academic argument which revisits the 1% rule and suggests some relaxation is appropriate.*

Bills C B, Grabowski J G, Li G. *Suicide by aircraft: a comparative analysis.* Aviation, Space and Environmental Medicine 2005; 76: 715–719.

CAA Safety Regulation Group. Aviation Safety Review 2005. CAP 763. 2005. Norwich: TSO. *As it says on the tin.*

Joy M. *Cardiovascular Disease,* in Ernsting's *Aviation Medicine – 4th edition;* eds Rainford D J, Gradwell D P 2006. London: Hodder Arnold; pp 567–604. *The textbook is a comprehensive treatment of the speciality. The cardiovascular chapter gives a general overview of cardiology in aviation. The 5th edition is due (2015).*

Orange V. *Dowding of Fighter Command: Victor of the Battle of Britain*. 2008. London: Grub Street. *This biography covers the life of Dowding, in addition to his Royal Air Force service before, and during, the Battle of Britain.*

CAA Safety Regulation Group. *Aviation Safety Review CAP 780.* 2008. Norwich: TSO. *As it says on the tin.*

Hannan E. L, Chuntao W, Walgord G et al. *Drug Eluting Stents vs Coronary-Artery Bypass Grafting in Multi-vessel Coronary Disease*. New England Journal of Medicine 2008; 358: 331–341. *A well-constructed paper debunking, again, the Holy Grail that coronary artery stenting is even equivalent to coronary surgery when it is generally neither, in terms of survival, nor of morbid event rate.*

Croft J. 2009. *Getting control of LOC. Flight International:* http://www.flightglobal.com/articles/2009/01/27/321563/getting-control-of-loc.html. Downloaded April 2015.

JAA Manual of Civil Aviation Medicine 2009. Cologne: Joint Aviation Authorities, Europe: JAR-FCL3: Joy M. 2-02. *The 'JAR Med' was the only comprehensive book of regulatory guidance material in medicine at the time. It was often to be seen on the desks of non-JAA regulators.*

Evans A D, Watson D B, Evans S A, Hastings J et al. *Safety Management as a Foundation for Evidence-based Aeromedical Standards and Reporting of Medical Events*. Aviation, Space and Environmental Medicine 2009; 80: 511–15.

Interim Report on the accident on 1ˢᵗ June 2009 to the Airbus A330-203 registered F-GZCP Operated by Air France flight AF 447, Rio de Janeiro–Paris. 2009. Paris: BEA

Tan S W, Sungar G W, Myers J et al. *A Simplified Electrocardiogram Score for the Prediction of Cardiovascular Mortality*. Clinical Cardiology 2009; 32: 82–86. *Justifies the use of the routine resting electrocardiography in screening for cardiovascular disease.*

Joy M. in *Evidence Based Cardiology*; eds Yusuf et al. 2010. Oxford: Wiley-Blackwell; *Chapter 7: The Application of Evidence-based Medicine to Employment Fitness Standards: the Transport Industries with Special Reference to Aviation.* pp 79–94. *A scientific treatment of evidence-based decision-making in cardiology.*

AAIB Report 11/2010. Piper PA-31P Pressurised Navajo, N95RS which crashed at Bladon, Oxfordshire, on January 10ᵗʰ 2010. 2010. Farnborough: AAIB

Hamilton-Paterson J. *Empire of the Clouds: when Britain's Aircraft ruled the World*. 2010. London: Faber and Faber. *A superbly illustrated treatment of the subject.*

McCaughran J. *Implied Terms: the Journey of the Man on the Clapham Omnibus*, 2011. *The Cambridge Law Journal*, 201: 70: 607 Cambridge University Press. (McQuire v. Western Morning News: Court of Appeal, 1903); *See also the Bondi tram.*

Manual of Civil Aviation Medicine. 3rd Edn. 2012. Doc 8984. AN/895. Montreal: International Civil Aviation Organization. Joy M. *Ch III-1-1 Cardiovascular System. ICAO guidance for cardiology in aviation.*

Grau-Sepulveda M V, Weintraub W S, Weiss J M et al. *Comparative Effectiveness of Revascularisation Targets.* New England Journal of Medicine 2012: 1056/NEJMoa1110717. Downloaded March 2015. *Another study, albeit in a population older than the pilot population, which confirms the better outcomes following coronary surgery, when compared with angioplasty, in terms of event-free and long-term survival.*

Final Report. On the accident on 1st June 2009 to the Airbus A330-203 registered F-GZCP operated by Air France flight AF 447 Rio de Janeiro–Paris. 2012. Paris; BEA. http://www.bea.aero/docspa/2009/f-cp090601.en/pdf/f-cp090601.en.pdf. Downloaded March 2015. *A seminal report to be taken very seriously.*

Evans S, Radcliffe S-A. *The annual incapacitation rate of commercial pilots.* Aviation, Space, and Environmental Medicine 2012; 83: 42–49. *An original approach to the prediction of risk of cardiovascular incapacitation in aircrew.*

Pursnani S, Korly F, Gopaul R et al. *Percutaneous Coronary Intervention versus Optimal Medical Therapy in Stable Coronary Artery Disease.* Circulatory and Cardiovascular Interventions 2012; 5: 476–490. *This analysis, in patients with stable coronary artery disease, demonstrated that percutaneous coronary intervention, as compared with ordinary medical treatment, failed to reduce mortality, cardiovascular death, non-fatal myocardial infarction, or revascularization. It had a small favourable impact on symptoms: aviators have to be asymptomatic.*

Jones M G. *Fairoaks Airport: an Illustrated History – the First Seventy-Five Years.* 2013. Woking: Michael G. Jones.

CAP 1036. CAA Global Fatal Accident Review 2002 to 2011: 2013: CAA; Norwich: TSO.

Federal Aviation Administration. Fact Sheet – FAA Forecast – Fiscal Years 2014–34. 2014. Washington DC: FAA.

EASA Safety Review 2013. 2014. EASA Cologne

Perrier P. *Letter*: Lancet, Diabetes and Endocrinology. March 2014 (DOI: http://dx.doi.org/10.1016/S2213-8587(14)70056-7)

Federal Aviation Administration. *FAA Aerospace Forecasts Fiscal Years 2003–2014*. 2014. Washington DC: FAA.

IATA Safety Report 2013: 50 years at the forefront of aviation safety. 2014; IATA: Geneva/Montreal.

Boeing: Current Market Outlook – *2012–2032*. 2013. Boeing: Seattle.

Zulfikar-Ali-Bhutto, 2013. http://www.britannica.com/EBchecked/topic/64265/Zulfikar-Ali-Bhutto. Downloaded March 2015.

Li J, Elrashidi M Y, Flammer E A et al. *Long term outcomes of fractional flow reserve-guided vs angiography-guided percutaneous coronary intervention in contemporary practice. European Heart Journal* 2013; doi:10.1093/eurheartj/eht005. Downloaded March 2015. *How to avoid angioplasty.*

ICAO Safety Report 2014: A Coordinated, Risk-based Approach to Improving Global Aviation Safety. 2014. ICAO: Montreal.

Manen O, Martel V, Germa R, Paris J F, Perrier E. *Lancet – Diabetes and Endocrinology* 2014; http://dx.doi.org/10.1016/S2213-8587(14)70056-7. Downloaded March 2015. *The interesting decision to permit injectable insulin use in professional pilots.*

Chiang Y P, Chikwe J, Moskowitz A J et al. *Survival and long-term outcomes following bioprosthetic vs mechanical aortic valve replacement in patients aged 50 to 69 years.* Journal of the American Medical Association 2014; 312: 1323–1329. *As it says.*

Statistical Summary of Commercial Jet Airplane Accidents: Worldwide Operations 1959–2013. 2014. Seattle: Boeing Commercial Airplanes.

Langewiesche W. *The Human Factor*. 2014. New York; Conde Naste; Vanity Fair: October 158–165 and 193–197. *A professional, and readable, account of the AF 447 tragedy.*

Learmount D. 2015. *Air Safety Network 2015*. Flight Safety Foundation. 2015: http://www.flightsafety.org

CAP 393 – Air Navigation: The Order and the Regulations. 1976, 1982, 2003, 2015 as amended. 2015. Norwich TSO; for London: CAA. *The Air Navigation Order.*

CAP 1214 – Consultation on Future Structure of the CAA's Medical Department. 2014. Norwich TSO; for London: CAA.

CAP 1276 – The Future Structure of the CAA's Medical Department – Response to views raised in consultation. 2015. Norwich TSO; for London: CAA.

European Aviation Safety Agency. *Notice of Proposed Amendment 2014–25. Requirements for relief pilots*. RMT.0190 (FCL.004 (A)); RMT.0191 (FCL.004 (B)). 2015. EASA: Cologne.

Learmount D. *The short flight of TransAsia GE235*. http://www.flightglobal.com/blogs/ learmount/2015/02/short-flight-transasia-ge235/ Downloaded April 2015.

European Aviation Safety Agency. Cologne: 2015. *Germanwings crash: EU concerns over German monitoring of crew health*. Agence France-Presse: Berlin: 5 April 2015.

And the workshops:

Joy M., Bennett G. *The First United Kingdom Workshop in Aviation Cardiology*. European Heart Journal 1984; 5 (Suppl A): 1–164.

Joy M., Bennett G. *The Second United Kingdom Workshop in Aviation Cardiology*. European Heart Journal 1988; 9 (Suppl G): 1–179.

Joy M. *The First European Workshop in Aviation Cardiology*. European Heart Journal 1992; 13 (Suppl H): 1–175.

Joy M. *The Second European Workshop in Aviation Cardiology*. European Heart Journal 1999; 1 (Suppl D): D1–D131.

INDEX

The index mainly relates to the characters, places and events in this tale. Emphasis is upon historical and civilian aspects of aviation, and of medicine, rather than the armed services.